Circuits, matrices, and linear vector spaces

circuits

matrices

and linear vector spaces

Lawrence P. Huelsman

Associate Professor of Electrical Engineering, University of Arizona

McGraw-Hill Book Company

New York   San Francisco   Toronto   London

Circuits, matrices, and linear vector spaces

to my father and mother

Preface

Courses in circuit theory may have many goals. The introductory courses usually develop basic concepts which are applied throughout all subsequent studies of electrical engineering. The later undergraduate courses are usually set up to provide the student with an insight into specific circuits and devices. A common factor in all this education, perhaps not always realized by the student, is that the training he receives in circuits provides him with a foundation of knowledge which is applicable to many disciplines. This is perhaps one of the most worthwhile results that can occur from a study of any subject.

It is the purpose of this book to add to the undergraduate knowledge of circuits possessed by a senior or first-year graduate student in such a way as to broaden his foundation of knowledge, not only with respect to circuits, but with respect to other areas of study as well. Among its specific purposes are the following:

First, to encourage the student to think in terms which are as general as possible. Thus, we introduce the subject of matrix algebra, which provides a general means of formulation for the details of a linear system.

Second, to select a broad and versatile framework on which to base his observations of electrical circuits and system phenomena. Thus, we present the basic theory of n-dimensional spaces and show how this can be applied to linear systems.

Third, to teach the student to differentiate between models useful because they approximate physical devices and models useful because they are theoretically powerful or analytically simple. Thus, we present such modern circuit elements as the ideal transformer, the negative-immittance converter, and the gyrator and show how these may be used in the synthesis and analysis of electric circuits.

Finally, to aid the student in preparing for his own explorations into the literature of current journals and publications.

There are two dominant premises which have been followed in the organization of the material. First, it was desired to have the book as completely self-contained as possible, in that all the required concepts of matrix algebra and linear vector spaces would be developed as an integral part of the book. In the presentation of this mathematical material, a middle course has been chosen, avoiding the extremes of mathematical rigor in favor of emphasizing the concepts which are important from the viewpoint of application. Second, it was felt that comprehension of the mathematical material would be gained only as a result of thorough application. Thus, each chapter devoted to a mathematical presentation is immediately followed by a chapter in which that material is used as fully as possible.

There are several main divisions of the material. Chapter 1 briefly reviews some introductory ideas pertinent to later material. In Chapter 2, the mathematics of matrix algebra and determinants is developed. Special emphasis is placed on the techniques of partitioning and matrix equations, both of which are used in later sections of the book. Chapter 3 applies matrix techniques to a general discussion of circuits. The differences between port notation and terminal notation are presented. The properties and uses of indefinite-admittance matrices are developed. The various types of network parameters are discussed. The effects of dependent and independent sources on the matrix formulation are described. In Chapter 4, the properties of active and passive two-port devices such as the ideal transformer, the negative-immittance converter, and the gyrator are discussed. Synthesis methods for voltage transfer functions and for non-p-r driving-point functions using RC elements and active devices are developed. A section on n-port synthesis is included. Chapter 5 presents the basic theory of linear vector spaces with special emphasis on the representation of a vector in an n-dimensional space. This material is applied to a discussion of the natural frequencies of a network in Chapter 6. Formulations are made in the time domain and the frequency domain for the RC network, the LC network, and the RLC network. The effect of driving sources is included. Appendices are used to present somewhat more sophisticated topics in the areas covered by Chapters 3, 4, and 6. Specifically, they cover the indefinite-transfer matrix, gyrators with complex gyration admittance, and network transformations.

Depending on the background of the students and the approach favored by the instructor, the book may be used in several ways. For example, a one-semester course for senior students of all engineering disciplines might include the material of Chapters 2, 5, and 6, with some of the material of Chapter 3. In this case, the material of Chapter 6 might be augmented by some examples of mechanical systems. A one-semester course for graduate electrical-engineering students might omit

Chapter 2 and cover Chapters 3 to 6, with collateral reading assignments on the material in Chapter 4.

I would like to express my thanks and appreciation to the following: Prof. D. O. Pederson of the University of California, whose enthusiasm as a teacher first awakened my interest in circuits; Prof. M. E. Van Valkenberg of the University of Illinois, for his encouragement during the months of writing; Prof. A. Gill of the University of California, for his helpful criticism of the manuscript; and my students, whose searching questions have led to much revision of my original thoughts.

L. P. Huelsman

Contents

Circuits, matrices, and linear vector spaces

Chapter 1 *Introduction*

1.1 *Circuits and circuit elements*

There are several classifications under which circuits, as they are studied today, may be grouped. Some of these classifications are determined by the properties of the circuit elements, and some of them are the result of the manner in which these elements are interconnected. In this chapter we shall present some of the basic ideas concerning the classification of circuits and circuit elements according to their properties. This material will serve to introduce some of the terms that will frequently appear in later sections of the book. It will also serve to review some of the basic ideas of circuit theory. Additional information on the topics of this chapter can be found in the references listed in the final section of the chapter.

1.2 *Classifications of circuit elements*

In a consideration of the elements of which a circuit is composed, a first distinction must be made as to the number of terminals that such elements possess. Since a one-terminal element is without physical significance, let us begin by considering elements with two terminals. These elements can, in general, be grouped according to the following divisions: linear or non-linear, lumped or distributed, passive or active. Let us consider each of these classifications and discuss its principal characteristics.

A *linear* element can be defined in terms of the requirements of superposition and homogeneity. *Superposition* requires that, if two inputs are simultaneously applied to an element, the result be the sum of the results obtained from separate application of those same inputs. Thus, if the result of applying a d-c voltage of 1 volt to a given element is a d-c current of 1 amp through the element, and the result of applying an a-c voltage, $\sin 2t$, to the element is a current $2 \sin 2t$, superposition requires that, if an input voltage $1 + \sin 2t$ is applied to the element, a current $1 + 2 \sin 2t$ results. The principle of *homogeneity* may be explained as follows: If a given input produces a certain result, then multiplying the magnitude of the input by a constant will multiply the value of the result by the same constant. A linear circuit element is one which satisfies the requirements of superposition and homogeneity. No physical device is actually linear; however, it is convenient to approximate such devices by models which are idealized in the sense that they are defined as being linear.

A *lumped* element is one whose properties can be considered as concentrated in space. From another viewpoint, it is one in which the time of propagation of electrical phenomena through the element is zero. A transmission line is an example of a nonlumped element, i.e., a *distributed* device. Actually, all physical devices can be considered as being distributed, since they have nonzero dimensions. It is convenient, however, to approximate physical devices by models which are considered as lumped. Thus, we shall treat our circuit elements as lumped and linear.

Three of the basic circuit elements which we shall consider are the *positive-valued resistor*, the *positive-valued inductor*, and the *positive-valued capacitor*. These are the elements that relate voltage and current, voltage and the derivative of current, and voltage and the integral of current, respectively. They will be treated as lumped linear elements. They are considered as *passive* elements in that they approximate physical devices which do not require a source of energy to achieve their specified properties. We shall see that elements which can be described as *negative-valued* resistors, inductors, and capacitors can also be considered in our circuit studies. The physical devices which these elements approximate, in general, require external power sources to sustain their operation. Thus, these elements will be referred to as *active* elements.

Two other elements which we shall use in our discussion of circuits are the voltage source and the current source. These are both models which may or may not approximate physical devices, depending on the inclusion of parasitic elements of resistance, capacitance, and inductance. The *voltage source* has zero internal impedance, i.e., the voltage existing at its terminals is independent of the current flowing through the element. If its output voltage is a function of some other voltage or current in the circuit, it is said to be a *dependent source*. If it has an output which is not a function of any of the circuit variables (it may still, of course, be a function of time), it is said to be an *independent source*. Similarly, the *current source* has infinite internal impedance, i.e., its output current is independent of the potential difference existing across its terminals. It may be a dependent source, in which case its output will be a function of some other voltage or current in the circuit, or an independent source.

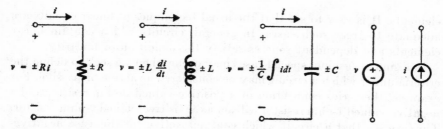

Figure 1.1   Symbols for circuit elements.

The usual symbols for the lumped linear passive and active circuit elements discussed above are shown in Fig. 1.1. In addition to these two-terminal elements, there are also some fundamental three-terminal and four-terminal circuit elements. These are the ideal transformer, the negative-immittance converter, and the gyrator. These are all linear elements. A more detailed discussion of them will be given in Chap. 4.

1.3   *Classifications of circuits*

Classifications similar to those made for the circuit elements described in the preceding section can be made for circuits comprised of such elements. There are, however, some interesting special cases. For example, we can consider a linear circuit as one comprised of linear elements, and thus we expect that the requirements of superposition and homogeneity will apply. An exception occurs when independent sources are present in the network. For example, consider the network shown in Fig. 1.2. If a voltage v of 5 volts is applied to this circuit, the current i is zero. Similarly, if a voltage v of 10 volts is applied, the current i is 1 amp. However, a voltage of 15 volts, which represents the simultaneous application of both the above inputs, causes a current of 2 amps to flow, in clear violation of the properties of linearity. Despite such discrepancies, it is convenient, in a broad sense, to consider as linear circuits those which are comprised of linear

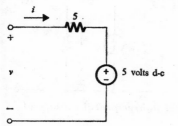

Figure 1.2   A circuit with an independent source.

elements. It is easy to see that the usual techniques of linear circuits are adequate to treat such cases. In general, circuits which contain linear elements and dependent sources satisfy the definition of linearity.

In a similar fashion, special cases may occur when we seek to define the criteria under which a circuit may be considered as active or passive. For example, the series connection of a positive-valued 3-ohm resistor and a negative-valued 1-ohm resistor will act as a positive-valued 2-ohm resistor. Thus we see that a circuit which contains active (in this case negative-valued) elements, can still act as a passive circuit. Despite this, however, it is convenient to define an active circuit as one which contains at least one active element. This definition will be used in the chapters that follow.

A classification that is made for circuits but which is not applicable to circuit elements is the division into reciprocal and nonreciprocal circuits. If, in a given circuit, when the points of excitation and observation of response are interchanged, the relationship between these two quantities remains the same, the circuit is said to be *reciprocal*. The interchange must not, of course, change the network. For a given circuit to be reciprocal, the above property must be true for any choice of the points of excitation and observation of response. A further discussion of the properties of reciprocal networks is given in Chap. 3. We shall point out at this time, however, that circuits composed entirely of linear R, L, and C elements, both negative- and positive-valued, are always reciprocal. Circuits which contain dependent sources may or may not be reciprocal. Nonreciprocal circuits usually fall into two categories. First, they may be unilateral, in the sense that when some points of excitation and observation of response are interchanged, no response is observed. Second, they may provide different relations between excitation and response when these quantities are interchanged. As examples, consider the networks shown in Figs. 1.3 to 1.5. The network shown in Fig. 1.3 is reciprocal; i.e., if a current is applied from terminal 1 to terminal 2, the resulting voltage, measured between terminals 3 and 4, will be the same as if the current had been

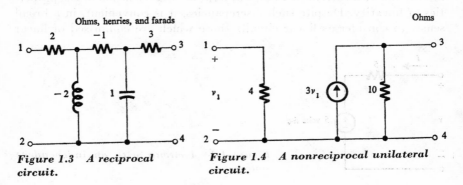

Figure 1.3   A reciprocal circuit.

Figure 1.4   A nonreciprocal unilateral circuit.

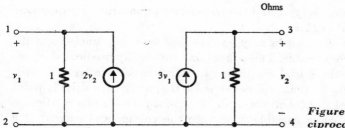

Figure 1.5   A nonre-
ciprocal circuit.

applied from terminal 3 to terminal 4 and the voltage measured between terminals 1 and 2. The network shown in Fig. 1.4 is unilateral in the sense that a voltage or current excitation applied at terminals 1 and 2 will produce an observable effect at terminals 3 and 4, but the converse is not true. In the network shown in Fig. 1.5, an excitation applied at terminals 1 and 2 will produce an observable effect at terminals 3 and 4, and vice versa; however, the relation between excitation and response in these two cases will be different. Thus we see that the networks shown in Figs. 1.4 and 1.5 are nonreciprocal.

1.4   *Network functions*

The actual variables of voltage, current, charge, etc., which are associated with a given circuit or with its elements are, of course, functions of time. The equations that relate these variables are linear differential equations, and if the values of the elements are constant, the coefficients of these equations are also constant. Thus we speak of time-invariant circuit elements and circuits. Some of the developments which will be made in future chapters will deal directly with these variables. Thus we will refer to an analysis as being made in the *time domain*. Other developments will deal with variables obtained by applying the one-sided Laplace transform to the original variables. Variables developed by the transformation are considered as functions of a complex frequency variable. Thus we have a *frequency domain*. The defining relation is[1]

$$A_i(p) = \int_0^\infty a_i(t)e^{-pt}\,dt \tag{1}$$

where $a_i(t)$ is any variable such as voltage, current, or charge. The functional notations (t) and (p) will be used where necessary for emphasis. Where feasible, the original quantities which are functions of time will be

---

[1] The letter s is used in many texts for the complex frequency variable. The use of p is preferable, however, since s is also widely used to denote elastance (reciprocal capacitance).

indicated by lowercase type, and the transformed quantities by uppercase type, as indicated in (1).

The properties of networks may be described by using functions of the complex frequency variable. These functions are usually predicated on the assumption that the initial conditions in the network are treated separately. The functions that will occur most frequently are driving-point functions and transfer functions. A *driving-point function* is a relation in the complex frequency variable p between the voltage and current at a given pair of terminals when the network is excited at these terminals. The ratio of $I(p)/V(p)$, i.e., the ratio of the transform of the current to the transform of the voltage, is referred to as a driving-point *admittance* function. The inverse ratio is referred to as a driving-point *impedance* function. Both relationships, collectively, are referred to as driving-point *immittance* functions.

Transfer functions relate transformed voltage and/or current variables at one point of a network to transformed voltage and/or current variables at some other point of the network. There are several combinations. For example, we can have *transfer-voltage ratios*, *transfer-current ratios*, and *transfer immittances*, depending on the quantities of interest. If the elements of the circuit are restricted to the lumped linear case, the functions will be ratios of polynomials in the variable p with real coefficients. In this case they are frequently referred to as rational functions.

1.5   *The use of examples*

The reader will find that Chaps. 2 and 5 are used to develop the basic mathematical concepts of matrices and linear vector spaces. Chapters 3, 4, and 6 cover the application of these concepts to general relationships in circuit analysis and synthesis. These applications are illustrated by examples which form an integral part of the presentation of the material. The reader is strongly urged to follow these examples through in detail and to complete any omitted steps. This procedure provides a powerful means of strengthening one's grasp of the basic concepts. It is an excellent self-test to make certain that new principles have been correctly assimilated. For convenience, the element values in the actual circuit examples have been chosen with a view toward simplifying the resulting computations. For example, liberal use has been made of 1-farad capacitors without regard for the availability of such elements. It should be realized, however, that these element values can be viewed as derived from frequency and impedance normalizations on the circuit. Thus, appropriate frequency and/or impedance *de*normalizations can always be made on these example networks to change them to more practical situations. Specifically, we may define a frequency-denormalization constant f_n and an impedance-denor-

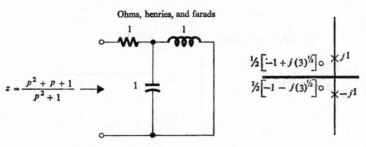

Figure 1.6   *A simple network.*

malization constant r_n. The relations between the given normalized network element values R, L, and C and the element values after denormalization R', L', and C' are

$$R' = r_n R$$
$$L' = \frac{r_n}{f_n} L$$
$$C' = \frac{1}{r_n f_n} C \qquad (1)$$

where r_n and f_n are real numbers. The frequency-denormalization constant will transform the frequency characteristics of the given network by the relation

$$p' = f_n p \qquad (2)$$

where p is the complex value of any point in the frequency plane characterizing the original normalized network, and p' is the complex value of the corresponding point in the frequency plane characterizing the denormalized network. A frequency denormalization leaves the impedance level of the network unchanged. Similarly, an impedance denormalization leaves the frequency characteristics of the network unchanged. As an example, consider the network shown in Fig. 1.6. The driving-point impedance z and the pole and zero locations on the p plane for this network are shown in the figure. Note that $z(0) = 1$; i.e., the impedance of

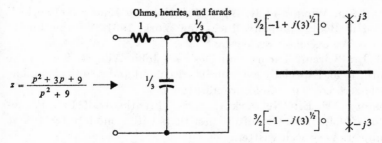

Figure 1.7   *The result of frequency denormalization* $(f_n = 3)$.

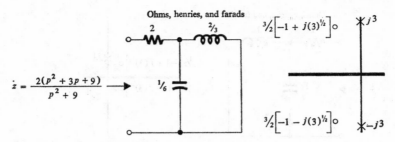

Figure 1.8   The result of impedance denormalization $(r_n = 2)$.

the network at zero frequency is unity. Now let us apply a frequency denormalization. Let $f_n = 3$. The network after frequency denormalization is shown in Fig. 1.7, together with its driving-point impedance and its pole and zero locations. It is easy to see that the complex values of the pole and zero locations have been shifted according to (2), but that $z(0) = 1$ as before. Now let us apply an impedance denormalization $r_n = 2$ to the network of Fig. 1.7. The result is shown in Fig. 1.8. Note that there are no changes in the pole and zero locations, but that the impedance $z(0) = 2$. Similar observations, of course, apply to the impedance at any other value of complex frequency, as may easily be verified by the reader.

1.6   *References for review*

Additional information on the topics of this chapter may be found in the texts referenced below. They are well equipped with problems which the reader may use for review. Due to the extensive quantity of material in this field, the compilation of a complete list has not been attempted. The entries listed should suffice to answer most questions.

Balabanian, N.: "Fundamentals of Circuit Theory," Allyn and Bacon, Inc., Englewood Cliffs, N.J., 1961. A clear and readable introductory treatment.

Friedland, B., O. Wing, and R. Ash: "Principles of Linear Networks," McGraw-Hill Book Company, Inc., New York, 1961. Notable for its conciseness. An excellent review text.

Stewart, J. L.: "Circuit Theory and Design," John Wiley & Sons, Inc., New York, 1956. Especially good for its treatment and practical emphasis of pole-zero concepts and normalizations.

Van Valkenburg, M. E.: "Network Analysis," Prentice-Hall, Inc., Englewood Cliffs, N.J., 1955. One of the first texts with a modern treatment of its subject. Very well written.

Chapter 2 *Matrices and determinants*

2.1 *Introduction*

In the last chapter, a review of some of the properties of various types of circuits was made. It was pointed out that we are restricting ourselves to circuits containing lumped linear time-invariant elements. In describing such circuits, frequent use is made of a linear equation or a set of linear equations. The latter is sometimes referred to as a *set of simultaneous equations*. In later chapters we shall see that there are several ways in which such equations can be developed. In this chapter, however, we are concerned with a study of the set of equations itself. An example of such a set can be made by writing the nodal equations for the circuit shown in Fig. 2.1. The equations are:

$$\begin{aligned} I_1 &= (Y_a + Y_b)V_1 - Y_bV_2 \\ I_2 &= -Y_bV_1 + (Y_b + Y_c)V_2 \end{aligned} \tag{1}$$

The quantities I_1 and I_2 may be considered as "known" quantities or independent variables. Similarly V_1 and V_2 are referred to as "unknowns" or dependent variables. Y_a, Y_b, and Y_c are admittances. All the above quantities are functions of the complex frequency variable p.

For more complicated networks we can generalize (1) by considering an n-node network ($n + 1$ nodes if the reference node is counted). For this network a set of n equations will result. These will have the form

$$\begin{aligned} I_1 &= Y_{11}V_1 + Y_{12}V_2 + \cdots + Y_{1n}V_n \\ I_2 &= Y_{21}V_1 + Y_{22}V_2 + \cdots + Y_{2n}V_n \\ &\;\; \cdots\cdots\cdots\cdots\cdots\cdots\cdots\cdots \\ I_n &= Y_{n1}V_1 + Y_{n2}V_2 + \cdots + Y_{nn}V_n \end{aligned} \tag{2}$$

A simplification of nomenclature has been achieved by the use of the

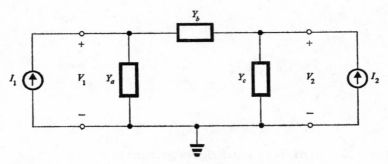

Figure 2.1 A network with two nodal voltage variables.

quantity Y_{ij}. The i subscript refers to the number of the equation (from 1 at the top to n at the bottom). This is also the number of the *row* in which the equation is located. The quantities $Y_{ij}V_j$ may be thought of as occurring in vertical *columns* (separated by addition symbols). Thus, the second subscript, j, refers to the column (numbered from 1 at the left to n at the right) in which the quantity Y_{ij} is located. Physically, the quantities Y_{ij} $(i = j)$ represent the totality of admittance connected to the ith node (or the jth node since $i = j$). Similarly the quantities Y_{ij} $(i \neq j)$ represent the mutual admittance between nodes i and j.[1]

A set of equations similar in their general form to (2) could be written on a loop (or mesh) basis. In this case the positions of all the voltage and current variables would be interchanged. Other sets of equations are possible if only part of the voltages and currents of (2) are interchanged. To achieve a maximum of generality we shall consider a set of equations of the form

$$
\begin{aligned}
U_1 &= a_{11}X_1 + a_{12}X_2 + \cdots + a_{1n}X_n \\
U_2 &= a_{21}X_1 + a_{22}X_2 + \cdots + a_{2n}X_n \\
&\;\cdots\cdots\cdots\cdots\cdots\cdots\cdots\cdots \\
U_n &= a_{n1}X_1 + a_{n2}X_2 + \cdots + a_{nn}X_n
\end{aligned}
\tag{3}
$$

If equations (3) are being used to describe a circuit, the quantities U_i will usually represent voltages and currents (as will the quantities X_i). The quantities a_{ij} will, in general, be restricted such that they are not functions of X_i or U_i and do not vary with time. Thus we shall restrict our interest to a *linear* set of equations with time-invariant coefficients. The set of equations (3) applies not only to linear circuits, but to any linear systems, e.g., mechanical, hydraulic, and economic. The purpose of this chapter is to discuss the properties of such a set of equations and to present methods for their manipulation which are of use in circuit and system theory.

[1] The value of the mutual admittance will be multiplied by $+1$ or -1, depending on the reference polarities of the nodal voltages.

2.2 *Matrices*

In the set of equations (3) in Sec. 2.1 let us "erase" the following quantities: the "plus" signs, the "equals" signs, the quantities U_i and X_i. What remains is an *array* of the elements a_{ij}:

$$
\begin{matrix}
a_{11} & a_{12} & \cdots & a_{1n} \\
a_{21} & a_{22} & \cdots & a_{2n} \\
\cdots & \cdots & \cdots & \cdots \\
a_{n1} & a_{n2} & \cdots & a_{nn}
\end{matrix}
\tag{1}
$$

This array is referred to as a matrix, and it is usually enclosed in brackets to emphasize its existence as a unique entity. We can make the following definition: A *matrix* is a rectangular array of elements arranged in horizontal lines (called rows) and vertical lines (called columns).

The elements referred to in the definition, in general, will be numbers (real or complex) or functions. Functions of the complex frequency variable form an especially important class of elements.

Several examples of matrices follow:

$$
\begin{bmatrix} 1 & 2 \\ 3 & 4 \\ 5 & 6 \end{bmatrix}
\quad
\begin{bmatrix} 1+j \\ 3 \\ 4+3j \end{bmatrix}
\quad
\underbrace{X_1 \quad X_2}
\quad
\begin{bmatrix} \dfrac{p}{p^2+3} & p+2 \\ p+4 & \dfrac{3}{p^2} \end{bmatrix}
\tag{2}
$$

A first method of characterizing matrices is by the numbers of rows and columns they contain. In general, we refer to a specific array as an $m \times n$ matrix if it has m rows and n columns. If $m = n$ the array is called a *square matrix*. If $m = 1$ and $n > 1$, i.e., if there is only one row, the array is called a *row matrix*. If $m > 1$ and $n = 1$, the array is called a *column matrix*. Row and column matrices are frequently shown with a slightly different arrangement of the brackets. Thus, the matrices shown in (2) are, respectively,

Size of array	*Type of matrix*
3×2	Rectangular
3×1	Column
1×2	Row
2×2	Square

One of the uses of matrices will be a simplification of notation where sets of equations are to be considered. Thus it will be convenient to express the matrix (1) in a system of notation whereby a single symbol represents the entire array. There are two convenient symbols frequently used for this purpose. We may define

$$[A] = [a_{ij}] = \begin{bmatrix} a_{11} & a_{12} & \cdots & a_{1n} \\ a_{21} & a_{22} & \cdots & a_{2n} \\ \cdots\cdots\cdots\cdots\cdots\cdots \\ a_{n1} & a_{n2} & \cdots & a_{nn} \end{bmatrix} \tag{3}$$

Note that the symbol $[A]$ or the symbol $[a_{ij}]$ can only *represent* the matrix, it cannot yield the information contained in the array. As a compact representation, however, it is a useful one. Frequently we shall omit the brackets and simply refer to the array by the letter alone, i.e., by A. Sometimes, however, for emphasis, it will be helpful to use the containing brackets to indicate that the matrix is square; thus we may write $[A]$. Similarly, a single bracket may be used to indicate a column matrix, as $B]$. A horizontal bracket may be used where it is necessary to emphasize that the matrix is a row matrix, as $\underline{C}$. Boldface type will be used whenever a symbol such as A is used to refer to an array of elements without regard to the size of the array. The distinction should be clearly made at this time by the student that a symbol such as A is a label for the matrix, while a_{ij} is a typical element of the matrix, common to row i and column j. This typical element will usually be written as the lowercase of the letter chosen for the label.

2.3   *Determinants*

In studying real or complex variables, considerable attention is given to *functions* of these variables. In the study of the properties of a matrix, there are also functions to be studied. Of particular interest at this point is a function of the *array* (more specifically of the *elements* of the *array*) called a determinant. To emphasize this point: the matrix *is* the array, the determinant is a *function* of the *elements* of the array. This function only applies to square arrays, i.e., to square matrices, and may be defined by the following steps:

Step 1. Form all possible combinations of products of the elements of the array such that each combination contains only one element from each row and each column. For an $n \times n$ array there will be $n!$ of these combinations.

Step 2. In each combination arrange the elements according to ascending order of the *first* subscript.

Step 3. Interchange elements in each combination in such a manner that they are now arranged according to the ascending order of the *second* subscript.

Step 4. Count the number of interchanges required in step 3. If the number is even, prefix a plus sign to the combination. If the number is odd, prefix a minus sign.

Step 5. Sum the combinations of products of the elements using the signs determined in step 4. The result is the determinant of the array. Since the determinant is unique, it follows that the parity determined by the interchanges in step 4 will also be unique, although the number of interchanges may be varied by different approaches to step 3.

As an example consider the following 2×2 array:

$$\begin{bmatrix} a_{11} & a_{12} \\ a_{21} & a_{22} \end{bmatrix}$$

Step 1. $a_{11}a_{22}$ and $a_{12}a_{21}$ are the only possible combinations.

Step 2. The combinations arranged according to the ascending order of the *first* subscript are:

$$a_{11}a_{22} \qquad a_{12}a_{21}$$

Step 3. The combinations arranged according to the ascending order of the second subscript (with the necessary interchanges of elements from step 2 indicated by arrows) are:

$$a_{11}a_{22} \qquad a_{21}a_{12}$$

Step 4. In going from step 2 to step 3, zero interchanges (an even number) are necessary in the first combination; one interchange (an odd number) is necessary in the second combination. The combinations with their proper signs are $+a_{11}a_{22}$ and $-a_{12}a_{21}$.

Step 5. Summing the above, we obtain

$$a_{11}a_{22} - a_{12}a_{21}$$

as the value of the determinant. Thus, as a numerical example, we see that

$$\text{determinant} \begin{bmatrix} 1 & 2 \\ 3 & 4 \end{bmatrix} = -2$$

As another example consider the following 3×3 array:

$$\begin{bmatrix} a_{11} & a_{12} & a_{13} \\ a_{21} & a_{22} & a_{23} \\ a_{31} & a_{32} & a_{33} \end{bmatrix}$$

Steps 1 and 2. The combinations grouped according to the ascending order of the first subscript are:

$$a_{11}a_{22}a_{33} \qquad a_{11}a_{23}a_{32} \qquad a_{12}a_{21}a_{33}$$
$$a_{12}a_{23}a_{31} \qquad a_{13}a_{22}a_{31} \qquad a_{13}a_{21}a_{32}$$

Step 3. The combinations grouped according to the ascending order of the second subscript (with the necessary interchanges of elements from step 2 indicated by arrows) are:

$$a_{11}a_{22}a_{33} \qquad a_{11}a_{32}a_{23} \qquad a_{21}a_{12}a_{33}$$

$$a_{31}a_{12}a_{23} \qquad a_{31}a_{22}a_{13} \qquad a_{21}a_{32}a_{13}$$

Steps 4 and 5. Summing the above terms with the **proper signs**, we obtain

$$a_{11}a_{22}a_{33} - a_{11}a_{32}a_{23} - a_{21}a_{12}a_{33}$$
$$+ a_{31}a_{12}a_{23} - a_{31}a_{22}a_{13} + a_{21}a_{32}a_{13}$$

as the value of the determinant.

It should be noted that for a 1×1 array, i.e., an array consisting of a single element, it is convenient to define the determinant as being equal to the element itself. This definition is consistent with the steps defined above. Thus,

$$\text{determinant } [a_{11}] = a_{11}$$

It will be convenient to adopt a symbolic means of referring to the determinant of an array. This will be parallel vertical lines on each side of the array. The determinant of a matrix A will also be indicated by "det A." Thus, we have

$$\det A = \begin{vmatrix} a_{11} & a_{12} & \cdots & a_{1n} \\ a_{21} & a_{22} & \cdots & a_{2n} \\ \cdots & \cdots & \cdots & \cdots \\ a_{n1} & a_{n2} & \cdots & a_{nn} \end{vmatrix} \tag{1}$$

Although the steps given above serve to define a determinant, in general, they do not provide the most convenient way for evaluating this function. Therefore, in the next section we shall introduce some easier methods of finding the determinant of a given array.

2.4   *Evaluating the determinant*

If, from an $n \times n$ array of elements, a row and a column are deleted, the elements that remain (after rearrangement to eliminate the empty spaces) form an $(n - 1) \times (n - 1)$ array of elements. For example, deletion of the second row and the third column of a 4×4 array may be performed as follows:

$$\begin{bmatrix} a_{11} & a_{12} & a_{13} & a_{14} \\ a_{21} & a_{22} & a_{23} & a_{24} \\ a_{31} & a_{32} & a_{33} & a_{34} \\ a_{41} & a_{42} & a_{43} & a_{44} \end{bmatrix} \rightarrow \begin{bmatrix} a_{11} & a_{12} & & a_{14} \\ & & & \\ a_{31} & a_{32} & & a_{34} \\ a_{41} & a_{42} & & a_{44} \end{bmatrix} \rightarrow \begin{bmatrix} a_{11} & a_{12} & a_{14} \\ a_{31} & a_{32} & a_{34} \\ a_{41} & a_{42} & a_{44} \end{bmatrix}$$

Thus a 3×3 array of elements is formed. The determinant of the 3×3 array of elements is called a *minor* of the 4×4 array of elements.[1] If we multiply the minor by $(-1)^{i+j}$, where i is the number of the row deleted and j is the number of the column deleted, the resulting function is called a *cofactor* and is indicated by the symbol A_{ij}. The cofactor is frequently referred to as a "signed" minor. Thus, in the above example,

$$A_{23} = (-1)^{2+3} \begin{vmatrix} a_{11} & a_{12} & a_{14} \\ a_{31} & a_{32} & a_{34} \\ a_{41} & a_{42} & a_{44} \end{vmatrix}$$

Similarly, for a 3×3 array,

$$\begin{bmatrix} a_{11} & a_{12} & a_{13} \\ a_{21} & a_{22} & a_{23} \\ a_{31} & a_{32} & a_{33} \end{bmatrix}$$

the cofactors for the elements in the first row are

$$A_{11} = (-1)^{1+1} \begin{vmatrix} a_{22} & a_{23} \\ a_{32} & a_{33} \end{vmatrix} \qquad A_{12} = (-1)^{1+2} \begin{vmatrix} a_{21} & a_{23} \\ a_{31} & a_{33} \end{vmatrix}$$

$$A_{13} = (-1)^{1+3} \begin{vmatrix} a_{21} & a_{22} \\ a_{31} & a_{32} \end{vmatrix} \quad (1)$$

It should be clear that there are n^2 cofactors for an $n \times n$ array.

One of the ways in which a determinant may be evaluated is by *expanding* the array in terms of the elements of a given row or column and the cofactors corresponding to these elements. For an expansion along the ith row of an $n \times n$ array $[a_{ij}]$, we may write

$$\det A = \sum_{k=1}^{n} a_{ik} A_{ik} \quad (2)$$

This says that we form a sum of the products of each of the elements in the ith row and the cofactor formed by deleting the ith row and the

[1] This is frequently termed a *first-order minor determinant* of the array. Higher-order minors are formed by simultaneously deleting more than one row and column.

column in which the element is located. For example, for a 3×3 array, expanding along the first row (i.e., for $i = 1$),

$$\det A = a_{11}A_{11} + a_{12}A_{12} + a_{13}A_{13}$$

From (1) we may write

$$\det A = a_{11}\begin{vmatrix} a_{22} & a_{23} \\ a_{32} & a_{33} \end{vmatrix} - a_{12}\begin{vmatrix} a_{21} & a_{23} \\ a_{31} & a_{33} \end{vmatrix} + a_{13}\begin{vmatrix} a_{21} & a_{22} \\ a_{31} & a_{32} \end{vmatrix} \tag{3}$$

Similarly, for a 2×2 matrix, expanding along the first row yields

$$\det A = a_{11}A_{11} + a_{12}A_{12}$$

The cofactors are found as follows:

$$A_{11} = (-1)^{1+1} \det [a_{22}] = a_{22}$$
$$A_{12} = (-1)^{1+2} \det [a_{21}] = -a_{21}$$

The determinant for a 2×2 array is now seen to be

$$\det A = a_{11}a_{22} - a_{12}a_{21} \tag{4}$$

We may apply this result to the 2×2 determinants which occur in the expression for the value of the determinant of a 3×3 array given in (3). This expression becomes

$$\det A = a_{11}(a_{22}a_{33} - a_{23}a_{32}) - a_{12}(a_{21}a_{33} - a_{23}a_{31}) + a_{13}(a_{21}a_{32} - a_{22}a_{31}) \tag{5}$$

The results of (4) and (5) for a 2×2 and a 3×3 array, respectively, may easily be seen to be identical with the results of the examples of Sec. 2.3.

If we expand the determinant along any *column*, e.g., the jth column, we get

$$\det A = \sum_{k=1}^{n} a_{kj}A_{kj} \tag{6}$$

The steps of the process are similar to those illustrated for the row expansions above.

By means of the expansion formulas (2) and (6), therefore, we may calculate the determinant of an $n \times n$ array in terms of determinants of $(n - 1) \times (n - 1)$ arrays. These determinants are called minors. These in turn may be expressed in terms of determinants of $(n - 2) \times (n - 2)$ arrays. The process may be continued until we finally arrive at determinants of 1×1 arrays which, as we have noted, are the elements themselves. Thus the equations (2) and (6) provide the means to evaluate a determinant of an array of any size by a systematic procedure. The equations are special cases of a more general method of evaluating a determinant known as Laplace's expansion.

When a 2×2 determinant is to be evaluated, an easily remembered procedure is as follows: Multiply elements along the diagonals and affix positive and negative signs as indicated below:

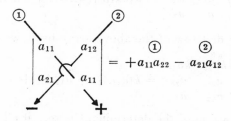

For a 3×3 matrix we may use a similar procedure. The first and second columns have been repeated for convenience:

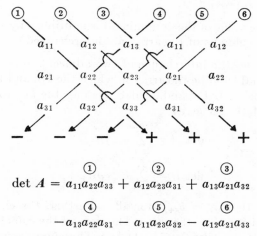

$$\det A = a_{11}a_{22}a_{33} + a_{12}a_{23}a_{31} + a_{13}a_{21}a_{32}$$

$$- a_{13}a_{22}a_{31} - a_{11}a_{23}a_{32} - a_{12}a_{21}a_{33}$$

It is easily seen that these results are the same as those previously determined.

2.5 *Properties of determinants*

Several of the most fundamental properties of a determinant may be developed by means of the Laplace expansion:

Property 1 The value of a determinant is multiplied by a constant k if all the elements of any row or column are multiplied by the constant k.

This is easily seen, since, if we expand about the row or column which has been so multiplied, each element of the expansion is multiplied by the same constant. For example,

$$\begin{vmatrix} a_{11} & a_{12} & a_{13} \\ a_{21} & a_{22} & a_{23} \\ a_{31} & a_{32} & a_{33} \end{vmatrix} = a_{11}A_{11} + a_{12}A_{12} + a_{13}A_{13}$$

If we multiply the first row of the above array by k, we obtain

$$\begin{vmatrix} ka_{11} & ka_{12} & ka_{13} \\ a_{21} & a_{22} & a_{23} \\ a_{31} & a_{32} & a_{33} \end{vmatrix} = k(a_{11}A_{11} + a_{12}A_{12} + a_{13}A_{13})$$

Property 2 The value of the determinant is zero if all the elements of any row or any column are zero.

In Property 1, we need only choose zero as the specific value of the multiplying constant to prove this.

Property 3 The value of the determinant is multiplied by -1 if any two rows or any two columns of the array are interchanged.

First let us consider the interchange of two adjacent rows. Let A be the original array, and let B be the array in which the kth and the $(k + 1)$th rows are interchanged. Expanding det A along the kth row and det B along the $(k + 1)$th row gives

$$\det A = \sum_{i=1}^{n} a_{ki}A_{ki}$$

$$\det B = \sum_{i=1}^{n} b_{k+1,i}B_{k+1,i}$$

It is easily seen that $a_{ki} = b_{k+1,i}$ for all i. Further, the elements of the cofactors A_{ki} and $B_{k+1,i}$ are the same. The signs of the cofactors, however, are opposite, since $(-1)^{k+i} = -(-1)^{k+1+i}$. Therefore, $A_{ki} = -B_{k+1,i}$ for all i. Thus, det $A = -$det B. This is illustrated below for a 3×3 array with the first and second rows interchanged:

$$\det A = \begin{vmatrix} a_{11} & a_{12} & a_{13} \\ a_{21} & a_{22} & a_{23} \\ a_{31} & a_{32} & a_{33} \end{vmatrix} = a_{11}(-1)^{1+1}\begin{vmatrix} a_{22} & a_{23} \\ a_{32} & a_{33} \end{vmatrix} + a_{12}(-1)^{1+2}\begin{vmatrix} a_{21} & a_{23} \\ a_{31} & a_{33} \end{vmatrix}$$

$$+ a_{13}(-1)^{1+3}\begin{vmatrix} a_{21} & a_{22} \\ a_{31} & a_{32} \end{vmatrix}$$

$$\det B = \begin{vmatrix} a_{21} & a_{22} & a_{23} \\ a_{11} & a_{12} & a_{13} \\ a_{31} & a_{32} & a_{33} \end{vmatrix} = a_{11}(-1)^{2+1}\begin{vmatrix} a_{22} & a_{23} \\ a_{32} & a_{33} \end{vmatrix} + a_{12}(-1)^{2+2}\begin{vmatrix} a_{21} & a_{23} \\ a_{31} & a_{33} \end{vmatrix}$$

$$+ a_{13}(-1)^{2+3}\begin{vmatrix} a_{21} & a_{22} \\ a_{31} & a_{32} \end{vmatrix}$$

It is easy to see that an identical proof holds true when adjacent columns are interchanged, since the expansions may be made equally well along columns.

Any interchange of two nonadjacent rows or columns can be accomplished by successive interchanges of adjacent rows or columns. Thus to interchange rows *1* and *3* below:

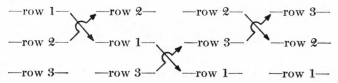

It may be shown that when k rows intervene between the rows being interchanged, exactly $2k + 1$ interchanges of *adjacent* rows will suffice. Since each interchange of adjacent rows multiplies the determinant by -1, and since $2k + 1$ is always odd, the result of the interchange of any two rows is to multiply the determinant by -1. The same is clearly true for any two columns.

Property 4 If a determinant has two identical rows or two identical columns, its value is zero.

By Property 3 above, if we interchange the two identical rows or columns we get the negative of the value of the determinant. After the interchange, however, the array is the same as before. Therefore, the value of the determinant must be the same. The only number that is equal to its negative is zero; therefore this is the value of the determinant.

Note that this property also applies when any row is a fixed multiple of another row or any column is a fixed multiple of another column. For example, if one row is k times another, then, by Property 1, we may divide this row by k and multiply the determinant by k, leaving its value unchanged. Since we now have two identical rows, however, by the above reasoning the value of the determinant is zero. Obviously the same holds true for columns.

Property 5 An expansion formed from the elements of one row and the cofactors of the corresponding elements of any other row has a value of zero. The same is true with respect to columns.

Assume that an expansion is made by using the elements of the first row associated with the cofactors of the elements of the second row of a given array. The elements of the second row do not appear in the expansion. In fact, the expansion is exactly that which would occur if the elements of the first and the second rows were identical. Therefore, by Property 4, the value of the determinant, i.e., the result of such an expansion, must be zero. For example, for the array

$$\begin{bmatrix} a_{11} & a_{12} & a_{13} \\ a_{21} & a_{22} & a_{23} \\ a_{31} & a_{32} & a_{33} \end{bmatrix}$$

an expansion in terms of the elements of the first row and the cofactors of the elements of the second row yields

$$a_{11}(-1)^{2+1}\begin{vmatrix} a_{12} & a_{13} \\ a_{32} & a_{33} \end{vmatrix} + a_{12}(-1)^{2+2}\begin{vmatrix} a_{11} & a_{13} \\ a_{31} & a_{33} \end{vmatrix} + a_{13}(-1)^{2+3}\begin{vmatrix} a_{11} & a_{12} \\ a_{31} & a_{32} \end{vmatrix}$$

It is easily seen that this is exactly the expansion that would result from expanding the array

$$\begin{bmatrix} a_{11} & a_{12} & a_{13} \\ a_{11} & a_{12} & a_{13} \\ a_{31} & a_{32} & a_{33} \end{bmatrix}$$

along its second row. A similar proof applies to columns.

Property 6 To any row of an array of elements can be added a multiple of any other row without changing the value of the determinant of the array. The same is true with respect to columns.

For example, consider the *i*th row of an array of elements. The determinant may be found by expanding along this row as follows:

$$\det A = \sum_{j=1}^{n} a_{ij}A_{ij}$$

If we add the k-multiplied mth row to the ith row, we may write the new expansion along the ith row as

$$\sum_{j=1}^{n} (a_{ij} + ka_{mj})A_{ij}$$

This can be written as the sum of two summations:

$$\sum_{j=1}^{n} a_{ij}A_{ij} + k \sum_{j=1}^{n} a_{mj}A_{ij}$$

The second summation above, however, is an expansion of the elements of one row with the cofactors of the corresponding elements of another row. By Property 5, this is equal to zero. Thus, the value of the determinant is unchanged. A similar proof holds with respect to modifying the elements of any column.

Property 7 The determinant of a triangular array is equal to the product of the diagonal elements.

We may define a triangular array as one in which all the elements below the main diagonal (the main diagonal of an array is the diagonal from the upper left-hand corner element of the array to the lower right-hand corner element) are equal to zero. Thus, if we expand along the first column, we obtain only the element a_{11} times its cofactor. To find the cofactor we take the new array of elements (formed by deleting the first row and column of the original array) and expand down its first column. The result is again the upper left-hand corner term times its cofactor. Continuing this process yields the product of the diagonal terms. The process is illustrated below:

$$\begin{vmatrix} a_{11} & a_{12} & a_{13} & a_{14} & \cdot \cdot \cdot & a_{1n} \\ 0 & a_{22} & a_{23} & a_{24} & \cdot \cdot \cdot & a_{2n} \\ 0 & 0 & a_{33} & a_{34} & \cdot \cdot \cdot & a_{3n} \\ 0 & 0 & 0 & a_{44} & \cdot \cdot \cdot & a_{4n} \\ \cdot & \cdot & \cdot & \cdot & \cdot \cdot \cdot \cdot & \cdot \\ 0 & 0 & 0 & 0 & \cdot \cdot \cdot & a_{nn} \end{vmatrix} = a_{11}a_{22}a_{33}a_{44} \cdot \cdot \cdot a_{nn}$$

Property 8 Any matrix can be reduced to triangular form without changing the value of the determinant.

This may be done in steps as follows:

Step 1. Multiply the first row of the array by $-a_{21}/a_{11}$ and add this row to the second row. Similarly, multiply the first row by $-a_{31}/a_{11}$ and add it to the third row. Continue, finally adding the first row, multiplied by $-a_{n1}/a_{11}$, to the nth row. By Property 6, the value of the determinant is not changed by these steps. The array now appears as follows:[1]

$$\begin{bmatrix} a_{11} & a_{12} & a_{13} & \cdot \cdot \cdot & a_{1n} \\ 0 & b_{22} & b_{23} & \cdot \cdot \cdot & b_{2n} \\ 0 & b_{32} & b_{33} & \cdot \cdot \cdot & b_{3n} \\ \cdot & \cdot & \cdot & \cdot \cdot \cdot \cdot & \cdot \\ 0 & b_{n2} & b_{n3} & \cdot \cdot \cdot & b_{nn} \end{bmatrix} \qquad (1)$$

where

$$b_{22} = a_{22} - \frac{a_{21}}{a_{11}} a_{12} \quad \cdot \cdot \cdot \quad b_{2n} = a_{2n} - \frac{a_{21}}{a_{11}} a_{1n}$$

$$b_{32} = a_{32} - \frac{a_{31}}{a_{11}} a_{12} \quad \cdot \cdot \cdot \quad b_{3n} = a_{3n} - \frac{a_{31}}{a_{11}} a_{1n}$$

$$\cdot \cdot \cdot \cdot \cdot \cdot \cdot \cdot \cdot \qquad \cdot \cdot \cdot \qquad \cdot \cdot \cdot \cdot \cdot \cdot \cdot \cdot$$

$$b_{n2} = a_{n2} - \frac{a_{n1}}{a_{11}} a_{12} \quad \cdot \cdot \cdot \quad b_{nn} = a_{nn} - \frac{a_{n1}}{a_{11}} a_{1n}$$

[1] If $a_{11} = 0$, then the rows or columns of the array should be rearranged so that the element in the first row and the first column is not zero. This can be done without changing the value of the determinant if appropriate sign corrections are made (see Property 3). The same comment applies to the following steps.

Step 2. Multiply the second row of (1) by $-b_{32}/b_{22}$ and add the result to the third row. Continue in this manner until the second row of (1) is multiplied by $-b_{n2}/b_{22}$ and added to the nth row. The resulting array, still with the same determinant, is

$$\begin{bmatrix} a_{11} & a_{12} & a_{13} & \cdots & a_{1n} \\ 0 & b_{22} & b_{23} & \cdots & b_{2n} \\ 0 & 0 & c_{33} & \cdots & c_{3n} \\ \cdot\cdot\cdot\cdot\cdot\cdot\cdot\cdot\cdot\cdot\cdot\cdot \\ 0 & 0 & c_{n3} & \cdots & c_{nn} \end{bmatrix}$$

where

$$c_{33} = b_{33} - \frac{b_{32}}{b_{22}} b_{23} \quad \cdots \quad c_{3n} = b_{3n} - \frac{b_{32}}{b_{22}} b_{2n}$$

$$\cdots\cdots\cdots\cdots \quad \cdots \quad \cdots\cdots\cdots\cdots$$

$$c_{n3} = b_{n3} - \frac{b_{n2}}{b_{22}} b_{23} \quad \cdots \quad c_{nn} = b_{nn} - \frac{b_{n2}}{b_{22}} b_{2n}$$

This process can be repeated as many times as necessary, each repetition creating a column of zeros below the main diagonal. After a maximum of $n - 1$ repetitions, the resulting array will be triangular but will have the same determinant as the original array. Since, by Property 7, the determinant of the array can now be found by a simple multiplication of the diagonal elements, this procedure provides a useful means of evaluating a determinant. Note, however, that even though the triangular array has the same determinant as the original array, the two arrays are not equal, for, obviously, their corresponding elements are not equal.

2.6 *Using determinants to solve a set of simultaneous equations*

We may apply the properties of determinants which were developed in the last section to solve a set of equations of the form

$$\begin{aligned} U_1 &= a_{11}X_1 + a_{12}X_2 + \cdots + a_{1n}X_n \\ U_2 &= a_{21}X_1 + a_{22}X_2 + \cdots + a_{2n}X_n \\ &\cdots\cdots\cdots\cdots\cdots\cdots\cdots\cdots \\ U_n &= a_{n1}X_1 + a_{n2}X_2 + \cdots + a_{nn}X_n \end{aligned} \tag{1}$$

The process of solving these equations may be described as finding the values of the variables X_i under the conditions that the terms U_i and a_{ij} are specified. In other words, we would like to determine the coefficients

b_{ij} in a set of equations

$$X_1 = b_{11}U_1 + b_{12}U_2 + \cdots + b_{1n}U_n$$
$$X_2 = b_{21}U_1 + b_{22}U_2 + \cdots + b_{2n}U_n$$
$$\cdots \cdots \cdots \cdots \cdots \cdots \cdots \cdots \cdots$$
$$X_n = b_{n1}U_1 + b_{n2}U_2 + \cdots + b_{nn}U_n \tag{2}$$

In equations (2), it should be clear that if the b_{ij} terms are known, then, when the U_i are specified, the values of the X_i are determined. The set of equations (1) and the set of equations (2) are usually referred to as sets of simultaneous equations. It is desired, not only to "solve" these equations by finding one set when the other is given, but it is also desirable to be able to state the conditions under which a solution is possible. This we shall now do.

Let us multiply the first equation of the set (1) by the cofactor A_{11}, the second by the cofactor A_{21}, the third by A_{31}, and so forth. We obtain

$$A_{11}U_1 = A_{11}(a_{11}X_1 + a_{12}X_2 + \cdots + a_{1n}X_n)$$
$$A_{21}U_2 = A_{21}(a_{21}X_1 + a_{22}X_2 + \cdots + a_{2n}X_n)$$
$$\cdots \cdots \cdots \cdots \cdots \cdots \cdots \cdots \cdots \cdots$$
$$A_{n1}U_n = A_{n1}(a_{n1}X_1 + a_{n2}X_2 + \cdots + a_{nn}X_n) \tag{3}$$

Adding the above equations together gives

$$(A_{11}U_1 + A_{21}U_2 + \cdots + A_{n1}U_n)$$
$$= X_1(a_{11}A_{11} + a_{21}A_{21} + \cdots + a_{n1}A_{n1})$$
$$+ X_2(a_{12}A_{11} + a_{22}A_{21} + \cdots + a_{n2}A_{n1})$$
$$+ \cdots \cdots \cdots \cdots \cdots \cdots \cdots \cdots$$
$$+ X_n(a_{1n}A_{11} + a_{2n}A_{21} + \cdots + a_{nn}A_{n1}) \tag{4}$$

In this equation the term $(a_{11}A_{11} + a_{21}A_{21} + \cdots + a_{n1}A_{n1})$ which multiplies X_1 is simply the expansion of the array of elements a_{ij} along the first column of the array. As such it is equal to det A. The term $(a_{12}A_{11} + a_{22}A_{21} + \cdots + a_{n2}A_{n1})$ which multiplies X_2 is the expansion of the array in terms of the elements of the *second* column and the cofactors of the elements of the *first* column. As such, by Property 5 of the preceding section, it is equal to zero. Similarly, the terms multiplying $X_3, \ldots, X_n$ are all zero. Thus (4) becomes

$$A_{11}U_1 + A_{21}U_2 + \cdots + A_{n1}U_n = X_1 \det A$$

This may also be written

$$X_1 = \frac{A_{11}}{\det A} U_1 + \frac{A_{21}}{\det A} U_2 + \cdots + \frac{A_{n1}}{\det A} U_n \tag{5}$$

We may perform an operation on the set of equations (1) similar to the above by multiplying the first equation of the set by the cofactor A_{12}, the second by the cofactor A_{22}, the third by the cofactor A_{32}, etc. Adding the resulting equations yields

$$A_{12}U_1 + A_{22}U_2 + \cdots + A_{n2}U_n$$
$$= X_1(a_{11}A_{12} + a_{21}A_{22} + \cdots + a_{n1}A_{n2})$$
$$+ X_2(a_{12}A_{12} + a_{22}A_{22} + \cdots + a_{n2}A_{n2})$$
$$+ \cdots \cdots \cdots \cdots \cdots \cdots \cdots$$
$$+ X_n(a_{1n}A_{12} + a_{2n}A_{22} + \cdots + a_{nn}A_{n2})$$

By following the above argument, we see that all the terms on the right side of the equation are zero except the term modifying X_2. This term is an expansion along the second column of the elements in the array and as such is equal to det A. Thus, after dividing both sides of the equation by det A, we may write

$$X_2 = \frac{A_{12}}{\det A}\, U_1 + \frac{A_{22}}{\det A}\, U_2 + \cdots + \frac{A_{n2}}{\det A}\, U_n$$

This procedure may be repeated to produce equations for $X_3, X_4, \ldots, X_n$. The final result is the set of equations

$$X_1 = \frac{A_{11}}{\det A}\, U_1 + \frac{A_{21}}{\det A}\, U_2 + \cdots + \frac{A_{n1}}{\det A}\, U_n$$
$$X_2 = \frac{A_{12}}{\det A}\, U_1 + \frac{A_{22}}{\det A}\, U_2 + \cdots + \frac{A_{n2}}{\det A}\, U_n \tag{6}$$
$$\cdots \cdots \cdots \cdots \cdots \cdots \cdots \cdots$$
$$X_n = \frac{A_{1n}}{\det A}\, U_1 + \frac{A_{2n}}{\det A}\, U_2 + \cdots + \frac{A_{nn}}{\det A}\, U_n$$

Comparing these equations with the set (2), we see that for the coefficients b_{ij} we may write[1]

$$b_{ij} = \frac{A_{ji}}{\det A} \tag{7}$$

In each of the terms b_{ij} as defined above, the quantity det A appears in the denominator. Thus, the condition that must be satisfied for a solution of (1) to exist is that det A be nonzero.

As an example of the above procedure, consider the set of equations

$$U_1 = 2X_1 + X_2$$
$$U_2 = 2X_1 + 3X_2$$

Suppose that it is desired to solve these equations, i.e., to express the vari-

---

[1] This is known as Cramer's rule.

ables X_i in terms of the variables U_i. Since $a_{11} = 2$, $a_{12} = 1$, $a_{21} = 2$, and $a_{22} = 3$,

$$\det A = \begin{vmatrix} 2 & 1 \\ 2 & 3 \end{vmatrix} = 4$$

Thus, we may compute the b_{ij} as follows:

$$b_{11} = \frac{A_{11}}{\det A} = \frac{(-1)^{1+1}|3|}{4} = \frac{3}{4}$$

$$b_{12} = \frac{A_{21}}{\det A} = \frac{(-1)^{2+1}|1|}{4} = \frac{-1}{4}$$

$$b_{21} = \frac{A_{12}}{\det A} = \frac{(-1)^{1+2}|2|}{4} = \frac{-1}{2}$$

$$b_{22} = \frac{A_{22}}{\det A} = \frac{(-1)^{2+2}|2|}{4} = \frac{1}{2}$$

the set of equations corresponding to (2) is

$$X_1 = \tfrac{3}{4}U_1 - \tfrac{1}{4}U_2$$
$$X_2 = -\tfrac{1}{2}U_1 + \tfrac{1}{2}U_2$$

The procedure is clearly applicable to more involved sets of equations.

A special case of interest occurs when all the U_i in (1) are zero. The resulting set of equations involving the elements a_{ij} and X_i is referred to as a *homogeneous* set of equations. Similarly, the original set of equations (1) in which the U_i are not all zero may be referred to as a nonhomogeneous set of equations.

Certain problems arise in the application of (6) in determining the values of X_i, i.e., in solving a homogeneous set of simultaneous equations. We shall consider two cases:

Case 1: det $A \neq 0$ In this case, every element on the right side of equations (6) is zero; therefore, we conclude that a solution to the original equations is given by $X_i = 0$. Substituting these values into (1) for $U_i = 0$ clearly satisfies the equations. This solution is frequently spoken of as the *trivial* solution. It may be shown that this is also the only solution.[1]

Case 2: det $A = 0$ In this case, the elements on the right side of equations (6) are indeterminate; i.e., they are of the form $0/0$. In this form we cannot find a solution for any particular X_i; however, it may be shown that an infinite number of solutions exist.[1] We can establish an intuitive feeling for this case by assuming for the moment that only one of the U_i is nonzero, and that det A is also nonzero. If we divide the first equation

[1] F. E. Hohn, "Elementary Matrix Algebra," chap. 5, The Macmillan Company, New York, 1958.

of (6) by the second, we obtain

$$\frac{X_1}{X_2} = \frac{A_{i1}U_i/\det A}{A_{i2}U_i/\det A} = \frac{A_{i1}}{A_{i2}}$$

This result is independent of both U_i and det A; therefore it should be valid for the case in which U_i and det A are zero. Thus, the choice of either of these variables determines the other. In considering both the above cases we conclude that a homogeneous set of equations has non-trivial solutions if and only if the determinant is equal to zero.

2.7   *Matrix algebra*

In Sec. 2.2 a definition of a matrix is given. In this section the algebraic operations which can be performed on matrices will be introduced.

Equality   Two matrices are equal if and only if each of their corresponding elements are equal. That is, $A = B$ only if $a_{ij} = b_{ij}$ for all i and j. As a consequence of this definition, we see that only matrices having the same number of rows and columns can be equal. As an example, if

$$A = \begin{bmatrix} 1 & 2 \\ 3 & 4 \end{bmatrix}$$

and if $A = B$, then

$$B = \begin{bmatrix} 1 & 2 \\ 3 & 4 \end{bmatrix}$$

Addition   The sum of two matrices is equal to a third matrix if and only if the sum of corresponding elements in the two matrices is equal to the value of the element in the corresponding position in the third matrix. Thus, $A + B = C$ only if $a_{ij} + b_{ij} = c_{ij}$ for all values of i and j. The operation of addition is defined only for matrices which have the same number of rows and columns. As an example,

$$\begin{bmatrix} 1 & 2 & 3 \\ 4 & 5 & 6 \end{bmatrix} + \begin{bmatrix} 1 & 1 & 1 \\ 1 & 1 & 1 \end{bmatrix} = \begin{bmatrix} 2 & 3 & 4 \\ 5 & 6 & 7 \end{bmatrix}$$

Multiplication by a scalar   Multiplying a matrix by a scalar multiplies each element of the matrix by the scalar. Thus, if k is a scalar, and A is a matrix with elements a_{ij}, the elements of the matrix kA are ka_{ij}. We shall consider the term scalar as including real numbers, complex numbers, and functions of the complex frequency variable. Note the difference between this case and the corresponding operation in a determinant (see Property 1, Sec. 2.5), where multiplying the determinant by a constant was the equivalent of multiplying the elements of a single row or a single column by the constant. As an example of multiplying a matrix by a scalar, consider the following:

$$k \begin{bmatrix} 5 & 1 & 2 \\ 3 & 4 & 5 \end{bmatrix} = \begin{bmatrix} 5k & k & 2k \\ 3k & 4k & 5k \end{bmatrix}$$

Subtraction   Subtraction can be defined in terms of multiplication by a scalar (-1) and addition. Thus $A - B = A + (-1)B$.

Multiplication of two matrices   We define this operation as follows: $A \times B = C$ (this will also frequently be written $AB = C$) implies that

$$c_{ij} = \sum_{k=1}^{n} a_{ik}b_{kj} \tag{1}$$

The following properties of this operation should be noted:

Property 1   The summation index that must be used for each term c_{ij} appears as the second subscript, i.e., the column subscript, of the a_{ik} term, but it appears as the first subscript, i.e., the row subscript, of the b_{kj} term. Thus, we conclude that the number of columns of the first matrix that enters into the product operation must be the same as the number of rows of the second matrix. Otherwise we are not able to run the summation index over its full range, and we say that multiplication is not defined in this case.

Property 2   Every value of the subscript i, i.e., the row subscript, that the element a_{ij} can have, as determined by the number of rows of the A matrix, determines a corresponding subscript (a row subscript) in the resulting element c_{ij}. Similarly, every value of the subscript j (the column subscript) that the element b_{ij} can have determines a corresponding subscript (the column subscript) in the element c_{ij}. Thus, the resulting C matrix has the same number of rows as the A matrix (the first one entering into matrix multiplication) and the same number of columns as the B matrix (the second one entering into the matrix multiplication).

Property 3   From a study of the first two properties, it should be clear that, in general, matrix multiplication is not commutative; i.e., $AB \neq BA$.

Property 4   It is easily shown that matrix multiplication is associative, i.e., $(AB)C = A(BC)$, and distributive, i.e., $A(B + C) = AB + AC$ and $(A + B)C = AC + BC$.

As an example of matrix multiplication, consider the following:

$$\begin{bmatrix} a_{11} & a_{12} & a_{13} \\ a_{21} & a_{22} & a_{23} \end{bmatrix} \begin{bmatrix} b_{11} & b_{12} \\ b_{21} & b_{22} \\ b_{31} & b_{32} \end{bmatrix} = \begin{bmatrix} c_{11} & c_{12} \\ c_{21} & c_{22} \end{bmatrix}$$

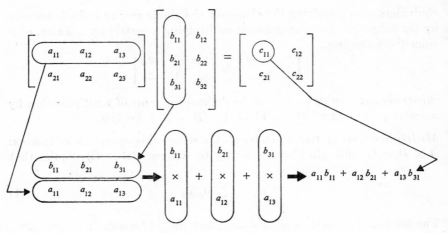

Figure 2.2   Matrix multiplication.

It should be noted that the first matrix has three columns and the second matrix has three rows. Thus, by Property 1, multiplication is possible. Since the first matrix has two rows and the second matrix has two columns, by Property 2 the resulting matrix will have two rows and two columns. The elements of the C matrix may be found as follows:

$$c_{11} = \sum_{k=1}^{3} a_{1k}b_{k1} = a_{11}b_{11} + a_{12}b_{21} + a_{13}b_{31}$$

$$c_{12} = \sum_{k=1}^{3} a_{1k}b_{k2} = a_{11}b_{12} + a_{12}b_{22} + a_{13}b_{32}$$

$$c_{21} = \sum_{k=1}^{3} a_{2k}b_{k1} = a_{21}b_{11} + a_{22}b_{21} + a_{23}b_{31}$$

$$c_{22} = \sum_{k=1}^{3} a_{2k}b_{k2} = a_{21}b_{12} + a_{22}b_{22} + a_{23}b_{32}$$

It may be helpful to indicate here that we can perform the summation indicated by (1) more easily if we visualize the appropriate column (the jth column) from the second matrix as removed from that matrix and associated with the appropriate row (the ith row) of the first matrix. The operations of multiplication and summation can then be performed directly. Practice in visualization may be achieved by performing a few examples as illustrated in Fig. 2.2 for c_{11}. The figure illustrates the removal of the first column from B and its placement above the first row of A. The elements of the two matrices which are in line vertically are then multiplied. The resulting products are summed horizontally. The result is the element c_{11}.

The set of equations (1) in Sec. 2.6 may be used as another example of matrix multiplication. They may also be written $U = AX$. In expanded form this is

$$
\begin{bmatrix} U_1 \\ U_2 \\ \cdot \cdot \\ U_n \end{bmatrix} = \begin{bmatrix} a_{11} & a_{12} & \cdots & a_{1n} \\ a_{21} & a_{22} & \cdots & a_{2n} \\ \cdot \cdot \cdot \cdot \cdot \cdot \cdot \cdot \cdot \cdot \cdot \cdot \\ a_{n1} & a_{n2} & \cdots & a_{nn} \end{bmatrix} \begin{bmatrix} X_1 \\ X_2 \\ \cdot \cdot \\ X_n \end{bmatrix}
$$

2.8   *Types of matrices and properties of matrices*

Identity matrix   The identity matrix (also referred to as the *unity* matrix) with symbol *1* is defined as follows:

$$
1 = \begin{bmatrix} 1 & 0 & \cdots & 0 \\ 0 & 1 & \cdots & 0 \\ \cdot & \cdot & \cdot \cdot \cdot \cdot & \cdot \\ 0 & 0 & \cdots & 1 \end{bmatrix}
$$

A property of the identity matrix is that any matrix premultiplied or post-multiplied by the identity matrix is equal to itself (we assume that multi-plication is defined, i.e., that the identity matrix is of the correct size in all cases). Thus, we may write $A1 = 1A = A$. If A is not a square matrix, then two different-sized identity matrices will be required in the last equation. The identity matrix itself is always a square matrix.

Inverse matrix   For a given matrix A there may exist a matrix A^{-1} de-fined by the relationship $A^{-1}A = 1$. This, of course, also implies a commu-tative law of multiplication; i.e., $AA^{-1} = 1$. The inverse matrix has the useful property of providing a solution to a set of equations. To see this, consider the equation

$$ U = AX $$

Premultiplying both sides of this equation by A^{-1}, we obtain

$$ A^{-1}U = A^{-1}AX = 1X = X $$

Comparing this with (2) of Sec. 2.6, we see that the elements of the A^{-1} matrix are the elements b_{ij} defined by (2) of Sec. 2.6. Thus, the condition for a matrix A^{-1} to exist is the same as the condition for the inverse set of equations (2) of Sec. 2.6 to exist, namely that det $A \neq 0$. This condition also requires that A be a square matrix, and thus that A^{-1} be a square matrix. A matrix that has an inverse is said to be a *nonsingular* matrix.

For example, for a 2×2 array,

$$A = \begin{bmatrix} a_{11} & a_{12} \\ a_{21} & a_{22} \end{bmatrix} \qquad A^{-1} = \frac{1}{\det A} \begin{bmatrix} a_{22} & -a_{12} \\ -a_{21} & a_{11} \end{bmatrix}$$

Thus, as a numerical example,

$$B = \begin{bmatrix} 2 & 4 \\ 1 & 3 \end{bmatrix} \qquad B^{-1} = \frac{1}{2} \begin{bmatrix} 3 & -4 \\ -1 & 2 \end{bmatrix}$$

As another example, a 3×3 array may have its inverse expressed in terms of its cofactors; thus

$$A = \begin{bmatrix} a_{11} & a_{12} & a_{13} \\ a_{21} & a_{22} & a_{23} \\ a_{31} & a_{32} & a_{33} \end{bmatrix} \qquad A^{-1} = \frac{1}{\det A} \begin{bmatrix} A_{11} & A_{21} & A_{31} \\ A_{12} & A_{22} & A_{32} \\ A_{13} & A_{23} & A_{33} \end{bmatrix}$$

Transpose matrix   If we interchange the rows and columns of a given matrix, we form the transpose of that matrix. This operation may be performed on a matrix of any size. For example, the transpose of a row matrix is a column matrix. The symbol for the transpose of the matrix A is A^t. For $B = A^t$ it follows that $b_{ij} = a_{ji}$. As examples, consider the following:

$$A = \begin{bmatrix} a_{11} & a_{12} & a_{13} \\ a_{21} & a_{22} & a_{23} \end{bmatrix} \qquad A^t = \begin{bmatrix} a_{11} & a_{21} \\ a_{12} & a_{22} \\ a_{13} & a_{23} \end{bmatrix}$$

$$B = \begin{bmatrix} 3 \\ 1 + j \\ 7 \end{bmatrix} \qquad B^t = \begin{bmatrix} 3 & 1 + j & 7 \end{bmatrix}$$

Conjugate matrix   If we replace every element in a matrix A by its complex conjugate, the resulting matrix is the conjugate matrix, denoted by the symbol A^*. If $B = A^*$, it follows that $b_{ij} = a_{ij}^*$.[1]

Symmetric matrix   If the elements of a given matrix are symmetric with respect to the main diagonal (the main diagonal of the matrix A consists of the elements a_{ii}), the matrix is said to be symmetric. Thus, A is symmetric if $a_{ij} = a_{ji}$. Only a square matrix can be symmetric. We may indicate this property by the superscript (S). An example of a symmetric matrix is the following:

$$A^{(S)} = \begin{bmatrix} p & p^2 + 1 & 3p \\ p^2 + 1 & 2p & 7 \\ 3p & 7 & 0 \end{bmatrix}$$

Skew-symmetric matrix   A skew-symmetric matrix A is defined by the relation $a_{ij} = -a_{ji}$. Since the only element that can equal its negative

[1] The superscript asterisk (*) will be used throughout this text to indicate the complex conjugate.

is zero, we conclude that the diagonal elements (i.e., $i = j$) of a skew-symmetric matrix are all zero. Only a square matrix can be skew symmetric. We will use the superscript (SS) to indicate this property of a matrix. An example of a skew-symmetric matrix is the following:

$$A^{(SS)} = \begin{bmatrix} 0 & 1+j & 3 \\ -1-j & 0 & -4 \\ -3 & 4 & 0 \end{bmatrix}$$

Hermitian matrix A matrix is said to be hermitian if the elements which are symmetrically located with respect to the main diagonal are complex conjugates. Thus, if A is a hermitian matrix, indicated by a superscript (H), it follows that $a_{ij} = a_{ji}{}^*$. The elements on the diagonal must, therefore, be real, since they are defined equal to their own complex conjugates. It should be clear that only a square matrix can be hermitian. An example of a hermitian matrix is the following:

$$A^{(H)} = \begin{bmatrix} 0 & 1+j & 0 \\ 1-j & 5 & -j6 \\ 0 & j6 & 8 \end{bmatrix}$$

Skew-hermitian matrix If the elements of a matrix A are defined by the relationship $a_{ij} = -a_{ji}{}^*$, the matrix is said to be skew hermitian. This property applies only to square matrices. It is indicated by the superscript letters (SH). Since the diagonal elements must be their own negative complex conjugates, they can only be imaginary or zero. An example of a skew-hermitian matrix is the following:

$$A^{(SH)} = \begin{bmatrix} j5 & 1 & -1+j3 \\ -1 & 0 & -j6 \\ 1+j3 & -j6 & j9 \end{bmatrix}$$

Dominant matrix A symmetric matrix whose elements are real is said to be dominant if each of the elements on the main diagonal is not less in value than the sum of the absolute values of all the other elements in the same row (or, since the matrix is symmetric, in the same column). In other words, if A is a dominant matrix, indicated by a superscript (D), with diagonal elements a_{ii}, these diagonal elements satisfy the restriction

$$a_{ii} \geq \sum_{j=1}^{n} |a_{ij}| \qquad j \neq i$$

for all values of i. An example of a dominant matrix is the following:

$$A^{(D)} = \begin{bmatrix} 7 & 2 & -1 \\ 2 & 4 & -1 \\ -1 & -1 & 2 \end{bmatrix}$$

2.9   *Theorems on matrices*

The following are presented as a collection of useful theorems on matrices. Many of these theorems will be used in later sections of the text. A discussion or a proof of these theorems is included only where this is pertinent to later theory. Several references with excellent proofs are available and are listed at the end of this chapter.

Theorem 1   The inverse of the product of two square matrices is equal to the product of the inverses taken in the opposite order.
Thus

$$(AB)^{-1} = B^{-1}A^{-1}$$

Theorem 2   The transpose of the product of two matrices is equal to the product of the transposes taken in the opposite order; the transpose of the sum of two matrices is equal to the sum of the transposes.
Thus,

$$(AB)^t = B^t A^t$$
$$(A + B)^t = A^t + B^t$$

Theorem 3   If a square matrix is equal to its transpose, it is symmetric. Similarly, a symmetric matrix is equal to its transpose.

Theorem 4   If a square matrix is equal to the negative of its transpose, the matrix is skew symmetric. Similarly, a skew-symmetric matrix is equal to the negative of its transpose.

Theorem 5   Any square matrix A with all real elements may be expressed as the sum of a symmetric matrix and a skew-symmetric matrix. The same is true of a matrix all of whose elements are functions of the complex frequency variable.

To see this, let

$$A = A_1{}^{(S)} + A_2{}^{(SS)}$$

Then, by Theorems 3 and 4,

$$A^t = A_1{}^{(S)} - A_2{}^{(SS)}$$

Adding and subtracting the above equations gives, respectively,

$$A_1{}^{(S)} = \tfrac{1}{2}(A + A^t) \qquad A_2{}^{(SS)} = \tfrac{1}{2}(A - A^t)$$

It is easy to see that $A_1{}^{(S)}$ and $A_2{}^{(SS)}$ have the desired properties and that their sum is equal to A.

Theorem 6 If a square matrix is equal to the conjugate of its transpose, the matrix is hermitian. Similarly, a hermitian matrix is equal to the conjugate of its transpose.

Theorem 7 If a square matrix is equal to the negative of the conjugate of its transpose, the matrix is skew hermitian. Similarly, a skew-hermitian matrix is equal to the negative of the conjugate of its transpose.

Theorem 8 Any square matrix A with real and complex elements may be expressed as the sum of a hermitian and a skew-hermitian matrix. To see this, let

$$A = A_1{}^{(H)} + A_2{}^{(SH)}$$

Then, by Theorems 6 and 7,

$$(A^t)^* = A_1{}^{(H)} - A_2{}^{(SH)}$$

Adding and subtracting the above equations gives, respectively,

$$A_1{}^{(H)} = \tfrac{1}{2}[A + (A^t)^*] \qquad A_2{}^{(SH)} = \tfrac{1}{2}[A - (A^t)^*]$$

It is easy to see that $A_1{}^{(H)}$ and $A_2{}^{(SH)}$ have the necessary properties.

Theorem 9 The inverse and the transpose of a matrix A may be taken in any order.

Thus,

$$(A^t)^{-1} = (A^{-1})^t$$

It is assumed, of course, that A has an inverse.

2.10 *Matrix partitioning*

When it is necessary to manipulate a matrix equation containing large matrices, it is frequently convenient to separate these matrices into smaller submatrices and perform the necessary operations on the submatrices rather than on the original matrices. The submatrices are considered to be the result of *partitioning* the original matrices. Matrix partitioning does not usually reduce the number of manipulations that are required, but it may simplify the procedure considerably and make it easier to prove general results. The partitioning procedures are applicable to matrices of all sizes. In forming the submatrices, certain rules must be followed so that the algebraic operations of the original matrix equation can still be performed. An example of partitioning is given in matrix A below. The 3×6 matrix has been partitioned into submatrices A_1, A_2, . . . , A_6. Dashed lines are used to indicate the bounds of the submatrices.

$$A = \begin{bmatrix} a_{11} & a_{12} & a_{13} & a_{14} & a_{15} & a_{16} \\ a_{21} & a_{22} & a_{23} & a_{24} & a_{25} & a_{26} \\ a_{31} & a_{32} & a_{33} & a_{34} & a_{35} & a_{36} \end{bmatrix} = \begin{bmatrix} A_1 & A_2 & A_3 \\ A_4 & A_5 & A_6 \end{bmatrix}$$

$$A_1 = \begin{bmatrix} a_{11} & a_{12} \\ a_{21} & a_{22} \end{bmatrix} \qquad A_2 = \begin{bmatrix} a_{13} & a_{14} & a_{15} \\ a_{23} & a_{24} & a_{25} \end{bmatrix} \quad \cdot \cdot \cdot$$

Now let us examine some of the algebraic matrix operations to see what restrictions they place on partitioning.

Addition   If $A + B = C$, then, for addition to be defined, we know that each matrix must have the same number of rows and columns. Similarly, if the A matrix is partitioned into submatrices A_i, and if identical partitionings are made for B and C into submatrices B_i and C_i, then we may write $A_i + B_i = C_i$ for all values of i. For example, let

$$A = \begin{bmatrix} a_{11} & a_{12} & a_{13} \\ a_{21} & a_{22} & a_{23} \end{bmatrix} = [A_1 \ \vdots \ A_2] \qquad A_1 = \begin{bmatrix} a_{11} & a_{12} \\ a_{21} & a_{22} \end{bmatrix} \qquad A_2 = \begin{bmatrix} a_{13} \\ a_{23} \end{bmatrix}$$

If B and C are identically partitioned and labeled then $A_1 + B_1 = C_1$ and $A_2 + B_2 = C_2$; that is

$$\begin{bmatrix} a_{11} & a_{12} \\ a_{21} & a_{22} \end{bmatrix} + \begin{bmatrix} b_{11} & b_{12} \\ b_{21} & b_{22} \end{bmatrix} = \begin{bmatrix} c_{11} & c_{12} \\ c_{21} & c_{22} \end{bmatrix}$$

and

$$\begin{bmatrix} a_{13} \\ a_{23} \end{bmatrix} + \begin{bmatrix} b_{13} \\ b_{23} \end{bmatrix} = \begin{bmatrix} c_{13} \\ c_{23} \end{bmatrix}$$

as is evident from the original matrix equation.

Multiplication   The restrictions on partitioning which are required so that matrix multiplication may be carried out follow directly from the properties of matrix multiplication given in Sec. 2.7. As a result of the first property, any vertical partitioning of the first matrix must be accompanied by a corresponding horizontal partitioning of the second. Otherwise matrix multiplication of the corresponding submatrices would not be possible. Similarly, as a result of the second property, the horizontal partitioning of the first matrix determines the horizontal partitioning of the resulting matrix. The vertical partitioning of the second matrix determines the vertical partitioning of the resulting matrix. These ideas are illustrated below. The superscript numbers in parentheses are used to indicate the numbers of rows and columns in the particular submatrix.

$$
\begin{bmatrix}
a_{11} & a_{12} & a_{13} & a_{14} \\
a_{21} & a_{22} & a_{23} & a_{24} \\
a_{31} & a_{32} & a_{33} & a_{34}
\end{bmatrix}
\begin{bmatrix}
b_{11} & b_{12} \\
b_{21} & b_{22} \\
b_{31} & b_{32} \\
b_{41} & b_{42}
\end{bmatrix}
=
\begin{bmatrix}
c_{11} & c_{12} \\
c_{21} & c_{22} \\
c_{31} & c_{32}
\end{bmatrix}
$$

$$
\begin{bmatrix}
A_1^{(2\times1)} & A_2^{(2\times2)} & A_3^{(2\times1)} \\
A_4^{(1\times1)} & A_5^{(1\times2)} & A_6^{(1\times1)}
\end{bmatrix}
\begin{bmatrix}
B_1^{(1\times1)} & B_2^{(1\times1)} \\
B_3^{(2\times1)} & B_4^{(2\times1)} \\
B_5^{(1\times1)} & B_6^{(1\times1)}
\end{bmatrix}
=
\begin{bmatrix}
C_1^{(2\times1)} & C_2^{(2\times1)} \\
C_3^{(1\times1)} & C_4^{(1\times1)}
\end{bmatrix}
$$

$$A_1B_1 + A_2B_3 + A_3B_5 = C_1$$
$$A_1B_2 + A_2B_4 + A_3B_6 = C_2$$
$$A_4B_1 + A_5B_3 + A_6B_5 = C_3$$
$$A_4B_2 + A_5B_4 + A_6B_6 = C_4$$

The same information is shown in three forms in the above equations. First, the original matrices are shown with a partitioning chosen so as to make multiplication of the submatrices possible. Next, the matrix equation in terms of the submatrices defined by the above partitioning is shown. The equations, now in terms of submatrices, are given as an additional form. The reader should check the individual submatrix products to ascertain that they obey the rules of matrix multiplication and that the indicated matrix addition is possible.

2.11 *Matrix equations*

When a real or a complex variable is defined, the next mathematical step of interest is usually to explore functions of such a variable. Similarly, having defined and specified a matrix A, we can specify the matrix product AA, which can also be written as A^2, or the matrix product $A \times A \times A \times \cdots \times A$ using n terms, which may be written as A^n. The matrix A must, of course, be a square matrix. Since multiplication of a matrix by a scalar is possible, we may define operations which appear in the form of polynomials with the matrix as the variable element. For example, we might write $A^3 + 3A^2 + 7A$. The rules of matrix equality require that, when a matrix equation is set equal to a constant (including zero), this constant be multiplied by the identity matrix. Thus, rather than writing

$$A^3 + 3A^2 + 7A = 5$$

we shall write

$$A^3 + 3A^2 + 7A = 5I$$

The matrix $5I$ is sometimes referred to as a *scalar matrix*. Note that all its elements are zero except those on the main diagonal, and that these latter are equal to each other.

The solutions to a matrix equation exemplify the fact that there are differences between scalar algebra and matrix algebra. For example, consider the equation $x^2 - 1 = 0$, where x is a real variable. The solutions of this equation are $x = 1$ and $x = -1$. If we write the matrix equation $A^2 - I = 0$, where 0 is the null matrix, it is easy to see that solutions to this equation are $A = I$ and $A = -I$. Unlike the scalar-algebra case, however, there may be additional solutions. For example, if the matrix A is a 2×2 matrix, to satisfy the above matrix equation it is necessary that the following relations hold among the matrix elements a_{11}, a_{12}, a_{21}, and a_{22}:

$$a_{11}^2 + a_{12}a_{21} = 1 \qquad a_{11}a_{12} + a_{22}a_{12} = 0$$
$$a_{22}^2 + a_{12}a_{21} = 1 \qquad a_{11}a_{21} + a_{22}a_{21} = 0$$

One set of coefficients that satisfies these relations and thus provides a solution to the matrix equation is $a_{11} = 2$, $a_{12} = 1$, $a_{21} = -3$, and $a_{22} = -2$. It is easily verified that the following matrix equation is true:

$$\begin{bmatrix} 2 & 1 \\ -3 & -2 \end{bmatrix} \begin{bmatrix} 2 & 1 \\ -3 & -2 \end{bmatrix} - \begin{bmatrix} 1 & 0 \\ 0 & 1 \end{bmatrix} = \begin{bmatrix} 0 & 0 \\ 0 & 0 \end{bmatrix}$$

Just as we may form infinite series of real or complex variables, so we may form infinite series of matrices. If we remember that a matrix equation is merely a representation for a certain number of ordinary equations, we may define the "convergence" of a series of matrices in terms of the convergence of the individual equations by well-known techniques.[1] As an example of an infinite series of matrices, consider the following:

$$I + A + \frac{1}{2!} A^2 + \frac{1}{3!} A^3 + \cdots + \frac{1}{n!} A^n + \cdots \tag{1}$$

If, for example, we choose

$$A = \begin{bmatrix} 1 & 0 \\ 0 & 2 \end{bmatrix}$$

then
$$A^2 = \begin{bmatrix} 1 & 0 \\ 0 & 2 \end{bmatrix} \begin{bmatrix} 1 & 0 \\ 0 & 2 \end{bmatrix} = \begin{bmatrix} 1 & 0 \\ 0 & 4 \end{bmatrix}$$

$$A^3 = \begin{bmatrix} 1 & 0 \\ 0 & 2 \end{bmatrix} \begin{bmatrix} 1 & 0 \\ 0 & 2 \end{bmatrix} \begin{bmatrix} 1 & 0 \\ 0 & 2 \end{bmatrix} = \begin{bmatrix} 1 & 0 \\ 0 & 8 \end{bmatrix}$$

$$\cdots\cdots\cdots\cdots\cdots\cdots\cdots\cdots\cdots\cdots$$

$$A^n = \begin{bmatrix} 1 & 0 \\ 0 & 2^n \end{bmatrix}$$

[1] See, for example, I. S. Sokolnikoff and R. M. Redheffer, "Mathematics of Physics and Modern Engineering," McGraw-Hill Book Company, Inc., New York, 1958.

The series (1) becomes

$$\begin{bmatrix} 1 & 0 \\ 0 & 1 \end{bmatrix} + \begin{bmatrix} 1 & 0 \\ 0 & 2 \end{bmatrix} + \frac{1}{2!}\begin{bmatrix} 1 & 0 \\ 0 & 4 \end{bmatrix} + \frac{1}{3!}\begin{bmatrix} 1 & 0 \\ 0 & 8 \end{bmatrix}$$

$$+ \cdot \cdot \cdot + \frac{1}{n!}\begin{bmatrix} 1 & 0 \\ 0 & 2^n \end{bmatrix} + \cdot \cdot \cdot$$

This matrix series simply represents the two convergent series of constants

$$1 + 1 + \frac{1}{2!} + \frac{1}{3!} + \cdot \cdot \cdot + \frac{1}{n!} + \cdot \cdot \cdot$$

and $$1 + 2 + \frac{4}{2!} + \frac{8}{3!} + \cdot \cdot \cdot + \frac{2^n}{n!} + \cdot \cdot \cdot$$

Thus we may say that the series of matrices "converges" in the sense that the individual series of which it is composed converge.

We may use the series (1) to define the term exp A, in light of its similarity to the expansion of exp x, where x is a real or complex variable. Similarly, we may define exp tA, where t is a real variable and A is a matrix, by the following:

$$e^{tA} = 1 + tA + \frac{t^2}{2!}A^2 + \cdot \cdot \cdot + \frac{t^n}{n!}A^n + \cdot \cdot \cdot \qquad (2)$$

Now we may define differentiation of exp tA with respect to t as the following:

$$\frac{d^n}{dt^n}e^{tA} = A^n e^{tA}$$

This definition may be justified by differentiating both sides of (2).

As an application of the definition of exp tA and its derivatives, consider a set of n functions $y_i(t)$, where t is a real variable. Suppose that we have available n first-order differential equations relating these functions. These equations may be written in matrix form as

$$Y'(t) = AY(t) \qquad (3)$$

The actual matrices will be

$$\begin{bmatrix} y_1'(t) \\ \cdot \cdot \cdot \\ y_n'(t) \end{bmatrix} = \begin{bmatrix} a_{11} & \cdot \cdot \cdot & a_{1n} \\ \cdot \cdot \cdot \cdot \cdot \cdot \cdot \cdot \cdot \cdot \\ a_{n1} & \cdot \cdot \cdot & a_{nn} \end{bmatrix} \begin{bmatrix} y_1(t) \\ \cdot \cdot \cdot \\ y_n(t) \end{bmatrix}$$

If we have available a set of n initial conditions $y_i(0)$ which are the elements of a column matrix $Y(0)$, then the solution to (3) is given explicitly by

$$Y(t) = e^{tA}Y(0) \qquad (4)$$

This may also be written

$$
\begin{bmatrix} y_1(t) \\ \cdots \\ y_n(t) \end{bmatrix} = \exp \left\{ t \begin{bmatrix} a_{11} & \cdots & a_{1n} \\ \cdots\cdots\cdots\cdots \\ a_{n1} & \cdots & a_{nn} \end{bmatrix} \right\} \begin{bmatrix} y_1(0) \\ \cdots \\ y_n(0) \end{bmatrix}
$$

In a purely formal manner we have been able to arrive at a solution for an arbitrarily complex set of first-order differential equations by an exceedingly simple technique. Needless to say, a considerable amount of actual labor may yet be required in actually obtaining the numerical solution for a specific problem. The salient point here, however, is that we have been able to complete all steps of the solution except the laborious details, and we have done this for a very general class of problems unrestricted in its number of variables. This example is typical of the powerful generality of matrix methods. It is this generality which makes matrix algebra so useful as an analytic tool in many system and circuit applications.

2.12 *Further reading*

The topics which have been presented in this chapter may also be found in a formidable number of other texts. Some of these are referenced in the list below. The entries have been chosen so as to include as wide as possible a range of level of presentation.

Hohn, F. E.: "Elementary Matrix Algebra," The Macmillan Company, New York, 1958. This is a clearly written and complete mathematical treatment. The material in Chaps. 1 to 3 is especially applicable.

Kemeny, J. G., H. Mirkil, J. L. Snell, and G. L. Thompson: "Finite Mathematical Structures," Prentice-Hall, Inc., Englewood Cliffs, N.J., 1959. Chapter 4 presents a treatment that is noteworthy for its wide scope of application to nonengineering fields; introductory in level.

Korn, G. A., and T. M. Korn: "Mathematical Handbook for Scientists and Engineers," McGraw-Hill Book Company, Inc., New York, 1961. A summary tabulation is given in Chap. 13. Excellent for review purposes.

Schwartz, J. T.: "Introduction to Matrices and Vectors," McGraw-Hill Book Company, Inc., New York, 1961. A clearly written introductory treatment with many examples of the mathematical operations.

Sokolnikoff, I. S., and R. M. Redheffer: "Mathematics of Physics and Modern Engineering," McGraw-Hill Book Company, Inc., New York, 1958. A concise presentation of the basic principles is given in Sec. 16, Chap. 4.

PROBLEMS

2.1 The determinants which follow are to be evaluated in two ways: (1) by expanding along a row or column and (2) by reducing the array to a triangular form.

$$(a) \begin{vmatrix} 0 & j & 1-j & 0 \\ 1 & 1 & 0 & j \\ j & -j & 0 & 1 \\ 1 & 0 & 0 & 1 \end{vmatrix} \quad (b) \begin{vmatrix} x & y & z \\ 1 & 2 & 1 \\ 0 & 1 & 1 \end{vmatrix} \quad (c) \begin{vmatrix} 2p+1 & p & 0 \\ p & 2p+2 & 2 \\ 0 & p & 2p+3 \end{vmatrix}$$

2.2 Is the determinant of the sum of two matrices equal to the sum of the determinants? Illustrate your answer with an example.

2.3 Prove that if the rows of an array of elements are interchanged with the columns, the value of the determinant is unchanged; i.e., prove that $\det A = \det A^t$.

2.4 If A is an $n \times n$ array of elements and k is a scalar, prove that

$$\det (kA) = k^n \det A$$

2.5 Make up a simple example which illustrates the fact that the determinant of the product of two square matrices is equal to the product of the determinants of the respective matrices.

2.6 Use the fact given in Prob. 2.5 to prove that $\det A = 1/(\det A^{-1})$.

2.7 If a matrix A may be written in terms of the component square matrices A_i and 0 as shown below (the 0 matrices have all elements zero), find an expression for the determinant of the matrix in terms of the determinants of the component square matrices.

$$A = \begin{bmatrix} A_1 & 0 & 0 & 0 \\ 0 & A_2 & 0 & 0 \\ 0 & 0 & A_3 & 0 \\ 0 & 0 & 0 & A_4 \end{bmatrix}$$

2.8 Show that the equation $\det (A - \lambda I) = 0$, where A is an $n \times n$ square matrix with real coefficients, forms an algebraic equation of degree n in the variable λ.

2.9 Solve the following set of equations:

$$X_1 + 2X_2 + X_3 = U_1$$
$$X_1 + X_2 - X_3 = U_2$$
$$X_2 + X_3 = U_3$$

2.10 Solve for x, y, and z in the following equations:

$$3x + y + z = 1$$
$$x + 2y + z = 2$$
$$x + y - z = 3$$

2.11 Perform the following matrix multiplications:

$$\begin{bmatrix} 1 & 2 & 3 \\ 4 & 5 & 6 \end{bmatrix} \begin{bmatrix} a \\ b \\ c \end{bmatrix} \qquad \begin{bmatrix} 1 & 2 \\ 3 & 4 \\ 5 & 6 \end{bmatrix} \begin{bmatrix} 1 & 0 \\ 2 & 1 \end{bmatrix}$$

$$(a) \qquad\qquad\qquad (b)$$

2.12 Show by a simple example that the distributive law of matrix multiplication applies, i.e., that $A(B + C) = AB + AC$.

2.13 Perform the following matrix multiplications:

$$\begin{bmatrix} 1 \\ 2 \\ 3 \\ 4 \end{bmatrix} \begin{bmatrix} 1 & 2 & 3 & 4 \end{bmatrix} \qquad \begin{bmatrix} 1 & 2 & 3 & 4 \end{bmatrix} \begin{bmatrix} 1 \\ 2 \\ 3 \\ 4 \end{bmatrix}$$

$$(a) \qquad\qquad\qquad (b)$$

2.14 Express the following matrix as the sum of a symmetric matrix and a skew-symmetric matrix:

$$\begin{bmatrix} 1 & a & b \\ 3 & c & 0 \\ 1 & 2 & 2 \end{bmatrix}$$

2.15 Express the following matrix as the sum of a hermitian matrix and a skew-hermitian matrix:

$$\begin{bmatrix} 1 & 3 + j & 4 \\ j & 0 & 5 \\ 2 + j & a + jb & 2 \end{bmatrix}$$

2.16 For the following matrices show that $(AB)^{-1} = B^{-1}A^{-1}$:

$$A = \begin{bmatrix} 1 & 1 \\ 2 & 1 \end{bmatrix} \qquad B = \begin{bmatrix} 1 & 2 \\ 3 & 4 \end{bmatrix}$$

2.17 For the matrices given in Prob. 2.16 show that $(AB)^t = B^tA^t$.

2.18 If A and B are diagonal matrices, show that multiplication is commutative, i.e., that $AB = BA$.

2.19 Given an arbitrary square matrix A, find a matrix B such that $(A + B)$ is commutative when multiplied by another arbitrary square matrix C.

2.20 Find the inverse of each of the following sets of equations:

$$V_1 = z_{11}I_1 + z_{12}I_2 \qquad I_1 = y_{11}V_1 + y_{12}V_2$$
$$V_2 = z_{21}I_1 + z_{22}I_2 \qquad I_2 = y_{21}V_1 + y_{22}V_2$$
$$(a) \qquad\qquad\qquad (b)$$

2.21 Given an $n \times n$ matrix, form an $(n + 1) \times (n + 1)$ matrix such that the sum of the elements in any row or any column is zero.

2.22 Find the conditions under which it is possible to interchange the variables A_i and B_j in the following matrix equation:

$$
\begin{bmatrix} A_1 \\ \cdot\, \cdot \\ A_i \\ \cdot\, \cdot \\ A_n \end{bmatrix}
=
\begin{bmatrix} c_{11} & \cdot\;\cdot & c_{1n} \\ \cdot\cdot\cdot\cdot\cdot\cdot\cdot\cdot\cdot\cdot \\ c_{n1} & \cdot\;\cdot & c_{nn} \end{bmatrix}
\begin{bmatrix} B_1 \\ \cdot\, \cdot \\ B_j \\ \cdot\, \cdot \\ B_n \end{bmatrix}
$$

2.23 Assume that A is a skew-symmetric matrix, all of whose elements are real. What properties will the diagonal elements of A^2 have?

2.24 The elements of the matrices A and B given below are assumed to be real. If A and B are both symmetric, will the product AB be symmetric? If not, find the conditions on the elements of A and B such that AB will be symmetric.

$$A = \begin{bmatrix} a_{11} & a_{12} \\ a_{21} & a_{22} \end{bmatrix} \qquad B = \begin{bmatrix} b_{11} & b_{12} \\ b_{21} & b_{22} \end{bmatrix}$$

2.25 If A, 1, and 0 are all $n \times n$ square matrices, find the total number of diagonal matrices which are solutions to the matrix equation $A^2 + 1 = 0$.

2.26 If the matrices of Prob. 2.25 are 2×2 matrices, find a solution which is not a diagonal matrix.

2.27 Find all diagonal 2×2 matrices which satisfy the following matrix equation:

$$A^2 + 3A + 1 = 0$$

2.28 Assume that A and P are square matrices and that P^{-1} exists. Let the matrix $B = PAP^{-1}$. Find an expression for B^k.

2.29 In the following matrix equation A is an $n \times n$ square matrix and the k_i are scalars:

$$f(A) = k_n A^n + \cdots + k_1 A + k_0 1 = 0$$

Show that if $B = PAP^{-1}$, then $f(B) = 0$.

2.30 Use the partitioning indicated by the dashed lines to compute the following matrix product:

$$
\begin{bmatrix} 1 & 0 & 1 \\ 2 & 0 & 1 \\ 0 & 1 & 1 \end{bmatrix}
\begin{bmatrix} 1 & 1 & 2 \\ 0 & 0 & 1 \\ 1 & 2 & 3 \end{bmatrix}
$$

2.31 Use the partitioning indicated by the dashed lines to compute the square of the following matrix:

$$
\begin{bmatrix}
1 & 1 & 1 & 0 & 0 \\
1 & 1 & 0 & 0 & 1 \\
1 & 0 & 1 & 0 & 0 \\
0 & 0 & 0 & 1 & 0 \\
0 & 1 & 0 & 0 & 1
\end{bmatrix}
$$

2.32 Given a matrix A partitioned into submatrices A_{ij} as indicated below, find an expression for A^{-1} in terms of the submatrices of A. Is it necessary that the A_{ij} submatrices be square?

$$
A = \begin{bmatrix} A_{11} & A_{12} \\ A_{21} & A_{22} \end{bmatrix}
$$

2.33 Show that the following matrix equation is equivalent to the set of equations (1) of Sec. 2.6.

$$
U^t = X^t A^t
$$

where
$$
U = \begin{bmatrix} U_1 \\ \cdot\, \cdot \\ U_n \end{bmatrix}
\qquad
X = \begin{bmatrix} X_1 \\ \cdot\, \cdot \\ X_n \end{bmatrix}
\qquad
A = \begin{bmatrix} a_{11} & \cdots & a_{1n} \\ \cdots\cdots\cdots\cdots \\ a_{n1} & \cdots & a_{nn} \end{bmatrix}
$$

2.34 Show that for an arbitrary row (column) matrix there exists a column (row) matrix with the property that when it is used to postmultiply (premultiply) the original matrix, the scalar 1 results.

2.35 Use Theorems 1 and 2 of Sec. 2.9 to prove Theorem 9.

2.36 Prove Theorem 1 of Sec. 2.9.

2.37 For the matrices of Prob. 2.16 show that Theorem 9 of Sec. 2.9 is true.

2.38 If $AB = CB$, can it be concluded that $A = C$? Give examples to show when this will not be true.

2.39 Given the matrix equation

$$
\alpha]\underline{X} = [G]B]\underline{X}
$$

show that it is possible to develop the equation

$$
\alpha] = [G]B]
$$

NOTE: Since X is a row matrix, it does not have an inverse; therefore it is not acceptable to simply postmultiply both sides of the first equation by X^{-1}.

2.40 What restrictions must be placed on A so that A^* will be hermitian?

2.41 The matrix shown below is partitioned into four square submatrices. If the 1 submatrices are identity matrices, the 0 submatrix is a null matrix (all the elements are zero), and the D submatrix has only diagonal elements, all of which are equal, find a general formula for the matrix raised to the nth power.

$$\begin{bmatrix} 1 & D \\ 0 & 1 \end{bmatrix}$$

2.42 If A is a diagonal matrix with the properties $a_{ij} = 0$, $i \neq j$ and $a_{ij} \neq 0$, $i = j$, show that it is always possible to specify a diagonal matrix B such that $B^t A B = 1$, where 1 is the identity matrix.

2.43 Under what conditions will $\det (B^t A B) = \det A$?

2.44 If $\det A = 0$, under what conditions will $\det (C^t A C) = 0$?

2.45 Assume a series of n matrix equations $C A_i = \lambda_i B A_i \, (i = 1, 2, \cdots, n)$ are satisfied where C and B are $n \times n$ square matrices, the A_i are $n \times 1$ column matrices, and the λ_i are scalars. Let A be an $n \times n$ matrix such that its columns are the A_i, and let D be a diagonal matrix such that $d_{ii} = \lambda_i$. Write all the individual matrix equations simultaneously as a single matrix equation.

2.46 Is $(A + B)^2$ ever equal to $A^2 + 2AB + B^2$? If so, when?

Chapter 3   *Circuit-theory applications of matrices*

3.1   *Introduction*

In this chapter we shall illustrate some of the basic applications of matrices to circuit theory. These applications will serve as useful tools in the study of the properties of active and passive networks which will fill later parts of this book.

In Chap. 2 we saw that one of the major uses of matrices was to provide a compact means of writing certain sets of equations. In investigating the applications of matrices to circuit theory, then, it seems reasonable to inquire as to the manner in which equations can be written in terms of the voltage and current variables of a given network. Several major categories of equations are of interest. For example, we may be interested in a given network solely from the viewpoint of its "appearance" at sets of external terminals. That is, we may be interested in the immittance between a pair of these terminals. This is called a *driving-point* immittance. We may also be interested in how a signal observed at some pair of terminals is related to an exciting or driving signal at some other pair of terminals. The ratio of these signals is called a *transfer function*. It may be a *transfer immittance*, a *transfer voltage ratio*, or a *transfer current ratio*. This "black-box" approach leaves us completely unconcerned with the internal structure of the network just so long as we can specify its external terminal behavior. If, in addition, we can also restrict ourselves to a situation in which the external terminals can be treated in pairs, such that the current into one terminal of the pair is equal to the current out of the other terminal of the pair, then we can reduce the number of equations required. How can we make such a restriction on an arbitrary network? Simply by specifying the type of device that is connected to these pairs of terminals. For example, a resistor, a voltage source, or a current source clearly requires that the currents follow this type of behavior. This is illustrated in Fig. 3.1. To define this case, that is, to specify the condition that the current into

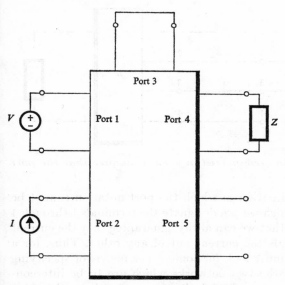

Figure 3.1 A five-port network.

one terminal is equal to the current out of another terminal, we use the word *port*. We may define a port of a given network as a pair of terminals connected to the network. The restriction on these terminals is that the current flowing into either of them must be equal to the current flowing out of the other.

Note that the use of the term "port" in referring to a pair of terminals is not a restriction on the form of the network to which those terminals belong, but a restriction on the type of circuitry which is externally connected to the terminals. Figure 3.2 gives an additional example of a case in which the port identification of a network may be used. For network A, terminals 1 and 2 certainly form a port. Since we may apply Kirchhoff's law to all the currents entering and leaving the various terminals of the network, the current into terminal 3 must be equal to the current flowing out of terminal 4. Thus, these two terminals also form a port. This logic may also be applied to the networks that follow in the cascade, justifying the use of the port notation for them.

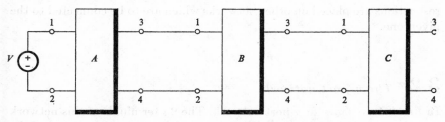

Figure 3.2 Three networks which may be treated as two-port networks.

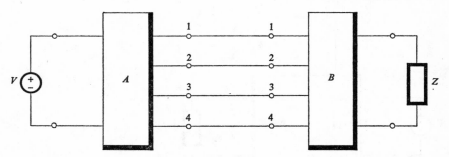

Figure 3.3   Two networks interconnected in such a manner that the port designation cannot be used.

In Fig. 3.3 is shown a situation in which the port notation cannot be used. There is no way in which we can designate the terminals 1 through 4 of networks A and B such that we can always guarantee that the current into any one of them equals the current out of any other. Thus, for a situation of this type, we must look for some other means of specifying the terminal properties of the two networks which are to be interconnected. Despite its limitations, much of the literature of active and passive network theory is developed with the network characteristics defined on a port basis. We shall make this our first topic of investigation in this chapter.

The second application of matrices to circuit theory will be an investigation of how we can characterize a network from the basis of its terminal properties when the port designation cannot be used. This will lead us to a study of the indefinite-admittance and indefinite-transfer matrices. Finally, we shall investigate the ways in which the internal network, that is, the actual configuration of active and passive elements connected to the terminals, can be characterized and represented in matrix notation.

It should be noted that, in all the discussion which follows, our goal is to arrive at a compact matrix notation for a network. This is the unifying theme of this chapter. However, as we have indicated above, the meaning of this matrix notation may differ considerably, depending on whether it represents the network from the viewpoint of its terminal properties or from the viewpoint of its internal configuration, and whether or not restrictions are placed on other networks which are to be connected to the given one.

3.2   *The n-port network*

In Fig. 3.4 we show an *n*-port network. The 2*n* terminals of this network have been grouped in pairs and labeled as the *n* ports. By reason of the

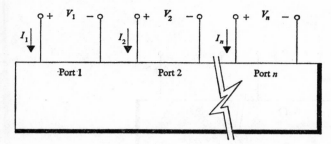

Figure 3.4 An n-port network with its voltage and current variables.

designation of port, defined in Sec. 3.1, we have not limited the network, but we have placed restrictions on the type of networks that may be connected to it. For the network illustrated, as many as n of the terminals shown may be connected to each other. For example, it frequently occurs that one terminal of each of the ports is "grounded," that is, that there are really only $n + 1$ distinct terminals. In this case, however, it is convenient to repeat the common terminals as illustrated in the figure. The n ports require the definition of $2n$ variables V_i and I_i. These are usually considered to be functions of the complex frequency variable p. The $2n$ variables may be expressed as a pair of column matrices, each with n rows. The two column matrices may then be related by an $n \times n$ square matrix. There are many ways in which the grouping of the variables may be made. For example,

$$\begin{bmatrix} V_1 \\ \cdot\cdot \\ V_n \end{bmatrix} = \begin{bmatrix} z_{11} & \cdots & z_{1n} \\ \cdots\cdots\cdots \\ z_{n1} & \cdots & z_{nn} \end{bmatrix} \begin{bmatrix} I_1 \\ \cdot\cdot \\ I_n \end{bmatrix} \tag{1}$$

This matrix equation may also be written $V = ZI$. It represents a set of n linear equations of the type

$$\begin{aligned} V_1 &= z_{11}I_1 + \cdots + z_{1n}I_n \\ &\cdots\cdots\cdots\cdots\cdots\cdots \\ V_n &= z_{n1}I_1 + \cdots + z_{nn}I_n \end{aligned} \tag{2}$$

The elements of the square $n \times n$ matrix obviously have the dimensions of impedance. This was the reason for the choice of the symbol z_{ij} to represent the elements of the matrix.

For a given network, the elements of the matrix can easily be found by applying testing conditions. For example, from (2), if all the currents except I_1 are made to equal 0, then z_{11} is simply the ratio of V_1 to I_1. Thus,

$$z_{11} = \frac{V_1}{I_1}\bigg|_{I_2 = I_3 = \cdots = I_n = 0}$$

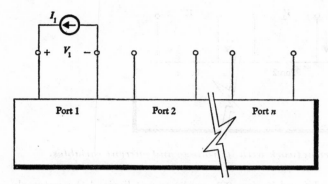

Figure 3.5   Finding z_{11} for an n-port network.

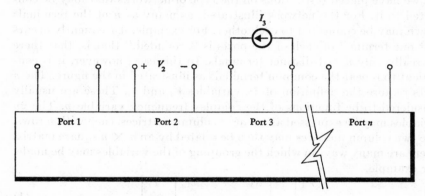

Figure 3.6   Finding z_{23} for an n-port network.

Note that the condition that all the currents except I_1 be zero is easily established by simply "testing" the network with all ports except port 1 open-circuited. A test current is applied to port 1 and the voltage across its terminals is measured. The ratio of voltage to current thus establishes z_{11}. This procedure is illustrated in Fig. 3.5. Similar tests may be made to establish the values of the terms z_{ij} for all values of i and j for any network for which these parameters are defined. Thus,[1]

$$z_{ij} = \frac{V_i}{I_j}\bigg|_{I_k=0 \quad k \neq j} \tag{3}$$

For example, if we apply this relationship to an n-port network to find z_{23}, we simply require a testing arrangement as shown in Fig. 3.6. In this

[1] The parameter z_{ij} is sometimes referred to as the voltage that will result at the ith port if a current $I_j = 1$ is applied at the jth port. Thus, in (3), if $I_j = 1$, $z_{ij} = V_i$. Since V_i and I_j are transformed variables, this process represents the application of an impulse of current to the network.

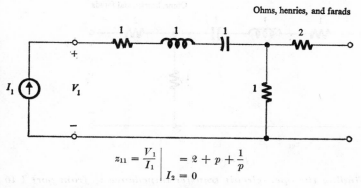

Figure 3.7 *Finding the open-circuit driving-point impedance z_{11} at port 1.*

figure a current is applied at port 3, and the resulting voltage is measured at port 2.

The terms z_{ij} are functions of the complex frequency variable p and are usually referred to as *network parameters*. They have the dimensions of impedance and are thus also called impedance network parameters or, more simply, *z parameters*. When a given network is tested to determine these parameters, all the ports are open-circuited (the impedance of the current generator is infinite, so we can also describe the port that the current generator is connected to as being open-circuited), so these terms may also be referred to as the *open-circuit parameters*. Specifically, any z_{ij} where $i = j$ may be referred to as the *open-circuit driving-point imped-ance* at the ith port. Similarly, any z_{ij} where $i \neq j$ may be referred to as the *open-circuit transfer impedance* from the jth port to the ith port.

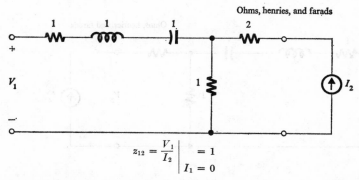

Figure 3.8 *Finding the open-circuit transfer impedance z_{12} from port 2 to port 1.*

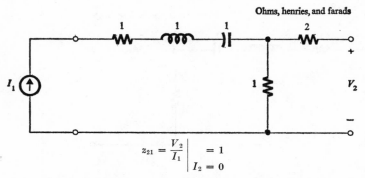

Ohms, henries, and farads

$$z_{21} = \frac{V_2}{I_1}\bigg|_{I_2 = 0} = 1$$

Figure 3.9   Finding the open-circuit transfer impedance z_{21} from port 1 to port 2.

As an example of how these parameters are determined, consider the two-port network shown in Figs. 3.7 to 3.10, in which are shown the conditions under which z_{11}, z_{12}, z_{21}, and z_{22}, respectively, can be found. In Fig. 3.11, the same network is considered as a four-port network by the addition of two more pairs of terminals. The open-circuit parameters given in the figure are found in the same manner as those of Figs. 3.7 to 3.10.

If we interchange the two column matrices containing the voltage and current variables of (1), we may write $I = YV$, where $Y = Z^{-1}$. The matrix equation is

$$\begin{bmatrix} I_1 \\ \cdots \\ I_n \end{bmatrix} = \begin{bmatrix} y_{11} & \cdots & y_{1n} \\ \cdots & \cdots & \cdots \\ y_{n1} & \cdots & y_{nn} \end{bmatrix} \begin{bmatrix} V_1 \\ \cdots \\ V_n \end{bmatrix} \tag{4}$$

We may use a testing procedure similar to that used for the z_{ij} terms to

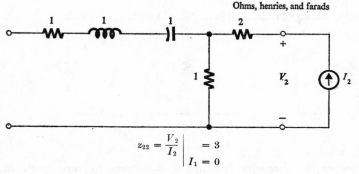

Ohms, henries, and farads

$$z_{22} = \frac{V_2}{I_2}\bigg|_{I_1 = 0} = 3$$

Figure 3.10   Finding the open-circuit driving-point impedance z_{22} at port 2.

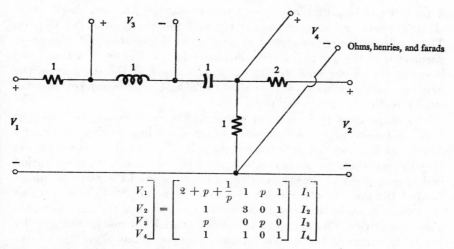

Figure 3.11   A four-port network and its z parameters.

determine the terms y_{ij}. For example, for y_{12} we may write

$$y_{12} = \frac{I_1}{V_2}\Bigg|_{V_1 = V_3 = \cdots = V_n = 0}$$

This requires placing a voltage source at port 2. The voltages at the other ports may be set equal to zero by short-circuiting these ports. Then we need only measure the current in the short circuit at port 1. The test is shown schematically in Fig. 3.12. In general, we may define

$$y_{ij} = \frac{I_i}{V_j}\Bigg|_{V_k = 0 \quad k \neq j} \tag{5}$$

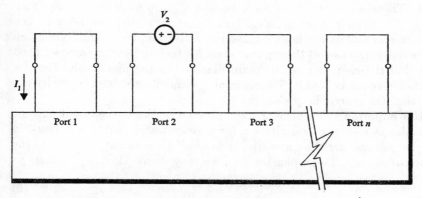

Figure 3.12   Finding y_{12} for an n-port network.

That is, to find y_{ij}, we place a voltage source at the jth port, short circuit all other ports, and measure the current in the short circuit at the ith port. The y_{ij} elements are frequently referred to as the *short-circuit admittance parameters* or the *y parameters* of the network. Specifically, y_{ij} where $i = j$ is called the *short-circuit driving-point admittance* at the ith port of the network, and y_{ij} where $i \neq j$ is called the *short-circuit transfer admittance* from the jth port to the ith port.

The property of reciprocity as applied to linear networks tells us that if an excitation is applied at one pair of terminals in a given network, and a response is measured at some second pair of terminals in the network, then the ratio of response to excitation will be the same as if the excitation had been applied at the second pair of terminals and the response measured at the first. In other words, in a reciprocal network, interchanging the points of excitation and response does not change the ratio between these quantities. The network, of course, must itself not be changed by the interchange of the excitation and response. Thus a voltage source being used to excite a given network may be interchanged with a short circuit in which the response current is being observed, and the ratio of these quantities will remain the same. In both cases, the network has zero-impedance elements connected to the terminal pairs. On the other hand, if a voltage source is being used to excite a network, and a voltage between two terminals is being measured as the response, then interchanging the response and the excitation will not yield the same result, since the network is changed by this operation.

In Figs. 3.8 and 3.9 the determination of z_{12} and z_{21} provides an example of a situation in which, if the network is reciprocal, the ratio of response to excitation is unchanged when the points of application and measurement are interchanged. More generally, this is the situation that occurs in the determination of z_{ij} and z_{ji} where $i \neq j$ in any network. Similarly, it is the situation that occurs in the determination of y_{ij} and y_{ji} in any network. Therefore we may conclude that, if a given network is reciprocal, then $z_{ij} = z_{ji}$ and $y_{ij} = y_{ji}$, i.e., that the z-parameter matrix and the y-parameter matrix are both symmetric. This provides a simplifying step in the determination of these parameters for such networks, since we need only find the elements on the main diagonal of the matrix and the elements above (or below) it. The remaining elements are determined by the fact that the matrix is symmetric.

It is important to realize the significance of the voltage and current variables as response *or* excitation for a given testing situation. Thus, in (1) the voltages are the quantities that result from the application of the various currents. To emphasize this, we may define the z parameters as

$$z_{ij} = \frac{\text{response}}{\text{excitation}} = \frac{V_i}{I_j}\bigg|_{I_k = 0 \quad k \neq j} \tag{6}$$

Similarly, in (4) the currents are the quantities that result from the application of various voltages, and thus we may define the y parameters as

$$y_{ij} = \frac{\text{response}}{\text{excitation}} = \frac{I_i}{V_j}\bigg|_{V_k=0 \quad k \neq j} \tag{7}$$

Note that where $i \neq j$, the port at which the response is to be determined may always be identified as the one at which some terminating condition is established. Thus, in the case of the z parameters, this port is open-circuited; in the case of the y parameters, this port is short-circuited. The other port then automatically becomes the one at which the excitation is applied. This distinction will be helpful when the transmission parameters for two-port networks are discussed, since these parameters are defined as a ratio of excitation to response, rather than the ratio of response to excitation indicated in (6) and (7).

The above two sets of parameters, the z and the y parameters, may be collectively referred to as the *immittance parameters*. Another very important set of parameters are the *hybrid parameters*. These are defined by the matrix equation $A = CB$, i.e.,

$$\begin{bmatrix} A_1 \\ \cdot\cdot \\ A_n \end{bmatrix} = \begin{bmatrix} c_{11} & \cdots & c_{1n} \\ \cdots\cdots\cdots \\ c_{n1} & \cdots & c_{nn} \end{bmatrix} \begin{bmatrix} B_1 \\ \cdot\cdot \\ B_n \end{bmatrix} \tag{8}$$

For the elements c_{ij} to be hybrid parameters, we require that the A_i be neither all voltage nor all current variables.

There are two types of hybrid parameters. The first type is determined by the condition that the A_i include one variable (either voltage or current) from each port. For example, for a three-port network, one possibility is

$$\begin{bmatrix} V_1 \\ I_2 \\ V_3 \end{bmatrix} = \begin{bmatrix} c_{11} & c_{12} & c_{13} \\ c_{21} & c_{22} & c_{23} \\ c_{31} & c_{32} & c_{33} \end{bmatrix} \begin{bmatrix} I_1 \\ V_2 \\ I_3 \end{bmatrix} \tag{9}$$

The second type of hybrid parameters is determined by the condition that the A_i include both variables (voltage *and* current) from at least one of the ports. For example, for a three-port network, one possibility is

$$\begin{bmatrix} V_1 \\ I_2 \\ V_2 \end{bmatrix} = \begin{bmatrix} d_{11} & d_{12} & d_{13} \\ d_{21} & d_{22} & d_{23} \\ d_{31} & d_{32} & d_{33} \end{bmatrix} \begin{bmatrix} I_1 \\ V_3 \\ I_3 \end{bmatrix} \tag{10}$$

The first type of hybrid parameters poses no new problems. For example, we may find c_{11} of (9) by the following equation:

$$c_{11} = \frac{V_1}{I_1}\bigg|_{V_2 = I_3 = 0}$$

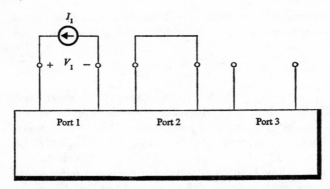

Figure 3.13   Determining c_{11} of equation (9) of Sec. 3.2.

Thus, our testing conditions simply require that port 2 be short-circuited and that port 3 be open-circuited. The situation is illustrated in Fig. 3.13.

For the second type of hybrid parameters, however, a new problem arises. For example, if in (10) we try to define d_{11}, we see that

$$d_{11} = \frac{V_1}{I_1}\bigg|_{V_3 = I_3 = 0}$$

The conditions here cannot be satisfied; that is, we cannot simultaneously require both the voltage and the current at a given port to be zero. Therefore, we must find some other means of determining the elements d_{ij}. We present the following theorem:

Theorem   If the elements c_{ij} of (8) are known, the necessary and sufficient condition that we may form a new matrix equation with the variables A_i and B_j interchanged is that $c_{ij} \neq 0$.[1]

As an example of the use of this theorem, consider the elements c_{ij} of (9), which we shall assume are known. Since we can form (10) by interchanging V_3 and V_2, the necessary and sufficient condition that the elements d_{ij} can be found is that $c_{32} \neq 0$. The elements can be found by matrix manipulation.

As another example consider the four-port network shown in Fig. 3.11. The impedance parameters are given by the matrix equation shown in the figure. Since the matrix element at the intersection of the second row and the third column is zero, the theorem tells us that we cannot form a hybrid set of parameters with the variables V_2 and I_3 interchanged. In other

[1] L. P. Huelsman, Transmission and Hybrid Parameters for n-Port Networks, *Proc. Natl. Electronics Conf.*, vol. 15, pp. 920–927, 1959.

words, the elements of the square matrix in the equation

$$\begin{bmatrix} V_1 \\ I_3 \\ V_3 \\ V_4 \end{bmatrix} = \begin{bmatrix} ? \\ \end{bmatrix} \begin{bmatrix} I_1 \\ I_2 \\ V_2 \\ I_4 \end{bmatrix} \tag{11}$$

do not exist. The other zeros in the matrix shown in Fig. 3.11 tell us that we cannot interchange variables V_3 and I_2, V_3 and I_4, or V_4 and I_3. Any other pairs of variables may be interchanged, and a new set of parameters may be found.

Let us now consider the effect of dependent and independent internal sources on the matrix formulation for n-port networks. We shall define *dependent sources* as voltage or current generators whose outputs depend on the voltage and current variables associated with the various ports. We shall define *independent sources* as voltage or current generators whose outputs are independent of the voltage and current variables associated with the various ports. Note that there are four possible dependent sources: (1) a voltage-controlled voltage source; (2) a current-controlled voltage source; (3) a current-controlled current source; and (4) a voltage-controlled current source. If dependent sources are present in the network, and if testing conditions are applied as previously described, the resulting matrix elements will include the effects of these dependent sources. This will be true whether the sources are directly dependent on the actual voltages and currents which are the port variables or whether they are dependent on internal voltages and currents. In this latter case, the internal voltages and currents themselves can be considered as functions of the port voltage and current variables, and thus the same criteria apply. This will be true for z, y, or hybrid parameters. As an example, consider the circuit shown in Fig. 3.14. The z-parameter matrix is easily found to be

$$\begin{bmatrix} \dfrac{R(5-k)}{3-k} & \dfrac{R}{3-k} \\[2mm] \dfrac{R(1+k)}{3-k} & \dfrac{R(5-k)}{3-k} \end{bmatrix} \tag{12}$$

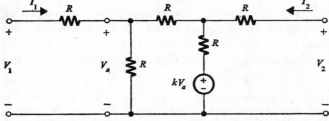

Figure 3.14   A two-port network with a dependent source.

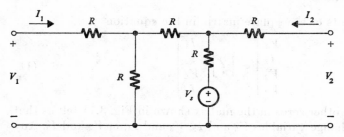

Figure 3.15   A two-port network with an independent source.

Let us now consider independent sources. If we are preparing to determine the z-parameter matrix for a given network, the presence of independent internal sources may be indicated by the fact that some of the voltages at the ports are nonzero even though all the currents are set equal to zero, i.e., even though all the ports are open-circuited.[1] Thus, the equations (1) become

$$\begin{bmatrix} V_1 \\ \cdot \cdot \\ V_n \end{bmatrix} = \begin{bmatrix} z_{11} & \cdots & z_{1n} \\ \cdots & \cdots & \cdots \\ z_{n1} & \cdots & z_{nn} \end{bmatrix} \begin{bmatrix} I_1 \\ \cdot \cdot \\ I_n \end{bmatrix} + \begin{bmatrix} V_{o1} \\ \cdot \cdot \\ V_{on} \end{bmatrix} \tag{13}$$

where the V_{oi} are the open-circuit voltages measured at the various ports when all the port currents are zero. The property of linearity easily establishes the validity of the superposition of the effects of independent sources and externally applied currents as indicated in the above equation.

A similar equation may be written for y parameters or for hybrid parameters. For example, for the network shown in Fig. 3.15, we can easily find the following matrix equation:

$$\begin{bmatrix} V_1 \\ V_2 \end{bmatrix} = \begin{bmatrix} \dfrac{5R}{3} & \dfrac{R}{3} \\ \dfrac{R}{3} & \dfrac{5R}{3} \end{bmatrix} \begin{bmatrix} I_1 \\ I_2 \end{bmatrix} + \begin{bmatrix} \dfrac{V_s}{3} \\ \dfrac{2V_s}{3} \end{bmatrix} \tag{14}$$

Note that an independent source need not have a d-c output. The equations associated with the n-port network deal with transformed quantities; hence any transformable d-c or time-varying output from an independent current or voltage generator may be expressed as the pertinent function of the complex frequency variable p. It is perhaps not amiss to remind the student at this point that the Laplace transform of a d-c source of k volts applied at $t = 0$ is k/p, not just k.

---

[1] Actually, there may still be independent sources present in the network even if the open-circuit port voltages are zero. Such sources, however, will not affect the relations among the voltage and current variables at the ports.

It is easy to show by combination theory that if we have $2n$ variables (the voltages and currents at n ports), and if these are to be arranged as the elements of two column matrices, each with n rows, there are c ways of arranging these elements, where

$$c = \frac{(2n)!}{(n!)^2}$$

This, of course, only takes account of the combinations, not the permutations, of the variables once they have been selected. In other words, there are c sets of different network parameters, although we may, of course, reposition the elements of a given array by permuting the variables. For example, for a two-port network, there are 6 sets of parameters; for a three-port network, 20 sets; for a four-port network, 70 sets, and so on, with the number rising very rapidly for networks with large numbers of ports.[1] Because of the frequency with which two-port networks occur, we shall treat the six possible sets of two-port network parameters in detail in the next section.

3.3 *Two-port-network parameters*

The various sets of two-port-network parameters are itemized below, together with their commonly accepted designations.[2] The appropriate testing conditions and the descriptions of the individual parameters are given in Table 3.1.

z parameters
$$\begin{bmatrix} V_1 \\ V_2 \end{bmatrix} = \begin{bmatrix} z_{11} & z_{12} \\ z_{21} & z_{22} \end{bmatrix} \begin{bmatrix} I_1 \\ I_2 \end{bmatrix}$$

y parameters
$$\begin{bmatrix} I_1 \\ I_2 \end{bmatrix} = \begin{bmatrix} y_{11} & y_{12} \\ y_{21} & y_{22} \end{bmatrix} \begin{bmatrix} V_1 \\ V_2 \end{bmatrix}$$

h parameters
$$\begin{bmatrix} V_1 \\ I_2 \end{bmatrix} = \begin{bmatrix} h_{11} & h_{12} \\ h_{21} & h_{22} \end{bmatrix} \begin{bmatrix} I_1 \\ V_2 \end{bmatrix}$$

g parameters
$$\begin{bmatrix} I_1 \\ V_2 \end{bmatrix} = \begin{bmatrix} g_{11} & g_{12} \\ g_{21} & g_{22} \end{bmatrix} \begin{bmatrix} V_1 \\ I_2 \end{bmatrix}$$

Transmission parameters
$$\begin{bmatrix} V_1 \\ I_1 \end{bmatrix} = \begin{bmatrix} A & B \\ C & D \end{bmatrix} \begin{bmatrix} V_2 \\ -I_2 \end{bmatrix}$$

Inverse-transmission parameters
$$\begin{bmatrix} V_2 \\ I_2 \end{bmatrix} = \begin{bmatrix} \mathcal{A} & \mathcal{B} \\ \mathcal{C} & \mathcal{D} \end{bmatrix} \begin{bmatrix} V_1 \\ -I_1 \end{bmatrix}$$

[1] Actually, we may also consider new variables formed by combinations of the voltage and current variables. An example of this is the scattering parameters discussed in Sec. 3.7.

[2] The term *four-pole* is also occasionally used in the literature to refer to a two-port network.

Table 3.1 Two-port-network parameters

Param-eter	Definition Formula	Condition	Description	Circuit
z_{11}	$\dfrac{V_1}{I_1}$	$I_2 = 0$	Open-circuit driving-point impedance at port 1	
z_{12}	$\dfrac{V_1}{I_2}$	$I_1 = 0$	Open-circuit transfer impedance from port 2 to port 1	
z_{21}	$\dfrac{V_2}{I_1}$	$I_2 = 0$	Open-circuit transfer impedance from port 1 to port 2	
z_{22}	$\dfrac{V_2}{I_2}$	$I_1 = 0$	Open-circuit driving-point impedance at port 2	
y_{11}	$\dfrac{I_1}{V_1}$	$V_2 = 0$	Short-circuit driving-point admittance at port 1	
y_{12}	$\dfrac{I_1}{V_2}$	$V_1 = 0$	Short-circuit transfer admittance from port 2 to port 1	
y_{21}	$\dfrac{I_2}{V_1}$	$V_2 = 0$	Short-circuit transfer admittance from port 1 to port 2	
y_{22}	$\dfrac{I_2}{V_2}$	$V_1 = 0$	Short-circuit driving-point admittance at port 2	

Table 3.1 (continued)

Param- eter	Definition Formula	Condition	Description	Circuit
h_{11}	$\dfrac{V_1}{I_1}$	$V_2 = 0$	Driving-point impedance at port 1 with port 2 short-circuited	
h_{12}	$\dfrac{V_1}{V_2}$	$I_1 = 0$	Voltage transfer ratio from port 2 to port 1 with port 1 open-circuited	
h_{21}	$\dfrac{I_2}{I_1}$	$V_2 = 0$	Current transfer ratio from port 1 to port 2 with port 2 short-circuited	
h_{22}	$\dfrac{I_2}{V_2}$	$I_1 = 0$	Driving-point admittance at port 2 with port 1 open-circuited	
g_{11}	$\dfrac{I_1}{V_1}$	$I_2 = 0$	Driving-point admittance at port 1 with port 2 open-circuited	
g_{12}	$\dfrac{I_1}{I_2}$	$V_1 = 0$	Current transfer ratio from port 2 to port 1 with port 1 short-circuited	
g_{21}	$\dfrac{V_2}{V_1}$	$I_2 = 0$	Voltage transfer ratio from port 1 to port 2 with port 2 open-circuited	
g_{22}	$\dfrac{V_2}{I_2}$	$V_1 = 0$	Driving-point impedance at port 2 with port 1 short-circuited	

Table 3.1   (*continued*)

Param-eter	Definition Formula	Condition	Description	Circuit
A	$\dfrac{V_1}{V_2}$	$I_2 = 0$	Inverse of voltage transfer ratio from port 1 to port 2 with port 2 open-circuited	
B	$\dfrac{V_1}{-I_2}$	$V_2 = 0$	Negative inverse of transfer admittance from port 1 to port 2 with port 2 short-circuited	
C	$\dfrac{I_1}{V_2}$	$I_2 = 0$	Inverse of transfer impedance from port 1 to port 2 with port 2 open-circuited	
D	$\dfrac{I_1}{-I_2}$	$V_2 = 0$	Negative inverse of current transfer ratio from port 1 to port 2 with port 2 short-circuited	
$\mathfrak{A}$	$\dfrac{V_2}{V_1}$	$I_1 = 0$	Inverse of voltage transfer ratio from port 2 to port 1 with port 1 open-circuited	
$\mathfrak{B}$	$\dfrac{V_2}{-I_1}$	$V_1 = 0$	Negative inverse of transfer admittance from port 2 to port 1 with port 1 short-circuited	
$\mathfrak{C}$	$\dfrac{I_2}{V_1}$	$I_1 = 0$	Inverse of transfer impedance from port 2 to port 1 with port 1 open-circuited	
$\mathfrak{D}$	$\dfrac{I_2}{-I_1}$	$V_1 = 0$	Negative inverse of current transfer ratio from port 2 to port 1 with port 1 short-circuited	

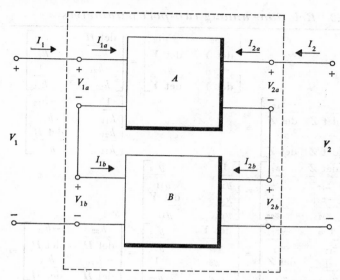

Figure 3.16   Two two-port networks connected in series.

It is easily seen that the z-parameter matrix is the inverse of the y-parameter matrix, the h-parameter matrix is the inverse of the g-parameter matrix, and the transmission-parameter (or $ABCD$-parameter) matrix is the inverse (with an additional sign change) of the inverse-transmission-parameter matrix. The theorem of the preceding section may be applied to easily establish whether or not it is possible to determine any set of the parameters once a given set is known. For example, if the z parameters are known, interchanging V_2 and I_2 yields the h parameters; therefore it is necessary and sufficient that $z_{22} \neq 0$ for the h parameters to exist. It is easy to establish the interrelations given in Table 3.2 between the various sets of parameters by substituting in the pertinent equations.[1] The validity of the theorem is seen in the appearance of the critical element in the denominator of the new set of parameters. Thus, corresponding to the above example, when the h parameters are expressed in terms of the z parameters, the term z_{22} appears in the denominator of each element.

The various sets of network parameters have several direct applications in terms of certain network configurations. For example, consider the two-port networks A and B connected as shown in Fig. 3.16. We shall refer to this connection as a *series* connection. For the two original networks we

[1] An even more extensive tabulation is given in E. F. Bolinder, Note on the Matrix Representation of Linear Two-port Networks, *IRE Trans. on Circuit Theory*, vol. CT-4, pp. 337–339, December, 1957.

Table 3.2   Relations among two-port parameters

$\begin{bmatrix} z_{11} & z_{12} \\ z_{21} & z_{22} \end{bmatrix} =$		$\begin{bmatrix} \dfrac{y_{22}}{\det Y} & \dfrac{-y_{12}}{\det Y} \\ \dfrac{-y_{21}}{\det Y} & \dfrac{y_{11}}{\det Y} \end{bmatrix} =$	$\begin{bmatrix} \dfrac{\det H}{h_{22}} & \dfrac{h_{12}}{h_{22}} \\ \dfrac{-h_{21}}{h_{22}} & \dfrac{1}{h_{22}} \end{bmatrix} =$
$\begin{bmatrix} y_{11} & y_{12} \\ y_{21} & y_{22} \end{bmatrix} =$	$\begin{bmatrix} \dfrac{z_{22}}{\det Z} & \dfrac{-z_{12}}{\det Z} \\ \dfrac{-z_{21}}{\det Z} & \dfrac{z_{11}}{\det Z} \end{bmatrix} =$		$\begin{bmatrix} \dfrac{1}{h_{11}} & \dfrac{-h_{12}}{h_{11}} \\ \dfrac{h_{21}}{h_{11}} & \dfrac{\det H}{h_{11}} \end{bmatrix} =$
$\begin{bmatrix} h_{11} & h_{12} \\ h_{21} & h_{22} \end{bmatrix} =$	$\begin{bmatrix} \dfrac{\det Z}{z_{22}} & \dfrac{z_{12}}{z_{22}} \\ \dfrac{-z_{21}}{z_{22}} & \dfrac{1}{z_{22}} \end{bmatrix} =$	$\begin{bmatrix} \dfrac{1}{y_{11}} & \dfrac{-y_{12}}{y_{11}} \\ \dfrac{y_{21}}{y_{11}} & \dfrac{\det Y}{y_{11}} \end{bmatrix} =$	
$\begin{bmatrix} g_{11} & g_{12} \\ g_{21} & g_{22} \end{bmatrix} =$	$\begin{bmatrix} \dfrac{1}{z_{11}} & \dfrac{-z_{12}}{z_{11}} \\ \dfrac{z_{21}}{z_{11}} & \dfrac{\det Z}{z_{11}} \end{bmatrix} =$	$\begin{bmatrix} \dfrac{\det Y}{y_{22}} & \dfrac{y_{12}}{y_{22}} \\ \dfrac{-y_{21}}{y_{22}} & \dfrac{1}{y_{22}} \end{bmatrix} =$	$\begin{bmatrix} \dfrac{h_{22}}{\det H} & \dfrac{-h_{12}}{\det H} \\ \dfrac{-h_{21}}{\det H} & \dfrac{h_{11}}{\det H} \end{bmatrix} =$
$\begin{bmatrix} A & B \\ C & D \end{bmatrix} =$	$\begin{bmatrix} \dfrac{z_{11}}{z_{21}} & \dfrac{\det Z}{z_{21}} \\ \dfrac{1}{z_{21}} & \dfrac{z_{22}}{z_{21}} \end{bmatrix} =$	$\begin{bmatrix} \dfrac{-y_{22}}{y_{21}} & \dfrac{-1}{y_{21}} \\ \dfrac{-\det Y}{y_{21}} & \dfrac{-y_{11}}{y_{21}} \end{bmatrix} =$	$\begin{bmatrix} \dfrac{-\det H}{h_{21}} & \dfrac{-h_{11}}{h_{21}} \\ \dfrac{-h_{22}}{h_{21}} & \dfrac{-1}{h_{21}} \end{bmatrix} =$
$\begin{bmatrix} \mathcal{A} & \mathcal{B} \\ \mathcal{C} & \mathcal{D} \end{bmatrix} =$	$\begin{bmatrix} \dfrac{z_{22}}{z_{12}} & \dfrac{\det Z}{z_{12}} \\ \dfrac{1}{z_{12}} & \dfrac{z_{11}}{z_{12}} \end{bmatrix} =$	$\begin{bmatrix} \dfrac{-y_{11}}{y_{12}} & \dfrac{-1}{y_{12}} \\ \dfrac{-\det Y}{y_{12}} & \dfrac{-y_{22}}{y_{12}} \end{bmatrix} =$	$\begin{bmatrix} \dfrac{1}{h_{12}} & \dfrac{h_{11}}{h_{12}} \\ \dfrac{h_{22}}{h_{12}} & \dfrac{\det H}{h_{12}} \end{bmatrix} =$

may write

$$V_a = Z_a I_a \qquad V_b = Z_b I_b \tag{1}$$

where $\quad V_a = \begin{bmatrix} V_{1a} \\ V_{2a} \end{bmatrix} \quad Z_a = \begin{bmatrix} z_{11a} & z_{12a} \\ z_{21a} & z_{22a} \end{bmatrix} \quad I_a = \begin{bmatrix} I_{1a} \\ I_{2a} \end{bmatrix} \quad \cdots \tag{2}$

For the new two-port network formed by the series combination of the two original networks and indicated by the dashed lines in Fig. 3.16, we may write

$$V = ZI \tag{3}$$

where $\quad V = \begin{bmatrix} V_1 \\ V_2 \end{bmatrix} \quad Z = \begin{bmatrix} z_{11} & z_{12} \\ z_{21} & z_{22} \end{bmatrix} \quad I = \begin{bmatrix} I_1 \\ I_2 \end{bmatrix} \tag{4}$

Since the voltages at the ports of networks A and B add to produce the voltages of the new two-port network, and since the input and output

$$\begin{bmatrix} \dfrac{1}{g_{11}} & \dfrac{-g_{12}}{g_{11}} \\[2mm] \dfrac{g_{21}}{g_{11}} & \dfrac{\det G}{g_{11}} \end{bmatrix} = \begin{bmatrix} \dfrac{A}{C} & \dfrac{\det A}{C} \\[2mm] \dfrac{1}{C} & \dfrac{D}{C} \end{bmatrix} = \begin{bmatrix} \dfrac{\mathcal{D}}{\mathcal{C}} & \dfrac{1}{\mathcal{C}} \\[2mm] \dfrac{\det \mathcal{A}}{\mathcal{C}} & \dfrac{\mathcal{A}}{\mathcal{C}} \end{bmatrix}$$

$$\begin{bmatrix} \dfrac{\det G}{g_{22}} & \dfrac{g_{12}}{g_{22}} \\[2mm] \dfrac{-g_{21}}{g_{22}} & \dfrac{1}{g_{22}} \end{bmatrix} = \begin{bmatrix} \dfrac{D}{B} & \dfrac{-\det A}{B} \\[2mm] \dfrac{-1}{B} & \dfrac{A}{B} \end{bmatrix} = \begin{bmatrix} \dfrac{\mathcal{A}}{\mathcal{B}} & \dfrac{-1}{\mathcal{B}} \\[2mm] \dfrac{-\det \mathcal{A}}{\mathcal{B}} & \dfrac{\mathcal{D}}{\mathcal{B}} \end{bmatrix}$$

$$\begin{bmatrix} \dfrac{g_{22}}{\det G} & \dfrac{-g_{12}}{\det G} \\[2mm] \dfrac{-g_{21}}{\det G} & \dfrac{g_{11}}{\det G} \end{bmatrix} = \begin{bmatrix} \dfrac{B}{D} & \dfrac{\det A}{D} \\[2mm] \dfrac{-1}{D} & \dfrac{C}{D} \end{bmatrix} = \begin{bmatrix} \dfrac{\mathcal{B}}{\mathcal{A}} & \dfrac{1}{\mathcal{A}} \\[2mm] \dfrac{-\det \mathcal{A}}{\mathcal{A}} & \dfrac{\mathcal{C}}{\mathcal{A}} \end{bmatrix}$$

$$\begin{bmatrix} \dfrac{C}{A} & \dfrac{-\det A}{A} \\[2mm] \dfrac{1}{A} & \dfrac{B}{A} \end{bmatrix} = \begin{bmatrix} \dfrac{\mathcal{C}}{\mathcal{D}} & \dfrac{-1}{\mathcal{D}} \\[2mm] \dfrac{\det \mathcal{A}}{\mathcal{D}} & \dfrac{\mathcal{B}}{\mathcal{D}} \end{bmatrix}$$

$$\begin{bmatrix} \dfrac{1}{g_{21}} & \dfrac{g_{22}}{g_{21}} \\[2mm] \dfrac{g_{11}}{g_{21}} & \dfrac{\det G}{g_{21}} \end{bmatrix} = \begin{bmatrix} \dfrac{\mathcal{D}}{\det \mathcal{A}} & \dfrac{\mathcal{B}}{\det \mathcal{A}} \\[2mm] \dfrac{\mathcal{C}}{\det \mathcal{A}} & \dfrac{\mathcal{A}}{\det \mathcal{A}} \end{bmatrix}$$

$$\begin{bmatrix} \dfrac{-\det G}{g_{12}} & \dfrac{-g_{22}}{g_{12}} \\[2mm] \dfrac{-g_{11}}{g_{12}} & \dfrac{-1}{g_{12}} \end{bmatrix} = \begin{bmatrix} \dfrac{D}{\det A} & \dfrac{B}{\det A} \\[2mm] \dfrac{C}{\det A} & \dfrac{A}{\det A} \end{bmatrix}$$

currents for the new two-port network flow in series through the original networks,[1]

$$V = V_a + V_b \qquad I = I_a = I_b \tag{5}$$

Therefore, we may write

$$V = Z_a I_a + Z_b I_b = (Z_a + Z_b)I \tag{6}$$

If we compare the right side of (6) with (3), we conclude that

$$Z = Z_a + Z_b \tag{7}$$

The conclusion of (7) is the following: When 2 two-port networks are connected in series as shown in Fig. 3.16, the z-parameter matrix of the resulting two-port network is equal to the sum of the z-parameter matrices of the original 2 two-port networks.

[1] The variables at port 1 will frequently be referred to as the "input" variables; similarly, those at port 2 will be called the "output" variables.

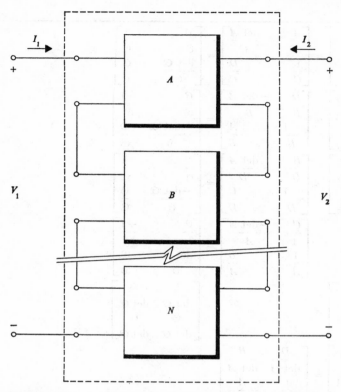

Figure 3.17   A series connection of n two-port networks.

The generality of matrix methods may now be called upon to extend this conclusion to n two-port networks connected in series as shown in Fig. 3.17. The only change in the development of the preceding equations is that there will be n defining equations of the type of (1) and there will be n terms inside the parentheses in (6). All other steps of the development and the resulting conclusion are exactly the same.

As an example of the above procedure, consider the networks and their z parameters shown in Fig. 3.18. It is readily established that the network resulting from the series connection of these networks has the z-parameter matrix formed by the addition of the two z-parameter matrices. Physically, if we consider the first network as a small-signal model of a vacuum tube, then the resulting network represents that same device with an unbypassed cathode resistor.

A case sometimes arises in which the conclusions of (7) are not applicable. As an illustration consider the series connection of the 2 two-port networks shown in Fig. 3.19. The z-parameter matrices are shown with

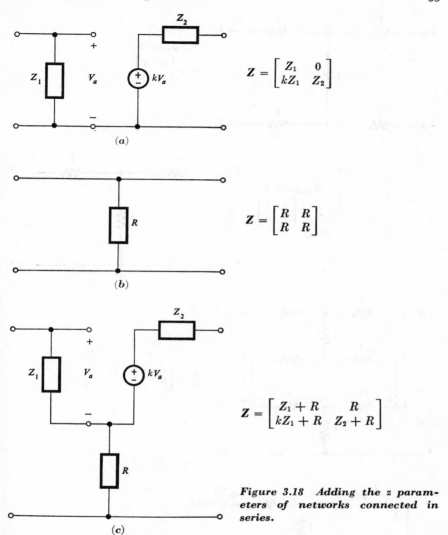

$$Z = \begin{bmatrix} Z_1 & 0 \\ kZ_1 & Z_2 \end{bmatrix}$$

(a)

$$Z = \begin{bmatrix} R & R \\ R & R \end{bmatrix}$$

(b)

$$Z = \begin{bmatrix} Z_1 + R & R \\ kZ_1 + R & Z_2 + R \end{bmatrix}$$

(c)

Figure 3.18 Adding the z parameters of networks connected in series.

the networks to which they refer. Clearly, the sum of the individual z-parameter matrices is not equal to the z-parameter matrix of the series connection of the networks. To see why this is so, consider part d of the figure. This illustrates the testing conditions appropriate for finding z_{11} or z_{21} of the over-all network. The definition of a port is violated for both network A and network B, since the currents at the terminals which form port 1 for either of these networks are not equal. Since we have violated

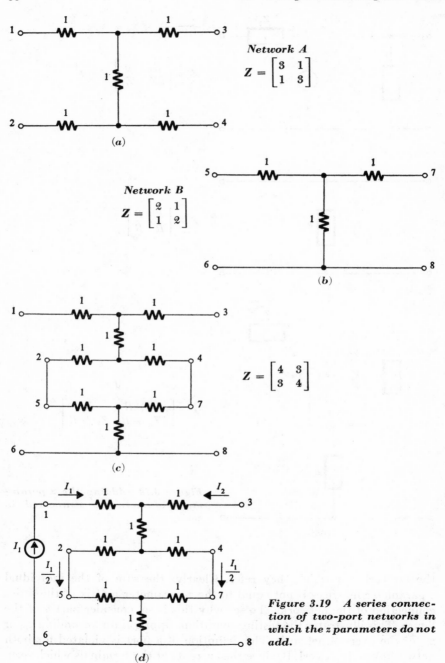

Network A
$$Z = \begin{bmatrix} 3 & 1 \\ 1 & 3 \end{bmatrix}$$

(a)

Network B
$$Z = \begin{bmatrix} 2 & 1 \\ 1 & 2 \end{bmatrix}$$

(b)

$$Z = \begin{bmatrix} 4 & 3 \\ 3 & 4 \end{bmatrix}$$

(c)

(d)

Figure 3.19   A series connection of two-port networks in which the z parameters do not add.

the conditions under which the original z parameters of each network were defined, we cannot expect to be able to add the original z-parameter matrices to find a resultant z-parameter matrix.

It is useful to be able to test an interconnection of networks to establish whether or not this problem will occur. Consider Fig. 3.19d. If we place an open circuit between terminals 4 and 7 (rather than the short circuit shown), then the currents at the terminals 1, 2, 5, and 6 of the network will be such that the port designation applies. We now simply must decide whether or not a current will flow between terminals 4 and 7 if the short circuit is reestablished. The criterion for the answer to this question is simply whether or not a voltage exists between terminals 4 and 7. If there is no voltage (while I_1 is flowing), then no current will flow when the short circuit is reestablished. In the circuit shown here, it is easy to see that there will be a voltage. A similar test can be made with a testing current I_2 applied between terminals 3 and 8 (with terminals 4 and 7 shorted) by measuring the voltage between terminals 2 and 5 when an open circuit exists between them.

The tests described are easily seen to apply to the general case. This is illustrated in Fig. 3.20a and b. We may conclude, with reference to these figures, that if V_a is zero for all values of I_1, and if V_b is zero for all values of I_2, then the series connection will give the results of (7). If either of the above tests fails, there is one other recourse left to us. We may modify either of the networks by connecting an ideal transformer[1] to one of its ports, as shown in Fig. 3.20c and d. An inspection of these figures will show that V_a and V_b will always be zero. Thus this modification of the networks ensures that the z parameters of the individual networks may be added to find the z parameters of the resulting network. The above tests may be generalized to the case of n two-port networks connected in series. It is easily shown that $n - 1$ isolating transformers will always make it possible to add the z-parameter matrices of the original networks to produce the z-parameter matrix of the network formed by the series connection of the original networks.

If n two-port networks are connected as shown in Fig. 3.21, we can describe the resulting two-port network shown by the dashed lines as the *parallel* connection of the original networks. If the original networks are defined by their y parameters, we may write

$$I_a = Y_a V_a \qquad I_b = Y_b V_b \qquad \cdot \ \cdot \ \cdot$$

$$\text{where} \quad I_a = \begin{bmatrix} I_{1a} \\ I_{2a} \end{bmatrix} \quad Y_a = \begin{bmatrix} y_{11a} & y_{12a} \\ y_{21a} & y_{22a} \end{bmatrix} \quad V_a = \begin{bmatrix} V_{1a} \\ V_{2a} \end{bmatrix} \quad \cdot \ \cdot \ \cdot$$

---

[1] The ideal transformer will be discussed in Sec. 4.2.

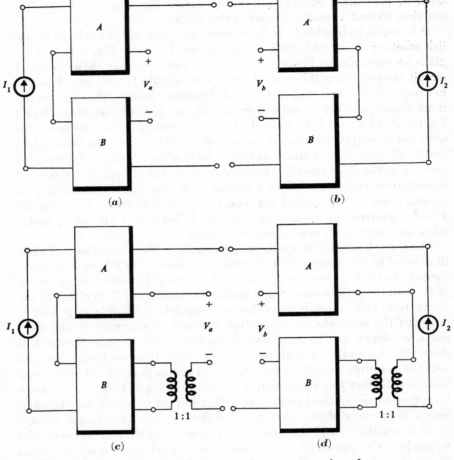

**Figure 3.20 The use of an ideal transformer to ensure that the
z parameters add.**

For the over-all two-port network we may write

$$I = YV$$

where $\qquad I = \begin{bmatrix} I_1 \\ I_2 \end{bmatrix} \qquad Y = \begin{bmatrix} y_{11} & y_{12} \\ y_{21} & y_{22} \end{bmatrix} \qquad V = \begin{bmatrix} V_1 \\ V_2 \end{bmatrix}$$

Since all the input voltages are in parallel, they are equal. Similarly,
the output voltages are equal. The individual network input and output
currents add to form the input and output currents for the over-all

network. Therefore, we may write

$$V = V_a = V_b = \cdots = V_n \qquad I = I_a + I_b + \cdots + I_n$$

For the over-all two-port network we may write

$$I = Y_a V_a + Y_b V_b + \cdots + Y_n V_n$$

Since the column matrices of voltages are all equal, we may write the above as

$$I = (Y_a + Y_b + \cdots + Y_n)V \tag{8}$$

From (8) we conclude that

$$Y = Y_a + Y_b + \cdots + Y_n \tag{9}$$

Thus we see that the y-parameter matrix of a two-port network formed by the parallel connection of a set of n two-port networks may be found by adding the individual y-parameter matrices. As in the case for the series-connected networks, interconnections of some networks may not follow (9). In general, this can be avoided by the use of isolating transformers as shown in Fig. 3.22.

Methods of interconnecting two-port networks such that their g-parameter matrices or their h-parameter matrices add to form the parameter matrix for the resulting two-port network are easily arrived at. These are left as exercises. Of more interest is the case shown in Fig. 3.23. The interconnection of two-port networks illustrated here will be referred to as a *cascade* connection. For the individual networks, in terms of their

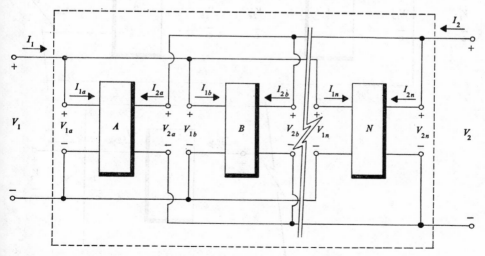

Figure 3.21   The parallel connection of n two-port networks.

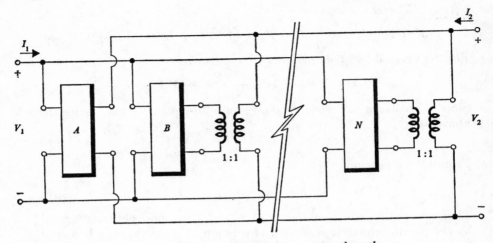

Figure 3.22   The use of ideal transformers to ensure that the
y parameters add.

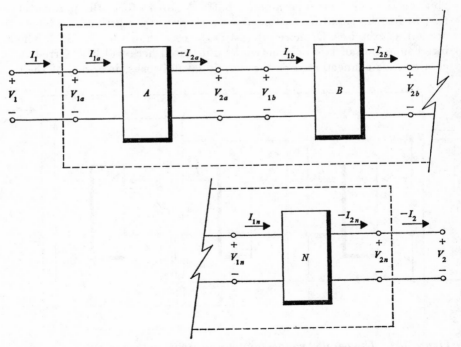

Figure 3.23   The cascade connection of *n* two-port networks.

transmission parameters, we may write

$$\begin{bmatrix} V_{1a} \\ I_{1a} \end{bmatrix} = \begin{bmatrix} A_a & B_a \\ C_a & D_a \end{bmatrix} \begin{bmatrix} V_{2a} \\ -I_{2a} \end{bmatrix} \qquad \begin{bmatrix} V_{1b} \\ I_{1b} \end{bmatrix} = \begin{bmatrix} A_b & B_b \\ C_b & D_b \end{bmatrix} \begin{bmatrix} V_{2b} \\ -I_{2b} \end{bmatrix} \quad \cdots$$

For the over-all two-port network as indicated by the dashed lines,

$$\begin{bmatrix} V_1 \\ I_1 \end{bmatrix} = \begin{bmatrix} A & B \\ C & D \end{bmatrix} \begin{bmatrix} V_2 \\ -I_2 \end{bmatrix} \tag{10}$$

Several matrix equalities exist, as may be seen from Fig. 3.23. For example,

$$\begin{bmatrix} V_1 \\ I_1 \end{bmatrix} = \begin{bmatrix} V_{1a} \\ I_{1a} \end{bmatrix} \qquad \begin{bmatrix} V_{2a} \\ -I_{2a} \end{bmatrix} = \begin{bmatrix} V_{1b} \\ I_{1b} \end{bmatrix} \quad \cdots \quad \begin{bmatrix} V_{2n} \\ -I_{2n} \end{bmatrix} = \begin{bmatrix} V_2 \\ -I_2 \end{bmatrix}$$

Thus we may write

$$\begin{bmatrix} V_1 \\ I_1 \end{bmatrix} = \begin{bmatrix} A_a & B_a \\ C_a & D_a \end{bmatrix} \begin{bmatrix} V_{2a} \\ -I_{2a} \end{bmatrix} = \begin{bmatrix} A_a & B_a \\ C_a & D_a \end{bmatrix} \begin{bmatrix} A_b & B_b \\ C_b & D_b \end{bmatrix} \begin{bmatrix} V_{2b} \\ -I_{2b} \end{bmatrix}$$

The process may be continued until we have

$$\begin{bmatrix} V_1 \\ I_1 \end{bmatrix} = \begin{bmatrix} A_a & B_a \\ C_a & D_a \end{bmatrix} \begin{bmatrix} A_b & B_b \\ C_b & D_b \end{bmatrix} \cdots \begin{bmatrix} A_n & B_n \\ C_n & D_n \end{bmatrix} \begin{bmatrix} V_2 \\ -I_2 \end{bmatrix}$$

Comparing this with (10), we see that

$$\begin{bmatrix} A & B \\ C & D \end{bmatrix} = \begin{bmatrix} A_a & B_a \\ C_a & D_a \end{bmatrix} \begin{bmatrix} A_b & B_b \\ C_b & D_b \end{bmatrix} \cdots \begin{bmatrix} A_n & B_n \\ C_n & D_n \end{bmatrix} \tag{11}$$

Therefore, we conclude that the transmission-parameter matrix of a cascade of two-port networks is equal to the matrix product of the transmission-parameter matrices of the two-port networks forming the cascade. Since matrix multiplication is, in general, noncommutative, the order of the transmission matrices in the multiplication must be the same as the order of the related networks in the cascade. As an example, consider the "T" configuration of 1-ohm resistors shown in Fig. 3.24. The transmission-

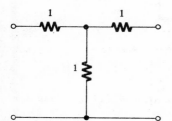

Figure 3.24   A "T" network of 1-ohm resistors.

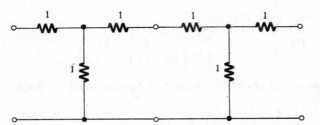

Figure 3.25 Two "T" networks connected in cascade.

parameter matrix is easily shown to be

$$\begin{bmatrix} 2 & 3 \\ 1 & 2 \end{bmatrix}$$

For the cascade of two of these networks as shown in Fig. 3.25, the transmission-parameter matrix may be found as follows:

$$\begin{bmatrix} 2 & 3 \\ 1 & 2 \end{bmatrix}\begin{bmatrix} 2 & 3 \\ 1 & 2 \end{bmatrix} = \begin{bmatrix} 7 & 12 \\ 4 & 7 \end{bmatrix}$$

Transmission parameters provide a convenient method for finding the transfer functions of ladder networks. The method considers the ladder network as a cascade of simple series impedances and shunt admittances. The transmission parameters of such elements are given in Fig. 3.26. Since the elements of the transmission-parameter matrices are quite simple, the multiplication of several of them together is usually fairly easy. As an example, consider the network shown in Fig. 3.27. The transmission parameters of this network may be found by performing the matrix multiplication

$$\begin{bmatrix} A & B \\ C & D \end{bmatrix} = \begin{bmatrix} 1 & 2 \\ 0 & 1 \end{bmatrix}\begin{bmatrix} 1 & 0 \\ 2p & 1 \end{bmatrix}\begin{bmatrix} 1 & p \\ 0 & 1 \end{bmatrix}\begin{bmatrix} 1 & 0 \\ p+1 & 1 \end{bmatrix}\begin{bmatrix} 1 & 2 \\ 0 & 1 \end{bmatrix}$$

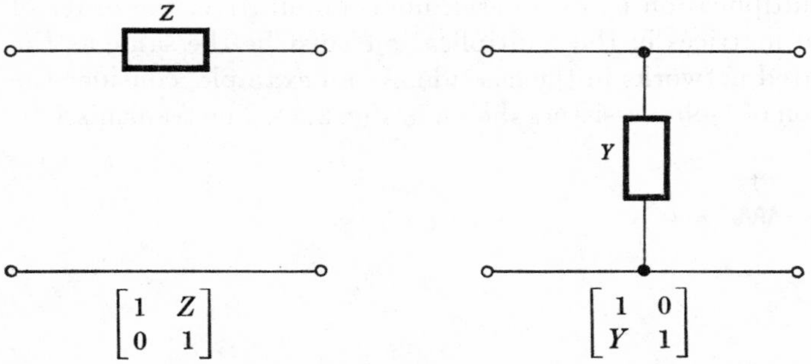

$$\begin{bmatrix} 1 & Z \\ 0 & 1 \end{bmatrix} \qquad\qquad \begin{bmatrix} 1 & 0 \\ Y & 1 \end{bmatrix}$$

Figure 3.26 Simple series and shunt ladder elements and their transmission parameters.

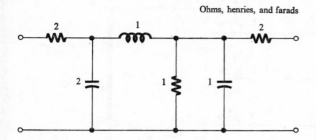

Ohms, henries, and farads

Figure 3.27   *A simple ladder network.*

The result is

$$\begin{bmatrix} 4p^3 + 5p^2 + 7p + 3 & 8p^3 + 14p^2 + 15p + 8 \\ 2p^3 + 2p^2 + 3p + 1 & 4p^3 + 6p^2 + 6p + 3 \end{bmatrix}$$

The student should compare the effort involved in obtaining any one of these parameters (the reciprocal short-circuit transfer impedance B, for example) by the above method and by any of the more conventional methods to appreciate the straightforwardness of this procedure.

3.4   *The n-terminal network*

We have seen that there are network situations in which the "port method" of describing a network cannot be used. This situation occurs whenever an unspecified multiterminal termination is connected to the network. An example was given in Fig. 3.3. Cases of this type may be considered by defining the properties of the network on a terminal basis rather than on a port basis. We shall have to make some different definitions of the voltage and current variables to do this. Consider the $(n + 1)$-terminal network shown in Fig. 3.28. We may define n current variables I_i as the input currents at the various terminals. Similarly, we may define n voltage variables V_i as the voltages at the various terminals, all taken with respect to the $(n + 1)$th terminal. Suppose that we specify certain numerical values for the current variables. For example, as shown in Fig. 3.29a, we might have d-c input and output currents whose magnitudes at the first three terminals at a given instant of time are 3, 1, and 2 amps, with the indicated directions. It should be noted that Kirchhoff's law is satisfied, i.e., that the net total current into the network is zero. Since the impedance of the current sources is infinite, the potential of the connection common to the three current sources is unspecified.

If the network is linear, i.e., one which is defined on the principle of superposition, then we may treat the three currents shown in Fig. 3.29a

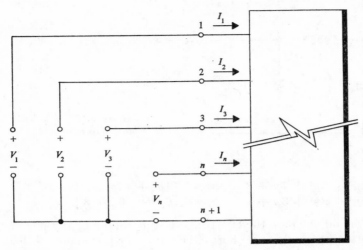

Figure 3.28   *An (n + 1)-terminal network with its voltage and current variables.*

as follows: (1) a current of 3 amps applied between terminals 1 and $n + 1$; (2) a current of 1 amp, applied in the direction shown between terminals 2 and $n + 1$; and (3) a current of 2 amps, applied between terminals 3 and $n + 1$. The voltages that will result at terminals 1, 2, and 3, as well as at all the other terminals, will simply be the sum of the voltages produced by each of the currents separately. This is just another

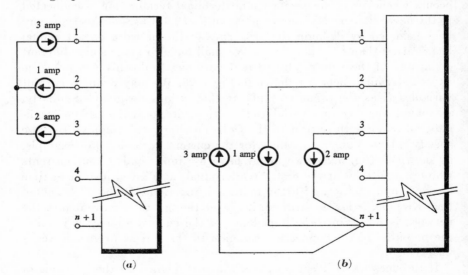

Figure 3.29   *The use of superposition in considering the current variables.*

way of stating the principle of superposition. Note this significant point:
Each of the currents shown in Fig. 3.29b satisfies the conditions used to
define a port, that is, that the current into one terminal must equal the
current out of the other terminal. Thus, terminals 1 and $n + 1$ may be
considered as forming a port; similarly, terminals 2 and $n + 1$ form a
port; etc. The terminal voltages are correctly defined as the port voltages
in this respect. Therefore, we conclude that an $(n + 1)$-terminal network
may be treated as an n-port network by defining a reference terminal
and measuring the terminal voltage variables with respect to it.

At this point the reader should note one other important distinction
between the two types of characterization, i.e., the terminal characterization and the port characterization of a given network. If the network is
to be used in such a manner that we may apply port terminology to it,
then a $2n$-terminal network may be characterized by n equations involving n current variables and n voltage variables. In other words, we may
characterize the network by an $n \times n$ square matrix. By different
groupings of the voltage and current variables, different matrix representations are possible, as was shown in the last section. By comparison,
if the network is to be used in such a manner that the terminal designation has to be used, then a $2n$-terminal network requires $2n - 1$ equations
and $2n - 1$ voltage variables, $2n - 1$ current variables, and a $(2n - 1) \times
(2n - 1)$ matrix to represent it. To summarize this point, the use of the
port designation for a given network requires approximately half the
number of equations and variables (for large n). This seems to be an
advantage in favor of the port designation; however, there is also a dis-
advantage. Since the port voltages are defined with respect to the potential difference existing between two terminals, no account is taken of the
potential of either of these terminals with respect to any ground or reference potential. Thus we might expect that a network will have the same
network parameters as defined on a port basis, independently of any
potential differences that exist between the ports, if the interconnection
between any of the ports reduces to a single branch at any point. The
definition of the port on the basis of current flow makes it impossible
for any current to flow along this single branch. To clarify the difference
between the port designation and the terminal designation, careful study
of Figs. 3.30 through 3.32 is essential at this point. For each figure the
circuit is drawn twice. The a portions of the figures indicate the circuit
with voltage and current variables defined on a port basis. The b portions
of the figures indicate the same circuit with a designation of the voltages
and currents on a terminal basis.

From these figures we may make certain quite general conclusions
about the two types of representations. The extension of the logic to the
general case will be quite apparent.

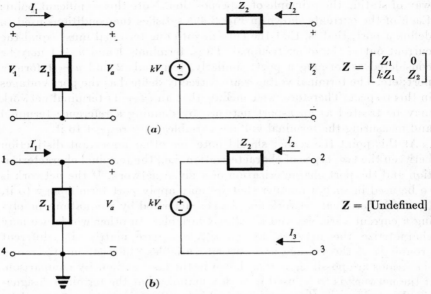

Figure 3.30   A network considered as (a) a two-port network; (b) a four-terminal network.

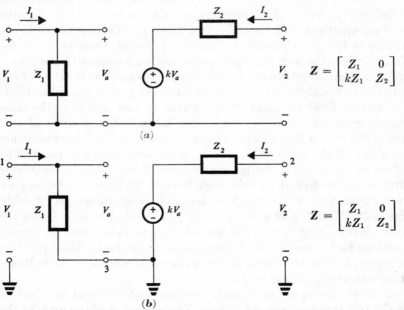

Figure 3.31   A network considered as (a) a two-port network; (b) a three-terminal network.

1. When any of the circuitry connected to any of the terminals of a network is isolated from any other terminal, a terminal-impedance representation is not possible, although a port-impedance representation may be used. As an example, see Fig. 3.30.

2. An *n*-port network, in which all the ports have a common terminal, can be represented by an $(n + 1)$-terminal network. Furthermore, the matrix representation and the physical significance of the variables will be identical. As an example, see Fig. 3.31.

3. When only a single branch links the circuitry connected to different ports, the port representation is unaffected by the elements of this branch; indeed, it is the same whether the branch is an open circuit

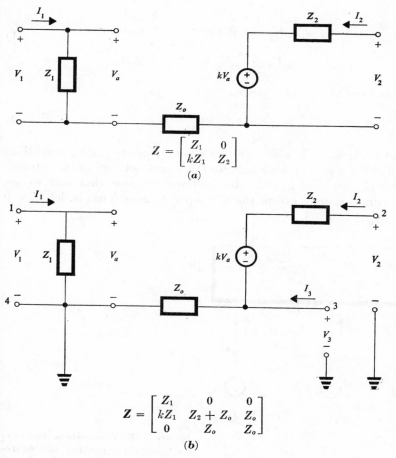

$$Z = \begin{bmatrix} Z_1 & 0 \\ kZ_1 & Z_2 \end{bmatrix}$$

(a)

$$Z = \begin{bmatrix} Z_1 & 0 & 0 \\ kZ_1 & Z_2 + Z_o & Z_o \\ 0 & Z_o & Z_o \end{bmatrix}$$

(b)

Figure 3.32 A network considered as (a) a two-port network; (b) a four-terminal network.

(Fig. 3.30) or a short circuit (Fig. 3.31) or has passive elements (Fig. 3.32). The terminal representation, however, definitely indicates the presence of this branch, as can be seen by studying the three figures.

3.5 *The indefinite-admittance matrix*

Consider an n-terminal network and an additional isolated node which we shall use as a reference node. If, as shown in Fig. 3.33, voltage sources are connected between the reference node and the n terminals, we may write a series of equations for the network as follows:

$$
\begin{aligned}
I_1 &= y_{11}V_1 + y_{12}V_2 + \cdots + y_{1n}V_n \\
I_2 &= y_{21}V_1 + y_{22}V_2 + \cdots + y_{2n}V_n \\
&\cdots\cdots\cdots\cdots\cdots\cdots\cdots\cdots\cdots \\
I_n &= y_{n1}V_1 + y_{n2}V_2 + \cdots + y_{nn}V_n
\end{aligned}
\tag{1}
$$

In matrix form (1) may be written

$$
I = YV
\tag{2}
$$

The matrix elements y_{ij} may be found by applying the testing conditions of (5) of Sec. 3.2 as they were used for the n-port network or the n-terminal network described in preceding sections. Suppose that now we set all the voltage sources except the first equal to zero. That is, let $V_i = 0$

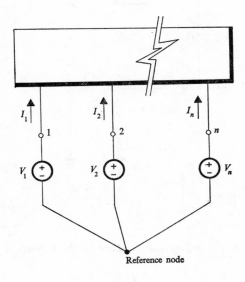

Reference node

Figure 3.33   The voltage and current variables for the indefinite-admittance matrix for an n-terminal network.

for all i except $i = 1$. The equations (1) become

$$I_1 = y_{11}V_1$$
$$I_2 = y_{21}V_1$$
$$\cdot \cdot \cdot \cdot \cdot \cdot \cdot$$
$$I_n = y_{n1}V_1$$

If we sum the above equations we see that

$$I_1 + I_2 + \cdots + I_n = y_{11}V_1 + y_{21}V_1 + \cdots + y_{n1}V_1$$

This may be written in the form

$$\sum_{k=1}^{n} I_k = V_1 \sum_{k=1}^{n} y_{k1}$$

The left side of this equation represents the summation of the currents flowing out of the reference node. Kirchhoff's law requires that this be zero. Therefore, the right side of the equation must also be zero. Since we have specifically chosen V_1 as *not* equal to zero, we conclude that the summation of the admittances must be zero.[1]

If the above procedure is followed in the more general case in which we require all the voltage sources except the ith one (i.e., V_i) to be zero, then summing the resulting equations gives

$$\sum_{k=1}^{n} I_k = V_i \sum_{k=1}^{n} y_{ki} \qquad i = 1, 2, \ldots, n \qquad (3)$$

Since the summation of the I_k, and therefore the left side of (3), is zero without regard for the choice of i,

$$\sum_{k=1}^{n} y_{ki} = 0 \qquad i = 1, 2, \ldots, n \qquad (4)$$

We have now established that the summation of the elements in any column of the matrix Y of (2) is zero.

A similar procedure may be used to establish the fact that the summation of the elements in any *row* of the matrix Y of (2) is zero. To see this, remove all the voltage sources except one (the jth one) in Fig. 3.33, leaving all the terminals except the jth one open-circuited. This will, of course, make all the currents at these terminals equal to zero. The current at the jth terminal will also be zero (by Kirchhoff's law). Since no current flows in the circuit, all the voltages are equal to the voltage

---

[1] It is assumed that none of the other terminals is common to terminal 1.

impressed at the jth terminal.[1] The equations (1) become

$$I_1 = y_{11}V_j + y_{12}V_j + \cdots + y_{1n}V_j$$
$$I_2 = y_{21}V_j + y_{22}V_j + \cdots + y_{2n}V_j$$
$$\cdots\cdots\cdots\cdots\cdots\cdots\cdots\cdots$$
$$I_n = y_{n1}V_j + y_{n2}V_j + \cdots + y_{nn}V_j$$

These may be written in the form

$$I_i = V_j \sum_{k=1}^{n} y_{ik} \qquad i = 1, 2, \ldots, n \tag{5}$$

Since all the I_i are zero, and since V_j is not zero, we conclude that the summation of the elements in any row of the Y matrix of (2) is equal to zero, i.e., that

$$\sum_{k=1}^{n} y_{ik} = 0 \qquad i = 1, 2, \ldots, n \tag{6}$$

The Y matrix of (2) is called the *indefinite-admittance matrix*.[2] Obviously, it may be used to characterize a network from the standpoint of its external behavior, just as the "port" designation and the "terminal" designation that have been treated previously. The indefinite matrix, however, has certain properties which make its use advantageous in many situations. For example, suppose that the indefinite-admittance matrix of a given network is known. In addition, suppose that it is decided to ground the jth terminal of this network, i.e., to connect the jth terminal directly to the reference node. There are two effects: (1) V_j becomes identically zero; therefore, the elements in the jth column of the matrix are each multiplied by zero, and thus these elements and V_j may be excluded from the equations; (2) I_j is now simply the negative of the summation of all the other currents. As such, it need no longer be retained as a variable, since it is clearly not independent of the other current variables. Thus, we may delete the jth row of the matrix (and thus the variable I_j) from our matrix equation. In summary, if the jth terminal of an n-terminal network is grounded, the resulting network description is that of an $(n - 1)$-terminal network, and it is found by deleting the jth row and column from the indefinite-admittance matrix which describes the network.

The above property also allows us to find easily the indefinite-admit-

---

[1] It is assumed that none of the terminals is completely isolated from the jth terminal.

[2] Many of the properties of the indefinite-admittance matrix presented in this section can be found in J. Shekel, Matrix Analysis of Multi-terminal Transducers, *Proc. IRE*, vol. 42, no. 5, pp. 840–847, May, 1954. Another excellent reference is L. A. Zadeh, Multi-pole Analysis of Active Networks, *IRE Trans. on Circuit Theory*, vol. CT-4, no. 3, pp. 97–105, September, 1957.

tance matrix for a given network. We need merely ground any arbitrary terminal, find the appropriate admittance matrix for the network on a terminal basis, and then add a row and a column to the matrix such that the summation of elements in the rows and the columns is zero. The process may be illustrated by the following example:

Consider the simple resistive network shown in Fig. 3.34. The values of the elements are given in mhos. In terms of the voltage and current variables defined in the figure, we may write the admittance matrix for the network, considering it as a three-terminal network, as follows:

$$\begin{bmatrix} I_1 \\ I_2 \end{bmatrix} = \begin{bmatrix} 3 & -2 \\ -2 & 5 \end{bmatrix} \begin{bmatrix} V_1 \\ V_2 \end{bmatrix}$$

The indefinite-admittance matrix may now be formed by adding a third row and column to the admittance matrix. Thus, we obtain

$$\begin{bmatrix} I_1 \\ I_2 \\ I_3 \end{bmatrix} = \begin{bmatrix} 3 & -2 & -1 \\ -2 & 5 & -3 \\ -1 & -3 & 4 \end{bmatrix} \begin{bmatrix} V_1 \\ V_2 \\ V_3 \end{bmatrix} \tag{7}$$

The network and the definition of the voltage and current variables are shown in Fig. 3.35. Note that this is just Fig. 3.34 with terminal 3 "ungrounded," i.e., separated from the reference or ground terminal. If terminal 2 of the network is now grounded, as shown in Fig. 3.36, it is easily seen that the admittance matrix for the three-terminal network is defined by the equation

$$\begin{bmatrix} I_1 \\ I_3 \end{bmatrix} = \begin{bmatrix} 3 & -1 \\ -1 & 4 \end{bmatrix} \begin{bmatrix} V_1 \\ V_3 \end{bmatrix} \tag{8}$$

Note that the admittance matrix is simply the indefinite-admittance matrix of (7) with the second row and column deleted. Similarly, if terminal 1 of the network is grounded, as shown in Fig. 3.37, the admit-

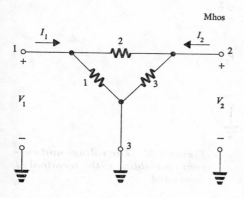

Figure 3.34 *A simple three-terminal network.*

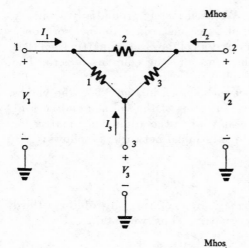

Figure 3.35 The voltage and current variables for the indefinite-admittance matrix.

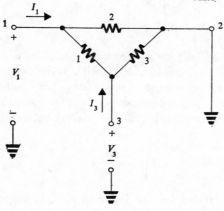

Figure 3.36 The voltage and current variables with terminal 2 grounded.

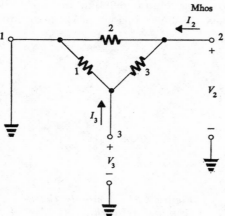

Figure 3.37 The voltage and current variables with terminal 1 grounded.

tance matrix for the resulting three-terminal network is defined by the equation

$$\begin{bmatrix} I_2 \\ I_3 \end{bmatrix} = \begin{bmatrix} 5 & -3 \\ -3 & 4 \end{bmatrix} \begin{bmatrix} V_2 \\ V_3 \end{bmatrix} \tag{9}$$

A second example of the flexibility of the indefinite-admittance matrix may be seen by considering the effects of shorting together two terminals of a network. In Fig. 3.38, an n-terminal network is shown with terminals 1 and 2 shorted together, but with the voltages and currents as originally defined in Fig. 3.33. We now have the additional constraint that $V_1 = V_2$. The network equations given in (1) may now be rewritten by letting $V_a = V_1 = V_2$. Thus, we obtain the following set of equations:

$$\begin{aligned}
I_1 &= (y_{11} + y_{12})V_a + y_{13}V_3 + \cdots + y_{1n}V_n \\
I_2 &= (y_{21} + y_{22})V_a + y_{23}V_3 + \cdots + y_{2n}V_n \\
I_3 &= (y_{31} + y_{32})V_a + y_{33}V_3 + \cdots + y_{3n}V_n \\
&\cdots\cdots\cdots\cdots\cdots\cdots\cdots\cdots\cdots\cdots \\
I_n &= (y_{n1} + y_{n2})V_a + y_{n3}V_3 + \cdots + y_{nn}V_n
\end{aligned} \tag{10}$$

If the first two equations of (10) are added, and if we let $I_a = I_1 + I_2$, then we obtain the following:

$$\begin{aligned}
I_a &= (y_{11} + y_{12} + y_{21} + y_{22})V_a + (y_{13} + y_{23})V_3 + \cdots + (y_{1n} + y_{2n})V_n \\
I_3 &= (y_{31} + y_{32})V_a + y_{33}V_3 + \cdots + y_{3n}V_n \\
&\cdots\cdots\cdots\cdots\cdots\cdots\cdots\cdots\cdots\cdots \\
I_n &= (y_{n1} + y_{n2})V_a + y_{n3}V_3 + \cdots + y_{nn}V_n
\end{aligned}$$

Thus, we have developed an indefinite-admittance matrix for an $(n - 1)$-terminal network, formed by shorting terminals 1 and 2 of the original

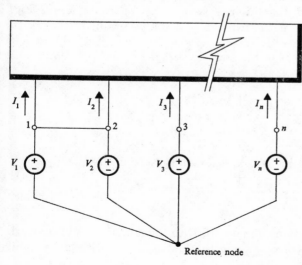

Figure 3.38 An n-terminal network with terminals 1 and 2 shorted together.

Reference node

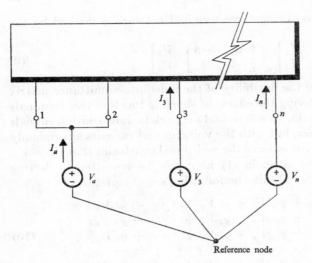

Figure 3.39 The modified voltage and current variables for the indefinite-admittance matrix of an $(n-1)$-terminal network.

network, simply by adding the related rows and columns (the first and second) of the original indefinite-admittance matrix. The variables and the $(n-1)$-terminal network are shown in Fig. 3.39. It is easy to see that, by the same proof, connecting any terminals together in a given network will yield a new network whose indefinite-admittance matrix may be formed by adding the appropriate rows and columns of the indefinite-admittance matrix of the original network.

Another property of the indefinite-admittance matrix is the following: When networks are connected in parallel, the indefinite-admittance matrix of the resulting network is formed by adding the indefinite-admittance matrices of the original networks. For example, in Fig. 3.40, consider the n-terminal network A and the m-terminal network B, where $n > m$. The reference terminals a and b may be connected together without altering conditions in the two networks. The network equations on an indefinite basis are

$$I_{1a} = y_{11a}V_{1a} + \cdots + y_{1ma}V_{ma} + \cdots + y_{1na}V_{na}$$
$$\cdots \cdots \cdots \cdots \cdots \cdots \cdots \cdots \cdots \cdots$$
$$I_{ma} = y_{m1a}V_{1a} + \cdots + y_{mma}V_{ma} + \cdots + y_{mna}V_{na}$$
$$\cdots \cdots \cdots \cdots \cdots \cdots \cdots \cdots \cdots \cdots$$
$$I_{na} = y_{n1a}V_{1a} + \cdots + y_{nma}V_{ma} + \cdots + y_{nna}V_{na}$$

and
$$I_{1b} = y_{11b}V_{1b} + \cdots + y_{1mb}V_{mb}$$
$$\cdots \cdots \cdots \cdots \cdots \cdots \cdots \cdots$$
$$I_{mb} = y_{m1b}V_{1b} + \cdots + y_{mmb}V_{mb}$$

If we add the m equations of network B to the n equations of network A, preserving the numbering among the first m of these equations and

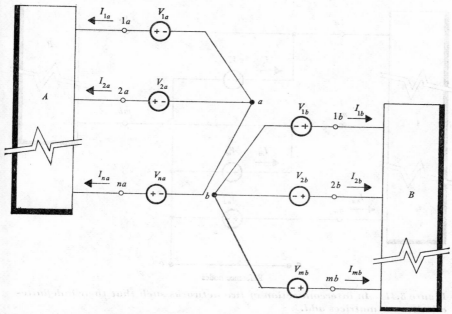

Figure 3.40 *The voltage and current variables for the indefinite-admittance matrices of an n-terminal network and an m-terminal network.*

setting $V_{1a} = V_{1b} = V_1, \ldots, V_{ma} = V_{mb} = V_m$, and $I_1 = I_{1a} + I_{1b}$, $\ldots, I_m = I_{ma} + I_{mb}$, we obtain

$$I_1 = (y_{11a} + y_{11b})V_1 + \cdots + (y_{1ma} + y_{1mb})V_m + \cdots + y_{1na}V_{na}$$
$$\cdots\cdots\cdots\cdots\cdots\cdots\cdots\cdots\cdots\cdots\cdots\cdots\cdots\cdots\cdots\cdots\cdots$$
$$I_m = (y_{m1a} + y_{m1b})V_1 + \cdots + (y_{mma} + y_{mmb})V_m + \cdots + y_{mna}V_{na}$$
$$\cdots\cdots\cdots\cdots\cdots\cdots\cdots\cdots\cdots\cdots\cdots\cdots\cdots\cdots\cdots\cdots\cdots$$
$$I_{na} = y_{n1a}V_1 + \cdots + y_{nma}V_m + \cdots + y_{nna}V_{na}$$

This represents the interconnection of the networks as shown in Fig. 3.41, which may be described as the parallel connection of the two networks. It also represents the addition of the two indefinite-admittance matrices, assuming that we add appropriate zeros to the smaller matrix so that the conditions for matrix addition are satisfied.

One other useful property of the indefinite-admittance matrix is the ease with which a given terminal may be "suppressed." In Fig. 3.33 an n-terminal network is shown. Suppose that it is desired to "suppress" the nth terminal. This means that we would like to eliminate the variables of voltage and current connected with this terminal from our indefinite-admittance matrix. In effect, we desire to leave this terminal open-circuited and eliminate it from consideration. Thus, I_n, the current associated with this terminal, will always be zero. Note that this is a

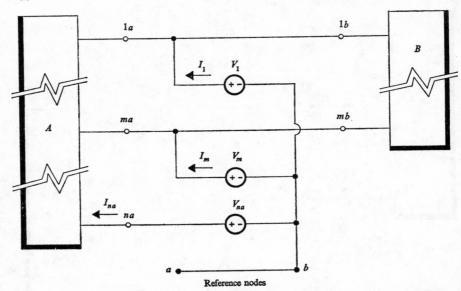

Figure 3.41   An interconnection of two networks such that their indefinite-admittance matrices add.

dual situation to the case in which the nth terminal was grounded, since in that case the voltage was always zero. When the nth terminal is suppressed, (1) becomes

$$
\begin{aligned}
I_1 &= y_{11}V_1 + y_{12}V_2 + \cdots + y_{1n}V_n \\
I_2 &= y_{21}V_1 + y_{22}V_2 + \cdots + y_{2n}V_n \\
&\cdots \cdots \cdots \cdots \cdots \cdots \cdots \cdots \cdots \\
0 &= y_{n1}V_1 + y_{n2}V_2 + \cdots + y_{nn}V_n
\end{aligned}
\tag{11}
$$

The last equation of (11) may be solved for V_n, where

$$
V_n = \frac{-1}{y_{nn}}(y_{n1}V_1 + y_{n2}V_2 + \cdots + y_{n,n-1}V_{n-1})
$$

Substituting this relation into (11) eliminates the variable V_n from the equations. The final result for the indefinite-admittance matrix for $n-1$ current variables and $n-1$ voltage variables is most easily expressed in matrix form:

$$
\begin{bmatrix} I_1 \\ \cdots \\ I_{n-1} \end{bmatrix} = \left\{ \begin{bmatrix} y_{11} & \cdots & y_{1,n-1} \\ \cdots \cdots & \cdots \cdots & \cdots \cdots \\ y_{n-1,1} & \cdots & y_{n-1,n-1} \end{bmatrix} \right.
$$
$$
\left. - \begin{bmatrix} y_{1n} \\ \cdots \\ y_{n-1,n} \end{bmatrix} \begin{bmatrix} \dfrac{1}{y_{nn}} \end{bmatrix} \underbrace{ y_{n1} \cdots y_{n,n-1} } \right\} \begin{bmatrix} V_1 \\ \cdots \\ V_{n-1} \end{bmatrix}
\tag{12}
$$

The matrix within the braces above defines the new indefinite-admittance matrix. The format of (12) may be emphasized if we define $Y^{(n)}$ as the original indefinite-admittance matrix for the n-terminal network. $Y^{(n)}$ may also be defined in terms of the submatrices Y_{ij} formed by the partitioning indicated in the following equation:

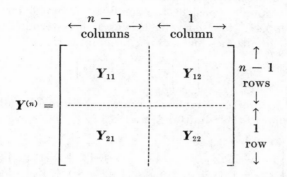

If we define $Y^{(n-1)}$ as the indefinite-admittance matrix for the $(n-1)$-terminal network formed by suppressing the nth terminal, it may be specified in terms of the above submatrices as

$$Y^{(n-1)} = Y_{11} - Y_{12}Y_{22}{}^{-1}Y_{21} \tag{13}$$

The reader should compare this with (12). Actually, the formulation of (13) may be considered as a general expression for the suppression of any number of terminals with the appropriate redefinitions of the submatrices. The proof is left to the reader as an exercise.

As a final property of the indefinite-admittance matrix we present the following: The effect of connecting an admittance Y between any two terminals of a network is to add or subtract Y to the elements at the intersections of the corresponding rows and columns of the indefinite-admittance matrix. It is added to the elements on the main diagonal and subtracted from the other elements. The proof is left to the reader as an exercise.

In the next section some examples of the application of the indefinite-admittance matrix to network problems are presented. The reader who is interested in an additional "indefinite" formulation is referred to Appendix A, where the properties of the indefinite-transmission matrix are discussed. This latter does not have as wide application as the indefinite-admittance matrix, although it does provide a means whereby the parameters of multiterminal networks connected in cascade may be found.

3.6 *Some applications of the indefinite-admittance matrix*

In this section we shall present two examples of the application of the indefinite-admittance matrix to network situations. These examples will illustrate some of the properties discussed in the last section.

As a first example, consider the small-signal model for a transistor shown in Fig. 3.42. If we consider this as a three-terminal network, we may write its admittance matrix on a terminal basis as

$$\begin{bmatrix} I_b \\ I_c \end{bmatrix} = \begin{bmatrix} Y_1 & 0 \\ aY_1 & Y_2 \end{bmatrix} \begin{bmatrix} V_b \\ V_c \end{bmatrix} \tag{1}$$

The indefinite-admittance matrix may now be formed by adding a third row and column to the admittance matrix of (1). Thus, we obtain

$$\begin{bmatrix} I_b \\ I_c \\ I_e \end{bmatrix} = \begin{bmatrix} Y_1 & 0 & -Y_1 \\ aY_1 & Y_2 & -(aY_1 + Y_2) \\ -Y_1(1+a) & -Y_2 & Y_1(1+a) + Y_2 \end{bmatrix} \begin{bmatrix} V_b \\ V_c \\ V_e \end{bmatrix} \tag{2}$$

The circuit and the definitions of the voltage and current variables are shown in Fig. 3.43. Note that this is just Fig. 3.42 with the emitter terminal "ungrounded," i.e., separated from the reference or ground terminal. Since the terminals correspond with the terminals of the transistor, as indicated in the figures, we may also consider the original circuit as the small-signal equivalent circuit for the transistor in a grounded-emitter configuration, as shown in Fig. 3.42. At this point, the versatility of the indefinite-admittance matrix is readily evident. Suppose that it is desired to find the admittance matrix for a transistor in a grounded-collector configuration. We need only delete the row and column of the

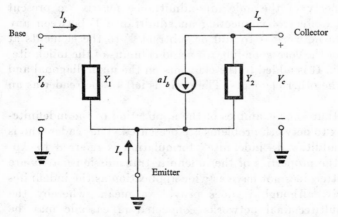

Figure 3.42   A small-signal equivalent circuit for a transistor.

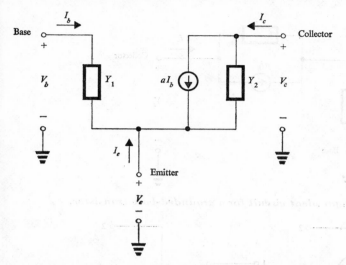

Figure 3.43 *The voltage and current variables for the indefinite-admittance matrix of the small-signal equivalent circuit for a transistor.*

matrix in (2) associated with the collector terminal. These are clearly the second row and column. The resulting model for the grounded-collector transistor considered as a three-terminal network is shown in Fig. 3.44. The equations for the network are

$$\begin{bmatrix} I_b \\ I_e \end{bmatrix} = \begin{bmatrix} Y_1 & -Y_1 \\ -Y_1(1+a) & Y_1(1+a)+Y_2 \end{bmatrix} \begin{bmatrix} V_b \\ V_e \end{bmatrix} \tag{3}$$

Similarly, we may develop the admittance matrix for a grounded-base transistor by deleting the first row and column of the indefinite-

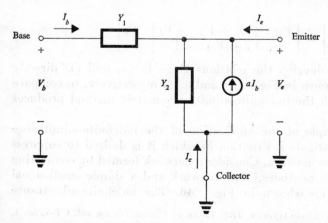

Figure 3.44 *An equivalent circuit for a grounded-collector transistor.*

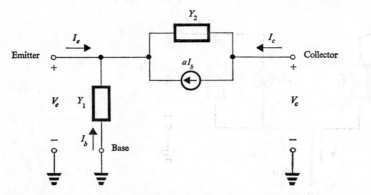

Figure 3.45   An equivalent circuit for a grounded-base transistor.

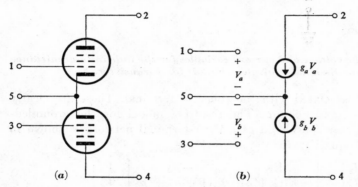

Figure 3.46   A connection of two pentodes and a simple equivalent circuit.

admittance matrix of (2). The circuit is shown in Fig. 3.45. The equations for the network are

$$
\begin{bmatrix} I_e \\ I_c \end{bmatrix} = \begin{bmatrix} Y_1(1+a) + Y_2 & -Y_2 \\ -(aY_1 + Y_2) & Y_2 \end{bmatrix} \begin{bmatrix} V_e \\ V_c \end{bmatrix}
\tag{4}
$$

The reader should develop the relations given in (3) and (4) directly from the circuits shown in Figs. 3.44 and 3.45, respectively, to compare the ease with which the indefinite-admittance-matrix method produces these relationships.

As another example of the application of the indefinite-admittance matrix, let us investigate a situation in which it is desired to suppress a terminal of a given network. Consider a network formed by connecting the cathodes of two pentodes.[1] The network and a simple small-signal equivalent circuit are shown in Fig. 3.46. The indefinite-admittance

---

[1] G. E. Sharpe, The Pentode Gyrator, *IRE Trans. on Circuit Theory*, vol. CT-4, no. 4, pp. 322–323, December, 1957.

matrix may be found by first considering the admittance parameters for the four-terminal network formed by grounding terminal 5. For this network, the admittance matrix is

$$
\begin{bmatrix}
0 & 0 & 0 & 0 \\
g_a & 0 & 0 & 0 \\
0 & 0 & 0 & 0 \\
0 & 0 & g_b & 0
\end{bmatrix}
$$

The indefinite-admittance matrix for the network is easily seen to be

$$
\begin{bmatrix}
0 & 0 & 0 & 0 & 0 \\
g_a & 0 & 0 & 0 & -g_a \\
0 & 0 & 0 & 0 & 0 \\
0 & 0 & g_b & 0 & -g_b \\
-g_a & 0 & -g_b & 0 & g_a + g_b
\end{bmatrix}
$$

To suppress terminal 5, we proceed as in (13) of Sec. 3.5. Thus, for our new indefinite-admittance matrix, we have

$$
\begin{bmatrix}
0 & 0 & 0 & 0 \\
g_a & 0 & 0 & 0 \\
0 & 0 & 0 & 0 \\
0 & 0 & g_b & 0
\end{bmatrix}
-
\begin{bmatrix}
0 \\
-g_a \\
0 \\
-g_b
\end{bmatrix}
\begin{bmatrix}
\dfrac{1}{g_a + g_b}
\end{bmatrix}
\begin{matrix}
-g_a & 0 & -g_b & 0
\end{matrix}
$$

After manipulation, the indefinite-admittance matrix for the four-terminal network is

$$
\begin{bmatrix}
0 & 0 & 0 & 0 \\
g & 0 & -g & 0 \\
0 & 0 & 0 & 0 \\
-g & 0 & g & 0
\end{bmatrix}
$$

where

$$
g = \frac{g_a g_b}{g_a + g_b}
$$

We shall make further use of this circuit and its indefinite-admittance matrix (with the suppressed terminal) in Sec. 4.7.

3.7 *The scattering matrix*

In the network descriptions presented in the previous sections of this chapter, various matrix representations have been discussed. We have seen that, in addition to the possibilities of choosing all the port currents or all the port voltages as the independent variables of the network equations, thus leading to immittance representations, it is possible to choose the voltage variables from some ports and the current variables from others, thus leading to hybrid representations for the network. There is one other choice of variables which is quite different in concept from the preceding ones. This is the choice of a *linear combination* of the voltages and the currents as a variable. Thus, at each port we might define one variable which is proportional to the *sum* of the voltage and the current at that port. As a second variable we might define one which is proportional to the *difference* between the voltage and current variables. In addition, we shall see that it is convenient to provide a normalization constant so that the actual impedances may be compared to some reference impedance. The representation that results from such a choice of variables is called the *scattering matrix*. The elements of the matrix are called the *scattering parameters*. The variables are called the *scattering variables*. In this section we shall briefly discuss this type of representation.

Let us begin by considering a one-port network with the variables V and I, both of which are functions of the complex frequency variable. These are shown together with their reference directions in Fig. 3.47. The impedance of the network is z. We shall now introduce a normalization constant r_o and use it to define new voltage and current variables $V^{(n)}$ and $I^{(n)}$. These latter will be referred to as the *normalized* voltage and current variables. The defining relations between the original variables and the normalized variables are

$$V^{(n)} = \frac{V}{r_o^{\frac{1}{2}}}$$
$$I^{(n)} = I r_o^{\frac{1}{2}}$$

(1)

We may also define a normalized impedance $z^{(n)}$, where

$$z^{(n)} = \frac{V^{(n)}}{I^{(n)}}$$

It is easy to see that

$$z^{(n)} = \frac{z}{r_o}$$

(2)

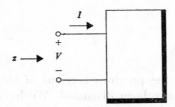

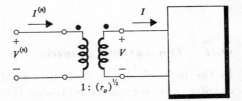

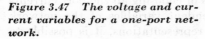

Figure 3.47   The voltage and current variables for a one-port network.

Figure 3.48   The normalized voltage and current variables for a one-port network.

Actually, the normalized variables may be thought of as the variables that result if an ideal transformer of turns ratio $1:r_o^{\frac{1}{2}}$ is connected to the one-port network as shown in Fig. 3.48. It is easily seen that the relations (1) and (2) are satisfied in this case.

We may now define the variables that we shall use with our scattering parameters as V_i and V_r (i is *not* used as a summation index here), where

$$V_i = \tfrac{1}{2}(V^{(n)} + I^{(n)})$$
$$V_r = \tfrac{1}{2}(V^{(n)} - I^{(n)}) \tag{3}$$

Thus we see that V_i is a variable which is proportional to the sum of the normalized voltage and current associated with the one-port network. Similarly, V_r is a variable which is proportional to the difference between the normalized variables. We shall refer to V_i and V_r as the scattering variables. It is easily shown that the normalized voltage and current variables can be expressed in terms of the scattering variables as

$$V^{(n)} = V_i + V_r$$
$$I^{(n)} = V_i - V_r \tag{4}$$

The variables V_i and V_r are sometimes referred to as the incident and reflected components of the voltage. This terminology stems from their original association with the voltages on a distributed-parameter transmission line. A development parallel to the above could be made using incident and reflected components of the current as the scattering variables. Similar results are obtained.

We may now define a scattering parameter s_{11} (there will be only one parameter since this is a one-port network) as

$$s_{11} = \frac{V_r}{V_i} = \frac{V^{(n)} - I^{(n)}}{V^{(n)} + I^{(n)}} = \frac{z^{(n)} - 1}{z^{(n)} + 1} \tag{5}$$

Note that s_{11} is a function of the complex frequency variable. From (5) we may express the normalized impedance $z^{(n)}$ in terms of s_{11} as

$$z^{(n)} = \frac{1 + s_{11}}{1 - s_{11}} \tag{6}$$

If we let the normalization constant r_o equal unity (this is sometimes referred to as choosing a 1-ohm reference impedance), then the normalized impedance $z^{(n)}$ will be equal to the actual impedance z. For this value of r_o, some simple examples of one-port scattering parameters are

$$
\begin{aligned}
z &= 0 & s_{11} &= -1 \\
z &= 1 & s_{11} &= 0 \\
z &= \infty & s_{11} &= 1 \\
z &= p & s_{11} &= \frac{p-1}{p+1}
\end{aligned} \tag{7}
$$

A similar procedure may be followed to define the scattering parameters for an n-port network. If we consider the network shown in Fig. 3.49, with variables V_j and I_j $(j = 1, 2, \ldots, n)$ as indicated, we may define a normalized set of variables $V_j^{(n)}$ and $I_j^{(n)}$ which are related to the original variables by the constants $r_{oj}^{\frac{1}{2}}$. The normalization relations are

$$V_j^{(n)} = \frac{V_j}{r_{oj}^{\frac{1}{2}}}$$
$$I_j^{(n)} = I_j \, r_{oj}^{\frac{1}{2}} \tag{8}$$

If we define a diagonal matrix R_o whose elements are $r_{oj}^{\frac{1}{2}}$, then

$$V^{(n)} = R_o^{-1} V$$
$$I^{(n)} = R_o I \tag{9}$$

where $V^{(n)}$ is the column matrix whose elements are the voltages $V_j^{(n)}$, etc. This normalization is equivalent to connecting an ideal transformer to each of the ports of the network as shown in Fig. 3.50. The voltage and current variables are related by the z-parameter matrix Z as follows:

$$V = ZI$$

We may also define a matrix $Z^{(n)}$ by the relation

$$V^{(n)} = Z^{(n)} I^{(n)}$$

It is easily seen that

$$Z^{(n)} = R_o^{-1} Z R_o^{-1} \tag{10}$$

The column matrices V_i and V_r whose elements are the scattering variables V_{ij} and V_{rj} $(j = 1, 2, \ldots, n)$ for the various ports may be defined

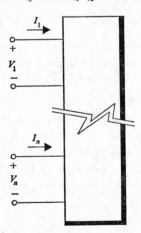

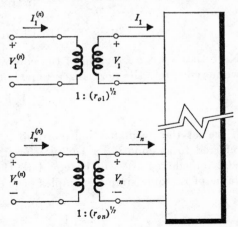

Figure 3.49   The voltage and current variables for an n-port network.

Figure 3.50   The normalized voltage and current variables for an n-port network.

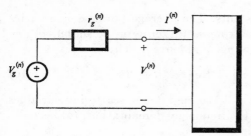

Figure 3.51 The normalized variables for a driving source and a one-port network.

in terms of the normalized voltage and current variables as

$$V_i = \tfrac{1}{2}(V^{(n)} + I^{(n)})$$
$$V_r = \tfrac{1}{2}(V^{(n)} - I^{(n)}) \tag{11}$$

We may now define the scattering matrix S by the relation

$$V_r = SV_i \tag{12}$$

From the above equations we see that

$$S = (Z^{(n)} - I)(Z^{(n)} + I)^{-1} \tag{13}$$

As an example of the significance and usefulness of the scattering parameters, let us again consider the one-port case. We will assume that a network with normalized variables $V^{(n)}$ and $I^{(n)}$ is driven by a source with normalized internal voltage $V_g^{(n)}$ and normalized internal impedance $r_g^{(n)}$ as shown in Fig. 3.51. From (3), we may solve for V_i by the relation

$$V_i = \tfrac{1}{2} \frac{V_g^{(n)}(z^{(n)} + 1)}{z^{(n)} + r_g^{(n)}} \tag{14}$$

If we set r_o equal to the source impedance r_g, then $r_g^{(n)}$ equals unity, and the above expression reduces to

$$V_i = \frac{V_g^{(n)}}{2} \tag{15}$$

Now let us consider these voltages and currents in the time domain under conditions of sinusoidal excitation. Specifically, let the normalized excitation to our network be $v_g^{(n)}(t)$, which may be defined as[1]

$$v_g^{(n)}(t) = ae^{j\omega t}$$

where a is a complex constant. With this excitation, the normalized voltage and current at the terminals of the network will be of the form

$$v^{(n)}(t) = be^{j\omega t}$$
$$i^{(n)}(t) = ce^{j\omega t}$$

[1] It is, of course, not possible for a physical voltage to be complex; however, this representation is a useful form that includes sinusoids of all phases and simplifies the transition between the time domain and the frequency domain.

where b and c are complex constants. The average power delivered by the source to the network may be expressed in terms of the actual voltage and current or the normalized voltage and current. Thus,

$$P = \text{Re}\,[i^*(t)v(t)] = \text{Re}\,[i^{(n)*}(t)v^{(n)}(t)] \tag{16}$$

where Re means "the real part of." We may define scattering variables in the time domain as well as in the frequency domain; thus, (4) becomes

$$v^{(n)}(t) = v_i(t) + v_r(t)$$
$$i^{(n)}(t) = v_i(t) - v_r(t)$$

The power may now be expressed in terms of the scattering variables as

$$P = \text{Re}\,[(v_i - v_r)^*(v_i + v_r)] = |v_i|^2 - |v_r|^2 \tag{17}$$

For the assumed exponential form of the voltage and current variables we may write (5) as

$$s_{11}(j\omega) = \frac{v_r}{v_i}$$

Thus, (17) may be written

$$P = |v_i|^2(1 - |s_{11}|^2) \tag{18}$$

Thus, we see that the maximum power that may be delivered by the source is

$$P_{\max} = \left| \frac{v_g{}^{(n)}}{2} \right|^2 = |v_i|^2 \tag{19}$$

From the above two equations, we see that

$$\frac{P}{P_{\max}} = 1 - |s_{11}|^2 \tag{20}$$

We see from this last equation that, for a passive network under conditions of sinusoidal excitation, it is not possible for the magnitude of the scattering parameter to be greater than unity, since it is not possible for a source to transfer negative power, i.e., to receive power, from the passive network. Thus we may visualize the scattering parameter as giving an indication of the existing deviation from maximum power-transfer conditions. For example, a normalized load impedance of unity, and thus a scattering parameter of zero, indicates maximum power transfer.

It is interesting to note that the scattering parameters will exist even when the z or y parameters for a given network do not exist. Thus, the scattering parameters are useful for describing networks such as multi-

port-transformer networks. Their application is well covered in the literature, to which the interested reader is referred.[1]

3.8 *Network descriptions*

The preceding sections of this chapter have described means by which a
network may be characterized. The characterization has been in terms
of the properties of the network as viewed from its external terminals.
These descriptions leave considerable freedom in the choice of elements
as well as in the configuration of these elements inside the network.
For example, from external circuit measurements, a 1-ohm resistor
appears the same as the parallel connection of two 2-ohm resistors. The
internal circuits, however, are certainly different. Our final goal in this
chapter is the application of matrix methods to the description of networks in terms of their internal configurations. In effect, we wish to
penetrate inside the "black box" and view its secrets.

The basic principles of circuit analysis, together with topological considerations, may always be applied to a given network to produce a set
of independent loop currents, which may then be used as the basis for
writing a set of loop equations for the network.[2] Each of these loops may
be divided into sections chosen such that each section contains the same
loop currents. In other words, as we follow along a certain loop, we start
a new section whenever some other loop current joins or leaves the loop
we are following. In the most general case each of these sections may have
resistance, inductance, elastance (reciprocal capacitance), and voltage
sources associated with it.

As an example, consider the ladder network shown in Fig. 3.52. If we
define

$$z_{11} = (r_1 + r_2) + p(l_1 + l_2) + \frac{1}{p}(s_1 + s_2)$$

$$z_{12} = z_{21} = r_2 + pl_2 + \frac{1}{p}s_2$$

$$z_{22} = (r_2 + r_3 + r_4) + p(l_2 + l_3 + l_4) + \frac{1}{p}(s_2 + s_3 + s_4) \qquad (1)$$

$$z_{23} = z_{32} = r_4 + pl_4 + \frac{1}{p}s_4$$

$$z_{33} = (r_4 + r_5) + p(l_4 + l_5) + \frac{1}{p}(s_4 + s_5)$$

---

[1] See H. J. Carlin, The Scattering Matrix in Network Theory, *IRE Trans. on Circuit
Theory*, vol. CT-3, no. 2, pp. 88–97, June, 1956. This issue of the transactions has several
other articles on the scattering matrix and its application.

[2] See E. A. Guillemin, "Introductory Circuit Theory," John Wiley & Sons, Inc., New
York, 1953.

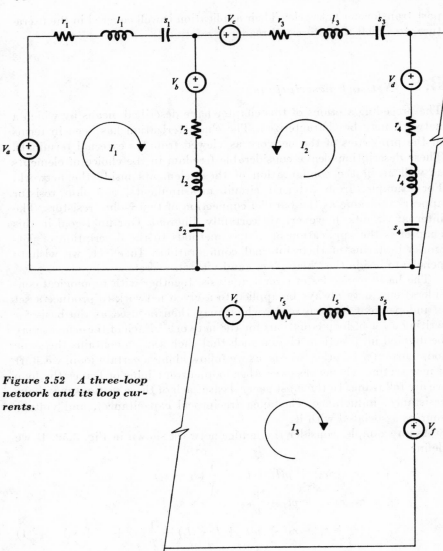

Figure 3.52 A three-loop network and its loop currents.

where p is the complex frequency variable, then we may write the loop equations as

$$V_a - V_b = z_{11}I_1 + z_{12}I_2$$
$$-V_b + V_c + V_d = z_{21}I_1 + z_{22}I_2 + z_{23}I_3 \qquad (2)$$
$$V_d - V_e - V_f = z_{32}I_2 + z_{33}I_3$$

Now let us define V_1, V_2, and V_3 as the totals of the voltages appearing in the first, second, and third loops, respectively. The definition may be made by the following matrix equation:

$$\begin{bmatrix} V_1 \\ V_2 \\ V_3 \end{bmatrix} = \begin{bmatrix} 1 & -1 & 0 & 0 & 0 & 0 \\ 0 & -1 & 1 & 1 & 0 & 0 \\ 0 & 0 & 0 & 1 & -1 & -1 \end{bmatrix} \begin{bmatrix} V_a \\ V_b \\ V_c \\ V_d \\ V_e \\ V_f \end{bmatrix} \tag{3}$$

We may now write the equations (2) in matrix form as follows:

$$\begin{bmatrix} V_1 \\ V_2 \\ V_3 \end{bmatrix} = \begin{bmatrix} z_{11} & z_{12} & 0 \\ z_{21} & z_{22} & z_{23} \\ 0 & z_{32} & z_{33} \end{bmatrix} \begin{bmatrix} I_1 \\ I_2 \\ I_3 \end{bmatrix} \tag{4}$$

At this point let us make and emphasize some observations about the elements of (4). The terms V_i $(i = 1, 2, 3)$ as defined by the matrix equation (3) represent the totality of voltage sources in the ith loop. The terms z_{ij} as defined by (1) may be separated into two categories. Where $i = j$, these elements give the total impedance in the ith loop. Where $i \neq j$, these elements give the impedance which is mutual to the ith and the jth loops, with negative or positive sign depending on whether the currents aid or oppose. Finally, the terms I_i represent the loop currents. All these elements and terms are functions of the complex frequency variable. The terms from the transformation which represent initial conditions have been ignored, since these may be represented by independent sources, which will be discussed later.

The above example was for a three-loop ladder network. It is easy to extend this method of development to a more general network. First, we may define

$$z_{ij} = r_{ij} + p l_{ij} + \frac{1}{p} s_{ij} \tag{5}$$

The matrix equation for the more general network is

$$\begin{bmatrix} V_1 \\ \cdot \cdot \\ V_n \end{bmatrix} = \begin{bmatrix} z_{11} & \cdots & z_{1n} \\ \cdot \cdot \cdot \cdot \cdot \cdot \cdot \cdot \cdot \\ z_{n1} & \cdots & z_{nn} \end{bmatrix} \begin{bmatrix} I_1 \\ \cdot \cdot \\ I_n \end{bmatrix} \tag{6}$$

We may, of course, write this equation in matrix notation as $V = ZI$. The elements V_i, z_{ij}, and I_i of (6) have exactly the same significance as they did in the simpler case of the ladder network. The matrix used in (3) to define the V_i will, of course, be different for different networks.

The elements of the matrix Z above may be replaced by their defining relations as given in (5). Thus, we may write

$$
\begin{bmatrix} z_{11} & \cdots & z_{1n} \\ \cdots & \cdots & \cdots \\ z_{n1} & \cdots & z_{nn} \end{bmatrix} = \begin{bmatrix} r_{11} & \cdots & r_{1n} \\ \cdots & \cdots & \cdots \\ r_{n1} & \cdots & r_{nn} \end{bmatrix} + p \begin{bmatrix} l_{11} & \cdots & l_{1n} \\ \cdots & \cdots & \cdots \\ l_{n1} & \cdots & l_{nn} \end{bmatrix}
$$
$$
+ \frac{1}{p} \begin{bmatrix} s_{11} & \cdots & s_{1n} \\ \cdots & \cdots & \cdots \\ s_{n1} & \cdots & s_{nn} \end{bmatrix} \tag{7}
$$

where r_{11} is the total amount of resistance in the first loop, etc. The first matrix in (7) is appropriately referred to as the Z matrix or the impedance matrix, the second as the R matrix or the resistance matrix, the third as the L matrix or the inductance matrix, and the fourth as the S matrix or the elastance matrix. We may now write a general matrix equation to represent the interior configuration on a mesh basis of a general network. The equation is

$$
V = \left(R + pL + \frac{1}{p} S \right) I \tag{8}
$$

The above equation is valid for networks containing passive elements and *independent voltage sources*. Other cases are easily treated. For example, if *independent current sources* are present, it is possible, by means of wye-delta transformations of some of the passive elements and the use of Thevenin equivalent circuits, to convert these to voltage generators in series with passive elements, thus producing sections of loops which are amenable to the above treatment. Other techniques, such as letting the current generator determine a specific loop current, are familiar artifices of network analysis, and the reader is referred to any of the many excellent texts on this subject.[1] If the network contains *dependent* current-controlled sources, they may easily be absorbed into the general matrix equation. For example, in Fig. 3.52 we might have $V_b = kI_3$. The first and second equations of (2) would then appear as

$$
\begin{aligned} V_a &= z_{11}I_1 + z_{12}I_2 + kI_3 \\ V_c + V_d &= z_{21}I_1 + z_{22}I_2 + z_{23}I_3 + kI_3 \end{aligned} \tag{9}
$$

The general matrix equation for the network then becomes

$$
V = \left(R + pL + \frac{1}{p} S + D \right) I \tag{10}
$$

where, in this case,

$$
D = \begin{bmatrix} 0 & 0 & k \\ 0 & 0 & k \\ 0 & 0 & 0 \end{bmatrix} \tag{11}
$$

[1] See, for example, M. E. Van Valkenburg, "Network Analysis," Prentice-Hall, Inc., Englewood Cliffs, N.J., 1955.

and the V_i elements forming the V matrix of (10) are redefined to include only the independent voltage sources. If the network contains *voltage-controlled* dependent voltage sources, the controlling voltage may usually be specified in terms of one or more of the current variables and the appropriate entries made in the D (we may consider "D" as standing for dependent source) matrix. In this case, of course, we may have functions of p appearing as elements of the D matrix. Dependent *current* sources, whether voltage or current controlled, may be treated by a combination of the techniques for independent current sources and dependent voltage sources. There are several variations, and these are left for the reader to explore.

The above procedure treats a general network defined on the basis of its loop equations. A similar procedure may be followed if we choose to describe a network on a node basis rather than on a loop basis. In this case, we shall be dealing with a Y matrix whose elements are defined as

$$y_{ij} = g_{ij} + pc_{ij} + \frac{1}{p}\, \gamma_{ij}$$

The g_{ij} terms are conductances, the c_{ij} are capacitances, and the γ_{ij} are values of reciprocal inductance. It is easy to see that y_{ij} for $i = j$ represents the total admittance of all elements connected to the ith node, while y_{ij} for $i \neq j$ represents the total admittance of all the elements connected between the ith and the jth nodes with appropriate plus or minus signs. If we have independent current sources I_i $(i = a, b, \cdot\cdot\cdot)$ connected to the various nodes, we may define variables I_i $(i = 1, 2, \cdot\cdot\cdot)$ as being the total currents entering the ith node. Similarly, we may treat *dependent* voltage-controlled or current-controlled current sources readily by techniques dual to the above. The over-all result of our efforts will be to produce a general matrix equation which will suffice to describe the internal configurations of an arbitrary linear network when its describing equations are written on a nodal basis. This will be of the form

$$I = \left(G + pC + \frac{1}{p}\, \Gamma + D \right) V \tag{12}$$

where the Y matrix has been resolved into separate G (conductance), C (capacitance), and Γ (reciprocal inductance) matrices, and the matrix D has been added to include the effect of dependent sources.

It is, of course, possible to write a set of independent equations for a given network by choosing both loop currents and nodal voltages as the independent variables. An example of this will be given in Chap. 6. However, the matrix formulation of such a case is of only limited interest and will not be discussed at this point.

PROBLEMS

3.1 Find all possible sets of network parameters for the networks shown in Fig. P3.1.

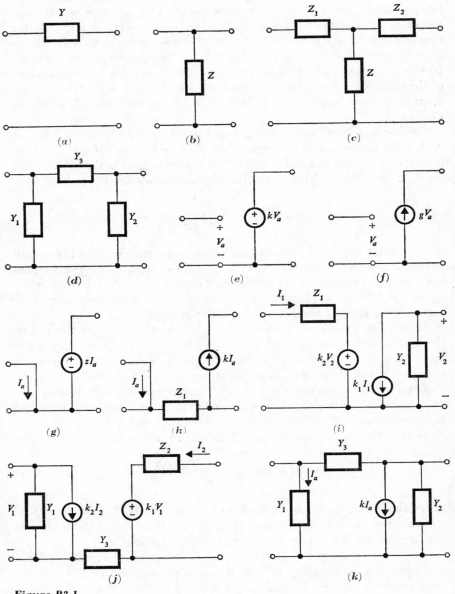

Figure P3.1

3.2 Divide each of the networks shown in Fig. P3.2 into subnetworks in such a manner that the parameters of the original network may be found by combining the parameters of the subnetworks.

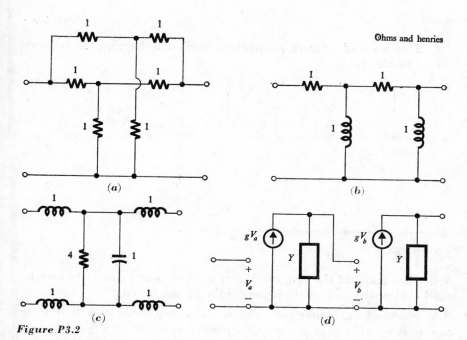

Ohms and henries

(a)

(b)

(c)

(d)

Figure P3.2

3.3 Find the z and y parameters (where possible) of the three-port networks shown in Fig. P3.3.

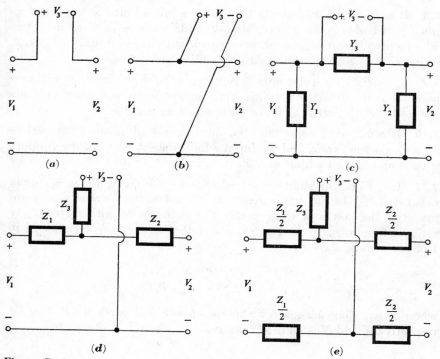

(a)

(b)

(c)

(d)

(e)

Figure P3.3

3.4 Find a set of network parameters which will describe the network shown in Fig. P3.4.

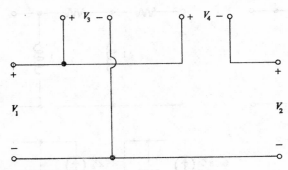

Figure P3.4

3.5 How many of the 20 possible sets of three-port parameters may be used to describe each of the networks shown in Fig. P3.3?

3.6 Show an interconnection of two n-port networks such that their z parameters will add to produce the z parameters of the resulting network.

3.7 Show an interconnection of two n-port networks such that their y parameters will add to produce the y parameters of the resulting network.

3.8 If a matrix Y represents the short-circuit admittance parameters (on a port basis) for an n-port network, find an expression for the matrix Y' which will represent the same network with impedances Z_i ($i = 1, 2, \cdots, n$) connected in series with the individual ports.

3.9 A matrix Y with elements y_{ij} represents the short-circuit admittance parameters for an n-port network. Find an expression for the input admittance at the ith port if all other ports are open-circuited.

3.10 If a matrix Y represents the short-circuit admittance parameters for an n-port network, find the input admittance at port 1 if the ith port is terminated in an admittance Y_i ($i = 2, 3, \cdots, n$).

3.11 Let Y' be the short-circuit admittance matrix of an $(n + r)$-port network. Let Y be short-circuit admittance matrix for a network comprised of the first n of these ports. The elements of both matrices are rational functions. If the last r ports of the network are terminated in 1-ohm resistors, show that

$$Y' = \begin{bmatrix} Y + NP_o^{-1}P^{-1}N^t & NP_o^{-1} \\ P_o^{-1}N^t & P_eP_o^{-1} \end{bmatrix}$$

where P is a diagonal matrix whose even and odd parts are P_e and P_o, respectively, and N is an $n \times r$ matrix.

3.12 Verify the z-parameter matrix (12) of Sec. 3.2 for the network shown in Fig. 3.14.

3.13 Verify the z-parameter matrix (14) of Sec. 3.2 for the network shown in Fig. 3.15.

3.14 Find the z-parameter matrix for the network shown in Fig. P3.14.

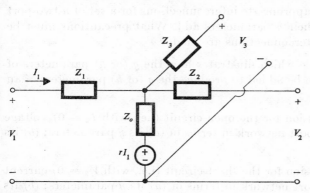

Figure P3.14

3.15 Find the z-parameter matrix for the network shown in Fig. P3.15.

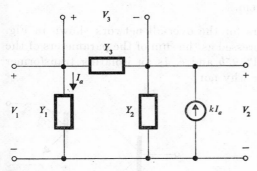

Figure P3.15

3.16 For the two-port network shown in Fig. 3.15, write separate matrix equations for the voltage and current variables such that they include: (a) a y-parameter matrix; (b) a g-parameter matrix; (c) an h-parameter matrix; (d) an *ABCD*-parameter matrix; (e) an 𝔞𝔟𝔠𝔡-parameter matrix.

3.17 For the three-port network shown in Fig. P3.14, assume that the voltage generator is independent of I_1 and, instead, has an output $V_o \sin 2t$. Write the matrix equation for the network in such a manner that it includes a z-parameter matrix.

3.18 Prove the theorem in Sec. 3.2. (HINT: Rearrange the variables so that A_i and B_j are at the bottom of their respective column matrices.)

3.19 Determine the appropriate interconnections for a set of n two-port networks such that their g parameters add. What precautions must be observed when the interconnections are made?

3.20 Determine the appropriate interconnections for a set of n two-port networks such that their h parameters add. What precautions must be observed when the interconnections are made?

3.21 Find an example which illustrates how the g (or h) parameters of two-port networks can be added to produce the g (or h) parameters of an over-all network.

3.22 Find an expression for the open-circuit (i.e., with $I_2 = 0$) voltage gain V_2/V_1 of a two-port network in terms of (a) its y parameters; (b) its z parameters.

3.23 Find an expression for the short-circuit (i.e., with $V_2 = 0$) current gain I_2/I_1 of a two-port network in terms of (a) its y parameters; (b) its z parameters.

3.24 Find a set of testing conditions which may be applied to any two-port networks which are to be connected in parallel to determine whether (9) of Sec. 3.3 will apply to them.

3.25 Find a set of parameters for the over-all network shown in Fig. P3.25a such that it may be expressed as the sum of the parameters of the two networks shown in Fig. P3.25b and c. Is an isolating transformer necessary in this case? Why or why not?

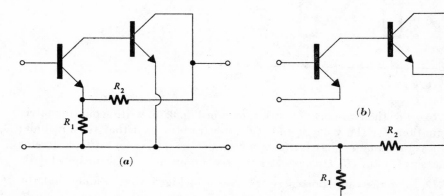

Figure P3.25

3.26 Determine whether or not the g-parameter matrices of the networks shown in Fig. P3.26a and b may be added to produce the g-parameter matrix of a resulting network. Assume that the networks are interconnected in such a manner that the matrices *should* add. If the port conditions are violated, add an isolating transformer to the circuit in such a manner that the parameter matrices will add.

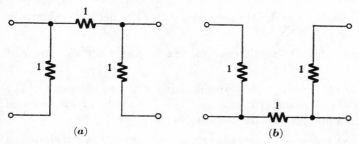

(a)   (b)

Figure P3.26

3.27 In Sec. 3.2 it is noted that the z-parameter matrix and the y-parameter matrix for a reciprocal network will be symmetric. Use this fact to find the relation that exists among the *ABCD* parameters for a reciprocal two-port network.

3.28 Find the open-circuit input impedance of the network shown in Fig. P3.28 by finding the transmission parameters of one section and then of the cascade of sections and converting to z parameters.

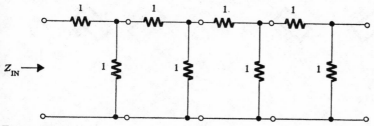

Figure P3.28

3.29 Find the properties of the hybrid parameters that exist for reciprocal two-port networks.

3.30 What relation must be satisfied by the inverse transmission parameters of a reciprocal two-port network?

3.31 If two-port networks are interconnected so that their transmission parameters multiply, is it ever necessary to use isolating transformers as must sometimes be done when networks are interconnected so that their z, y, g, or h parameters add? Explain.

3.32 If, for a two-port network, y_{12} or y_{21} is zero, show that $y_{11} = 1/z_{11}$.

3.33 The network shown in Fig. P3.1j is to be considered as a four-terminal network. If the lower left-hand terminal is taken as a reference, find the z and y parameters for the network.

3.34 Find the y parameters on a terminal basis of the networks shown in Figs. P3.3d and e.

3.35 Find the indefinite-admittance matrices for the networks shown in Fig. P3.1.

3.36 Find the indefinite-admittance matrix for the network shown in Fig. P3.3e.

3.37 Prove that by appropriate respecification of the partitioning of the submatrices, the expression (13) of Sec. 3.5 can be applied to the case in which more than one node of the network is suppressed.

3.38 Show that the suppression of terminal 4 of the network shown in Fig. P3.38a in the indefinite-admittance matrix for that network leads to the indefinite-admittance matrix for the network shown in Fig. P3.38b.

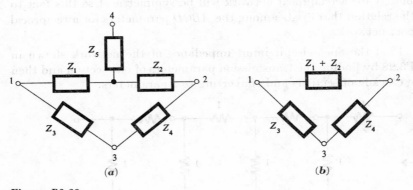

Figure P3.38

3.39 Show that the effect of connecting an admittance Y between any two terminals of a network is to add or subtract Y to the corresponding elements at the intersections of the rows and columns in the indefinite-admittance matrix. Specifically, Y is added to the diagonal elements and subtracted from the off-diagonal elements.

3.40 Find the indefinite-admittance matrix of the network shown in Fig. P3.40b by proceeding as follows: (1) Find the indefinite-admittance matrix of the network shown in Fig. P3.40a; (2) add an admittance Y_3 between terminals 2 and 4 by the method of Prob. 3.39; and (3) suppress terminal 3.

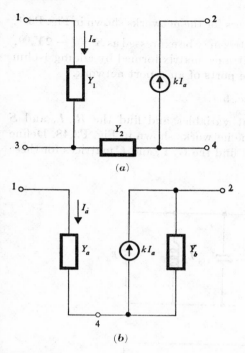

Figure P3.40

3.41 Formulate an indefinite-impedance matrix by following the general form of the development of the indefinite-admittance matrix.

3.42 Show how the indefinite-admittance matrix for a given network may be modified to take into account the grounding of one terminal of the network through an impedance Z.

3.43 Find an expression for the short-circuit current gain between any two terminals of a network in terms of the elements of the indefinite-admittance matrix for that network. The output terminal should be considered as short-circuited, i.e., grounded.

3.44 The following open-circuit parameters were measured as the small-signal parameters for a transistor in a grounded-base configuration:

$$z_{11} = 500 \text{ ohms} \qquad z_{12} = 100 \text{ ohms}$$
$$z_{21} = 50K \text{ ohms} \qquad z_{22} = 20K \text{ ohms}$$

(a) Find the indefinite-admittance matrix; (b) which terminal of the transistor should be grounded to produce the highest input impedance when the output is grounded?

3.45 Find the scattering parameters for the networks shown in Fig. P3.1.

3.46 Show that the scattering matrix may be expressed as $S = 1 - 2Y_a{}^{(n)}$, where $Y_a{}^{(n)}$ is an augmented admittance matrix formed by adding 1-ohm resistors in series with each of the ports of an n-port network.

3.47 Derive equation (13) of Sec. 3.7.

3.48 Define appropriate current variables and find the R, L, and S matrices defined in Sec. 3.8 for the networks shown in Fig. P3.48. Define appropriate voltage variables and find the G, Γ, and C matrices for these networks.

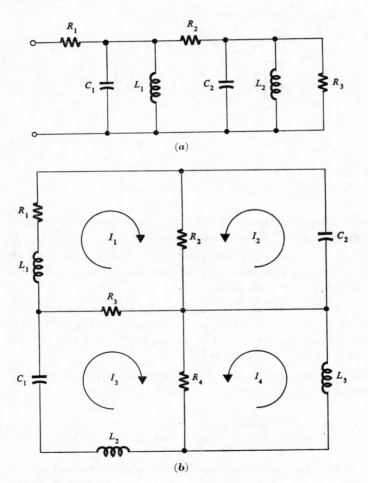

(a)

(b)

Figure P3.48

3.49 Write the matrix equation on a nodal basis for the network shown in Fig. P3.49. The various matrices should be grouped separately as shown in (12) of Sec. 3.8.

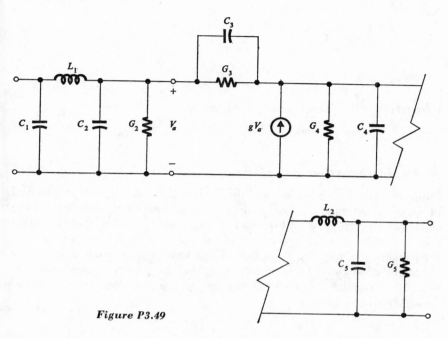

Figure P3.49

Chapter 4 Two-port devices

4.1 Introduction

Suppose we had no knowledge of the devices that we might expect to find in electrical networks, but only a knowledge of basic mathematics and the electrical quantities of voltage and current. The knowledge of the latter might have been developed from basic concepts of charge as known from the principles of physics. We might expect that devices would exist whose characteristics would be specified by relations between voltage and current. If we restricted ourselves to linear algebraic relationships, we could investigate the equations

$$v = k_1 i \qquad k_1 > 0$$
$$v = -k_2 i \qquad k_2 > 0$$

The use of the lowercase letter for the quantities v and i indicates that these are functions of time. The positive constants k_i are assumed to be real and time-invariant. Other basic relationships that we might explore would be those involving first-order derivatives with respect to time. Four possible combinations are

$$v = k_3 \frac{di}{dt} \qquad v = -k_4 \frac{di}{dt}$$
$$i = k_5 \frac{dv}{dt} \qquad i = -k_6 \frac{dv}{dt} \tag{1}$$

The constants k_i in (1) are considered as positive, real, and time-invariant. The above relationships, of course, actually define the familiar concepts of positive-valued resistance (k_1), inductance (k_3), and capacitance (k_5), and the not-so-familiar concepts of *negative-valued* resistance $(-k_2)$, inductance $(-k_4)$, and capacitance $(-k_6)$.

The positive-valued quantities define the commonly accepted passive network elements. We know, of course, that elements defined by these

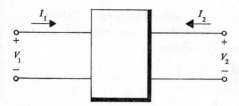

*Figure 4.1 A two-port network
with its voltage and current variables.*

relationships are considered ideal; that is, they serve as models for actual
physical devices which, over certain ranges of voltages, currents, and frequencies, and under certain other operating conditions, more or less
closely approach the characteristics predicated by the model. The negative-valued quantities define network elements which might be considered
as active in that they, in general, require power sources for their operation.
How this type of element is produced and used will be the subject of much
of the material which follows.

   If we were satisfied that the above exploration had exhausted the possibilities for two-terminal (i.e., one-port) network elements, we might next
turn our attention to two-port devices. We may define two voltage variables $v_1(t)$ and $v_2(t)$ and two current variables $i_1(t)$ and $i_2(t)$. These have
the Laplace transforms V_1, V_2, I_1, and I_2, as shown in Fig. 4.1. The reference directions are, of course, arbitrary and are chosen to agree with the
usual conventions. There are many possibilities of interrelations between
these variables. Let us explore only the relations that are (1) linear, (2)
algebraic, and (3) expressible by a set of two equations in which each
equation contains only one variable from each of the ports. Two basic
types of relationships are permitted under the above restrictions. These
are:

$$V_1 = aV_2 \qquad I_1 = bI_2 \tag{2}$$

and
$$V_1 = aI_2 \qquad I_1 = bV_2 \tag{3}$$

If we consider the constants a and b as positive, then we may treat four
different possibilities for each of the above sets of equations. For (2) we
have

$$V_1 = aV_2 \qquad I_1 = -bI_2 \tag{4a}$$
$$V_1 = -aV_2 \qquad I_1 = bI_2 \tag{4b}$$
$$V_1 = aV_2 \qquad I_1 = bI_2 \tag{4c}$$
$$V_1 = -aV_2 \qquad I_1 = -bI_2 \tag{4d}$$

Similarly, for (3), we have

$$V_1 = -aI_2 \qquad I_1 = bV_2 \tag{5a}$$
$$V_1 = aI_2 \qquad I_1 = -bV_2 \tag{5b}$$
$$V_1 = aI_2 \qquad I_1 = bV_2 \tag{5c}$$
$$V_1 = -aI_2 \qquad I_1 = -bV_2 \tag{5d}$$

Actually, all the above equations may be expressed in terms of the trans-mission-parameter matrix which was defined for the two-port case in Sec. 3.3. In this form, the equations (4) become

$$\begin{bmatrix} V_1 \\ I_1 \end{bmatrix} = \begin{bmatrix} a & 0 \\ 0 & b \end{bmatrix} \begin{bmatrix} V_2 \\ -I_2 \end{bmatrix} \tag{6a}$$

$$\begin{bmatrix} V_1 \\ I_1 \end{bmatrix} = \begin{bmatrix} -a & 0 \\ 0 & -b \end{bmatrix} \begin{bmatrix} V_2 \\ -I_2 \end{bmatrix} \tag{6b}$$

$$\begin{bmatrix} V_1 \\ I_1 \end{bmatrix} = \begin{bmatrix} a & 0 \\ 0 & -b \end{bmatrix} \begin{bmatrix} V_2 \\ -I_2 \end{bmatrix} \tag{6c}$$

$$\begin{bmatrix} V_1 \\ I_1 \end{bmatrix} = \begin{bmatrix} -a & 0 \\ 0 & b \end{bmatrix} \begin{bmatrix} V_2 \\ -I_2 \end{bmatrix} \tag{6d}$$

Similarly, for (5),

$$\begin{bmatrix} V_1 \\ I_1 \end{bmatrix} = \begin{bmatrix} 0 & a \\ b & 0 \end{bmatrix} \begin{bmatrix} V_2 \\ -I_2 \end{bmatrix} \tag{7a}$$

$$\begin{bmatrix} V_1 \\ I_1 \end{bmatrix} = \begin{bmatrix} 0 & -a \\ -b & 0 \end{bmatrix} \begin{bmatrix} V_2 \\ -I_2 \end{bmatrix} \tag{7b}$$

$$\begin{bmatrix} V_1 \\ I_1 \end{bmatrix} = \begin{bmatrix} 0 & -a \\ b & 0 \end{bmatrix} \begin{bmatrix} V_2 \\ -I_2 \end{bmatrix} \tag{7c}$$

$$\begin{bmatrix} V_1 \\ I_1 \end{bmatrix} = \begin{bmatrix} 0 & a \\ -b & 0 \end{bmatrix} \begin{bmatrix} V_2 \\ -I_2 \end{bmatrix} \tag{7d}$$

The matrix notation of the above equations emphasizes the similarities and differences between the various combinations. The rest of this chapter will be devoted to studying these various sets of transmission parameters. We shall see how they lead to the definitions of such basic two-port net-work devices as ideal transformers, gyrators, and negative-immittance converters.

Each of the eight sets of transmission parameters given in (6) and (7) defines a specific two-port network in terms of its behavior as a "black box." The internal workings of the network, however, as is always the case in "port" descriptions, are not unique. As an example of this non-uniqueness, any of these networks may be realized through the use of con-trolled sources, i.e., voltage and current generators whose outputs are proportional to some other voltages or currents. To illustrate this, con-sider the general equations for a two-port network as specified by the transmission parameters. These are

$$V_1 = AV_2 - BI_2$$
$$I_1 = CV_2 - DI_2$$

The second equation may also be written

$$-I_2 = \frac{1}{D} I_1 - \frac{C}{D} V_2$$

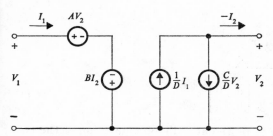

Figure 4.2 A controlled-source representation of the transmission parameters for a two-port network.

The controlled-source representation of these equations is shown in Fig. 4.2. Any of the eight equations specified in (6) or (7) may be represented in this fashion. For example, (6a) is shown in Fig. 4.3. The unfortunate part of this representation may be seen from the fact that the transmission parameters of (6a), when $a = b = 1$, also specify a simple pair of wires as shown in Fig. 4.4. In other words, the two representations shown in Figs. 4.3 and 4.4 have exactly the same transmission parameters when $a = b = 1$. The amount of introspection necessary to deduce this conclusion from Fig. 4.3 is considerable. For example, try to explain the effect of a voltage applied at port 1 in producing a voltage at port 2, or try explaining the effect of a current applied at port 2 in producing a current through an arbitrary impedance connected to port 1.

In general, the controlled-source representation will not be used for the two-port devices to be discussed in this section. When we discuss the actual implementation of some of these devices, however, we will use models of active devices such as vacuum tubes or transistors, and these models will in general have controlled sources in them.

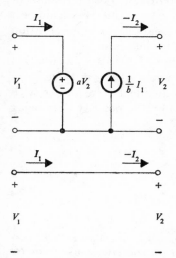

Figure 4.3 A controlled-source representation for the transmission parameters of (6a) of Sec. 4.1.

Figure 4.4 A realization for the transmission parameters of (6a) of Sec. 4.1 when $a = b = 1$.

4.2   *The ideal transformer*

The transmission-parameter matrix

$$\begin{bmatrix} a & 0 \\ 0 & b \end{bmatrix} \tag{1}$$

was shown in the last section to represent a direct connection of the two ports when $a = b = 1$. It may also be considered as representing an ideal transformer of unity turns ratio as defined by the relations $V_1 = V_2$ and $I_1 = -I_2$. In defining the ideal transformer, if the turns ratio is not unity, we have the usual relations $V_1 = nV_2$ and $I_1 = -(1/n)I_2$. Thus, we need only make the restriction that $b = 1/a = 1/n$ in (1) to specify an ideal transformer of turns ratio $n:1$. The symbol for this transformer with its identifying polarity dots is shown in Fig. 4.5. The quantity n is assumed real and positive. Note that the transmission matrix requires the transmission of d-c signals as well as a-c signals. The circuit symbol of Fig. 4.5, however, indicates that the circuits connected to port 1 are isolated from those connected to port 2. This is entirely consistent with the conclusions of Sec. 3.3, regarding the use of ideal transformers for isolation, and the remarks of Sec. 3.4, where it was emphasized that the port notation does not recognize differences of potential between circuits which are connected together. Thus, any d-c potential difference which is established between the two terminals of port 1 will appear (after having been multiplied by the pertinent turns ratio) at port 2. On the other hand, any raising or lowering of the potential at both terminals of port 1 will not affect the voltages at port 2. In view of the remarks in Sec. 3.3 and Figs. 3.30 through 3.32, it should be clear that a representation for an ideal transformer is not possible on a terminal basis.

The transmission matrix of (6b) of Sec. 4.1 may be written in equation form as $V_1 = -aV_2$ and $I_1 = bI_2$. If we set $a = 1/b = n$, then $V_1 = -nV_2$ and $I_1 = (1/n)I_2$, the equations for an ideal transformer with one of its windings reversed. This is indicated by the polarity dots being

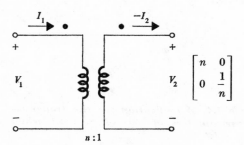

Figure 4.5   An ideal transformer and its transmission-parameter matrix.

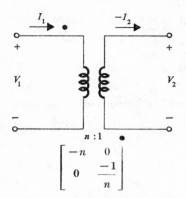

$$\begin{bmatrix} -n & 0 \\ 0 & \dfrac{-1}{n} \end{bmatrix}$$

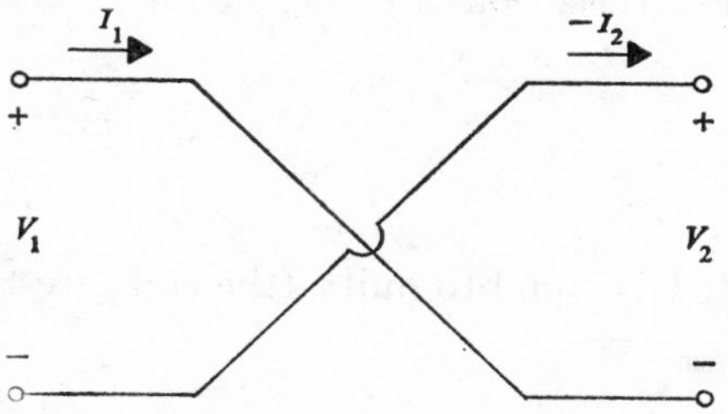

$$\begin{bmatrix} -1 & 0 \\ 0 & -1 \end{bmatrix}$$

Figure 4.6 An ideal transformer with a reversed winding and its transmission-parameter matrix.

Figure 4.7 A simple two-port network and its transmission-parameter matrix.

placed at opposite ends of the respective windings, as shown in Fig. 4.6. For the case in which $a = b = 1$, i.e., for an ideal transformer of unity turns ratio so connected as to invert the polarity, the two-port parameters are exactly the same as those of a pair of crossed wires, as shown in Fig. 4.7. Needless to say, there are many situations in which a pair of crossed wires cannot be used to replace a unity-turns-ratio ideal transformer; however, on a port basis, it should be recognized that the networks of Figs. 4.6 and 4.7 have the same network parameters when $a = b = 1$.

It is interesting to compare the ideal transformer with its physical counterpart. A practical transformer may be represented in its basic form by a pair of coupled coils whose self-inductances are L_1 and L_2 with a mutual inductance of M. This latter quantity may be positive or negative. The arrangement of the coils and the voltage and current variables is shown in Fig. 4.8. In the time domain, we may write the following equations:

$$v_1(t) = L_1 \frac{di_1}{dt} + M \frac{di_2}{dt}$$

$$v_2(t) = M \frac{di_1}{dt} + L_2 \frac{di_2}{dt} \tag{2}$$

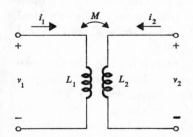

Figure 4.8 A pair of coupled coils.

For these coils we may define a coefficient of coupling k, where

$$k = \frac{|M|}{(L_1 L_2)^{\frac{1}{2}}} \tag{3}$$

If k is equal to unity (the coils are then said to be perfectly coupled),

$$\frac{L_1}{M} = \frac{M}{L_2}$$

In this case we may write (2) as

$$\begin{aligned}
\frac{v_1(t)}{L_1} &= \frac{di_1}{dt} + \frac{M}{L_1}\frac{di_2}{dt} \\
\frac{v_2(t)}{M} &= \frac{di_1}{dt} + \frac{M}{L_1}\frac{di_2}{dt}
\end{aligned} \tag{4}$$

Setting the above equations equal, we see that

$$\frac{v_2(t)}{v_1(t)} = \frac{M}{L_1} \tag{5}$$

Now let the values of L_1, L_2, and M go to infinity while the ratio M/L_1 is kept constant. From (4) we see that, in the limit,

$$0 = \frac{di_1}{dt} + \frac{M}{L_1}\frac{di_2}{dt} \tag{6}$$

Thus, we see that

$$\frac{i_2(t)}{i_1(t)} = -\frac{L_1}{M} \tag{7}$$

If we define $L_1/M = n$, then (5) and (7) are the equations of the ideal transformer in the time domain. Thus we see that we may define an ideal transformer in terms of a pair of coupled coils with infinite self and mutual inductance and with unity coefficient of coupling.

We have now covered the two-port devices represented by the first two transmission-parameter matrices of equations (6) of Sec. 4.1. The properties and representations of these devices are summarized in Table 4.1 on pages 120 and 121. The reader is referred to this table in following the progress of this chapter through other fundamental two-port devices.

4.3   *The negative-immittance converter*

The transmission matrix of (6c) of Sec. 4.1 represents the equations

$$
\begin{aligned}
V_1 &= a V_2 \\
I_1 &= (-b)(-I_2)
\end{aligned}
$$

$$(1)$$

If we divide corresponding members of these equations, we obtain

$$
\frac{V_1}{I_1} = -\frac{a}{b}\frac{V_2}{-I_2}
$$

The ratio $V_2/-I_2$, however, is just the impedance of a load connected to port 2 as shown in Fig. 4.9. Thus, if we have a two-port device whose transmission parameters are those of (6c) of Sec. 4.1, the input impedance to this device at port 1 (i.e., the ratio V_1/I_1) is $-(a/b)\,Z_2$, where Z_2 is the impedance connected to port 2. If the ratio a/b is equal to unity, then we may say that the input impedance is the negative of the impedance connected to the output. Obviously this statement is true on an impedance or an admittance basis. We see, therefore, that the action of this device is such that it may be described as a negative-immittance converter. It is interesting to note how this "negative" action comes about. From (1) we see that the device, in effect, monitors the current flowing *out* of the upper terminal of port 2 and requires that the same current (times a constant multiplier) flow *out* of the upper terminal of port 1. Normally, we would expect that if a current flowed out of port 2, a current would have to flow *into* port 1. Thus the action of the device has been to reverse the normal flow of current by some means. To emphasize this fact, we shall call this device a *current* negative-immittance converter, or an INIC for short.

We shall investigate the properties of the INIC in more detail shortly, but first let us consider the transmission matrix of (6d) of Sec. 4.1, which represents the equations

$$
\begin{aligned}
V_1 &= -a V_2 \\
I_1 &= b(-I_2)
\end{aligned}
$$

$$(2)$$

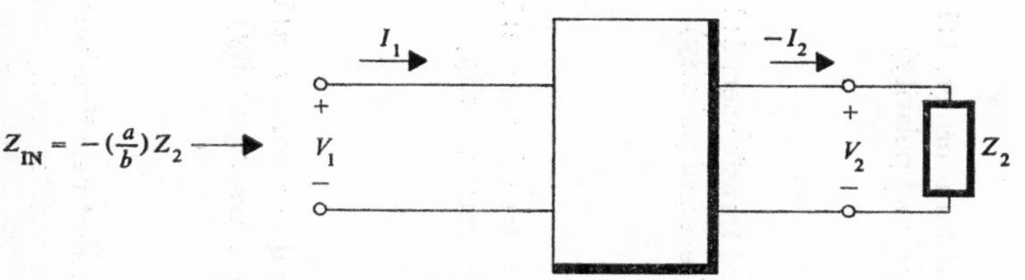

Figure 4.9   Producing a negative impedance.

Table 4.1 Two-port devices

Description	Symbol	ABCD Parameters	Properties
Ideal transformer; 1:1 (normal polarity)	1:1	$\begin{bmatrix} 1 & 0 \\ 0 & 1 \end{bmatrix}$	$Z = Z_1$ $Z = Z_2$
Ideal transformer; 1:1 (reversed polarity)	1:1	$\begin{bmatrix} -1 & 0 \\ 0 & -1 \end{bmatrix}$	$Z = Z_1$ $Z = Z_2$
Ideal transformer; $n:1$ (normal polarity)	$n:1$	$\begin{bmatrix} n & 0 \\ 0 & \dfrac{1}{n} \end{bmatrix}$	$Z = Z_1/n^2$ $Z = n^2 Z_2$
Ideal transformer; $n:1$ (reversed polarity)	$n:1$	$\begin{bmatrix} -n & 0 \\ 0 & -\dfrac{1}{n} \end{bmatrix}$	$Z = Z_1/n^2$ $Z = n^2 Z_2$
Current negative-immittance converter (unity ratio)	INIC	$\begin{bmatrix} 1 & 0 \\ 0 & -1 \end{bmatrix}$	$Z = -Z_1$ $Z = -Z_2$

Element	Symbol	Matrix	Output (terminated z_2)	Input (terminated z_1)
Voltage negative-immittance converter (unity ratio)	VNIC	$\begin{bmatrix} -1 & 0 \\ 0 & 1 \end{bmatrix}$	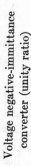 $z = -z_2$	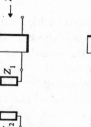 $z = -z_1$
Current negative-immittance converter (ratio of conversion k)	INIC	$\begin{bmatrix} \dfrac{1}{k} & 0 \\ 0 & -k \end{bmatrix}$	$z = -z_2/k^2$	$z = -k^2 z_1$
Voltage negative-immittance converter (ratio of conversion k)	VNIC	$\begin{bmatrix} -\dfrac{1}{k} & 0 \\ 0 & k \end{bmatrix}$	$z = -z_2/k^2$	$z = -k^2 z_1$
Gyrator (unity gyration conductance)	$\xrightarrow{1}$	$\begin{bmatrix} 0 & 1 \\ 1 & 0 \end{bmatrix}$	$z = 1/z_2$	$z = 1/z_1$
Gyrator (gyration conductance G)	$\xrightarrow{G}$	$\begin{bmatrix} 0 & \dfrac{1}{G} \\ G & 0 \end{bmatrix}$	$z = 1/G^2 z_2$	$z = 1/G^2 z_1$

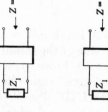
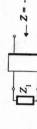

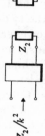

If we divide corresponding members of these equations, we obtain

$$\frac{V_1}{I_1} = -\frac{a}{b}\frac{V_2}{-I_2}$$

Once more, we have the situation represented in Fig. 4.9, i.e., if $a/b = 1$, the input immittance to port 1 of our device is the negative of the immittance connected to port 2. If we examine the equations (2), however, we see that there is an important difference in how the "negative" action has come about as compared with how it is produced by the INIC described above. In (2) we see that the current flowing out of the two-port device is matched by current flowing into it. The voltage, however, has been inverted in polarity and multiplied by a constant. Thus, the action of this type of device depends on inverting the voltage. It is thus called a *voltage negative-immittance converter* and it will be referred to as a VNIC. In general, we shall only be interested in negative-immittance converters in which $a/b = 1$. Before we can continue our discussion of the properties of the two types of NICs (negative-immittance converters), it is necessary to set up some criteria to permit us to determine when a two-port device is an NIC. In short, we would like to develop a set of necessary and sufficient conditions which may be applied to an arbitrary two-port network which will guarantee that it perform in such a manner that the input immittance seen at one set of terminals is exactly the negative of the immittance connected at the other set of terminals. To establish these conditions, consider a network described in terms of its g parameters. The equations are

$$\begin{aligned} I_1 &= g_{11}V_1 + g_{12}I_2 \\ V_2 &= g_{21}V_1 + g_{22}I_2 \end{aligned} \tag{3}$$

Terminating the two-port network in an impedance Z_2 adds the additional relationship $V_2 = Z_2(-I_2)$ to the above. We may now solve the equations for the ratio V_1/I_1, i.e., for the input impedance of the device. The input impedance is

$$\frac{V_1}{I_1} = \frac{1}{g_{11} - g_{12}g_{21}/(Z_2 + g_{22})} \tag{4}$$

Thus we see that it is both necessary and sufficient that

$$g_{11} = 0 \qquad g_{22} = 0 \qquad g_{12}g_{21} = 1 \tag{5}$$

for the input immittance to be the negative of the terminating immittance, i.e., for the device to act as an NIC.[1]

There are several ways in which the product $g_{12}g_{21}$ (we assume that these are real constants) may be set equal to unity as required by (5). The

---

[1] The conditions in this form were first reported in A. I. Larky, Negative-impedance Converters, *IRE Trans. on Circuit Theory*, vol. CT-4, no. 3, pp. 124–131, September, 1957.

only criteria required of g_{12} and g_{21} are (1) that they be of the same sign
and (2) that $|g_{12}| = |1/g_{21}|$. For example, if both are positive, then (3)
becomes

$$I_1 = g_{12}I_2 \qquad g_{12} > 0$$
$$V_1 = \frac{1}{g_{21}} V_2 \qquad g_{21} > 0 \tag{6}$$

With the appropriate changes in the variable from I_2 to $-I_2$ and the
identification of $g_{12} = b$ and $g_{21} = 1/a$, these are the same equations as
(1), and we see that requiring $g_{12}g_{21} = 1$ is the same as requiring $a/b = 1$.
We conclude that if both g_{12} and g_{21} are positive, the device is an INIC.
Similarly, if both g_{12} and g_{21} are negative (we may consider the symbols as
positive and prefix negative signs), then equations (3) become

$$I_1 = -g_{12}I_2 \qquad g_{12} > 0$$
$$V_1 = -\frac{1}{g_{21}} V_2 \qquad g_{21} > 0 \tag{7}$$

We may make identifications similar to the above and compare these with
(2), thus establishing that if the g_{12} and g_{21} parameters are negative, the
device is a VNIC. In later sections we shall illustrate some applications
which depend entirely on the choice of either an INIC or a VNIC as the
active element. At this time, however, we will develop more of the properties of the NIC without regard to its type.

For the first property, consider Fig. 4.10, where a two-port network is
terminated in an impedance Z_1 at port 1. This establishes the relationship
$V_1 = Z_1(-I_1)$ between the variables V_1 and I_1. If we substitute this relation in (3) and solve for the ratio V_2/I_2, i.e., the input impedance seen
looking into the terminals of port 2, we obtain

$$\frac{V_2}{I_2} = g_{22} - \frac{g_{12}g_{21}}{1/Z_1 + g_{11}} \tag{8}$$

The conditions of (5) therefore also require that the input immittance seen
looking into port 2 is the negative of the immittance connected to port 1.
We conclude that the negative-immittance conversion operation takes
place equally well in either direction.

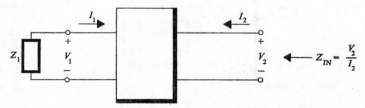

Figure 4.10   A two-port network terminated at port 1.

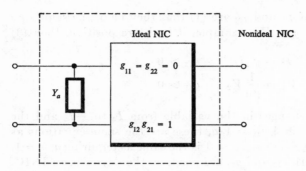

Figure 4.11 A non-ideal NIC with $g_{11} \neq 0$.

For the second property, let us consider the case in which g_{11} (the open-circuit input admittance at port 1) is not equal to zero. Specifically, let $g_{11} = Y_a$. This situation is shown in Fig. 4.11, where an ideal NIC which satisfies the conditions of (5) has an admittance Y_a connected in shunt with port 1. The resulting g parameters for the nonideal NIC (including Y_a) are

$$\begin{bmatrix} Y_a & g_{12} \\ g_{21} & 0 \end{bmatrix}$$

The nonidealness of this NIC may easily be compensated for by an external admittance Y_b connected as shown in Fig. 4.12. We may consider this as part of the load impedance Z_2 in (4). That equation becomes

$$\frac{V_1}{I_1} = \cfrac{1}{Y_a - \cfrac{1}{1/(Y_2' + Y_b) + 0}} = \frac{1}{Y_a - (Y_2' + Y_b)}$$

If we make Y_b equal to Y_a, we see from the above that we again have ideal NIC action. In a similar manner we may compensate an NIC if it is nonideal in the sense that $g_{22} \neq 0$. The process is illustrated in Fig. 4.13. In this figure, Z_a is g_{22}, i.e., the short-circuit impedance at port 2, of the non-

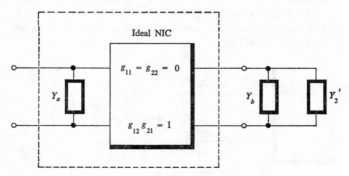

Figure 4.12   Compensating the NIC when $g_{11} \neq 0$.

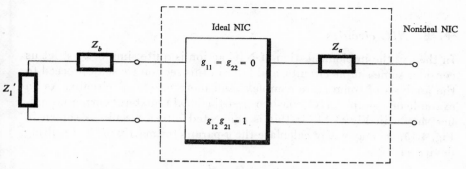

Figure 4.13 *Compensating the NIC when $g_{22} \neq 0$.*

ideal NIC. The Z_1 of Fig. 4.10 is now the series sum of the load impedance Z_1' and the compensating impedance Z_b. If we substitute in (8), we obtain

$$\frac{V_2}{I_2} = Z_a - \frac{1}{1/(Z_1' + Z_b) + 0} = Z_a - (Z_1' + Z_b)$$

If we make Z_b equal to Z_a, ideal NIC action is once more obtained; i.e., the parameters of the over-all NIC, including its inherent imperfection of a nonzero g_{22} and its compensating impedance Z_b, again satisfy the conditions (5). The above development leads to the following conclusion: If an NIC is nonideal in the sense that either g_{11} or g_{22} is not equal to zero, it may be compensated by an external immittance in such a manner that the resulting device is an ideal NIC. Clearly, this property of an NIC to be amenable to compensation for its own nonidealness is a most unusual and important property.

A third property of the NIC may be seen if we establish the conditions on a two-port network that $g_{11} = g_{22} = 0$ and that $g_{12}g_{21} = k^2$, where k is an arbitrary positive number. Under these conditions the input impedance of this device when terminated in an impedance Z_2 at port 2 may be found from (4) as

$$\frac{V_1}{I_1} = - \frac{Z_2}{k^2} \tag{9}$$

Similarly, the input impedance at port 2 when the device is terminated in Z_1 at port 1 may be found from (8) as

$$\frac{V_2}{I_2} = -k^2 Z_1 \tag{10}$$

The device defined by the g parameters, as specified above, thus provides a "negative" action in both directions, as well as a transformation ratio. It represents an ideal transformer of turns ratio $1/k$ in cascade with an NIC.

4.4 *NIC circuits*

In theory, the implementation of NIC action is quite simple. First let us consider some simple circuits, and later in this section we shall proceed to the analysis of some more complex (and more practical) circuits. As an example of a simple NIC, consider first the ideal unilateral current amplifier shown in Fig. 4.14. If this is connected into a circuit as shown in Fig. 4.15, we may easily calculate the g-parameter matrix of the resulting device as

$$\begin{bmatrix} 0 & -(1+k) \\ 1 & 0 \end{bmatrix} \tag{1}$$

In order that the product $g_{12}g_{21}$ be equal to unity, it is only necessary to require that $k = -2$. Since the g_{11} and g_{22} parameters already satisfy the conditions (5) of Sec. 4.3, this circuit is an NIC. With the value of k specified above, both g_{12} and g_{21} are positive; therefore, the circuit is an INIC. The configuration shown in Fig. 4.15 is redrawn in Fig. 4.16 to illustrate the INIC action more clearly.

In a similar fashion, we may use the ideal voltage amplifier shown in

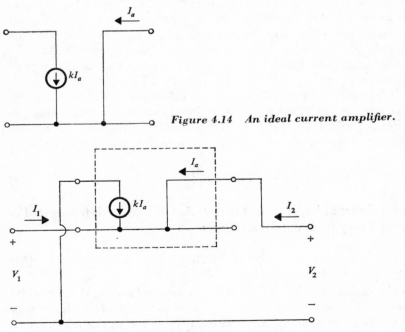

Figure 4.14   *An ideal current amplifier.*

Figure 4.15   *Connecting the ideal current amplifier as an INIC.*

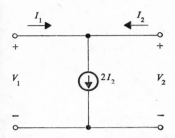

Figure 4.16 A simplified representation of the INIC of Fig. 4.15.

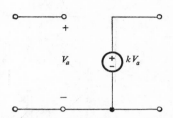

Figure 4.17 An ideal voltage amplifier.

Fig. 4.17 as the nucleus of the circuit shown in Fig. 4.18a. The g-parameter matrix of this device is

$$\begin{bmatrix} 0 & -1 \\ 1-k & 0 \end{bmatrix}$$

In order that the product $g_{12}g_{21}$ be equal to unity, it is only necessary that $k = 2$. Since g_{12} and g_{21} are both negative, we conclude that this device is a VNIC. Its circuit is redrawn in Fig. 4.18b to indicate the VNIC action more clearly.

Owing to difficulties in grounding, locating the controlling parameter, and other problems, the circuits indicated above do not provide a practical means of obtaining NIC action. A further deficiency of these circuits (as if one were needed) is that their operation is very sensitive to changes in the parameters of the active element, i.e., the ideal voltage or current generator. We shall analyze two additional circuits which are considerably more practical. One of these is an INIC circuit, the other a VNIC circuit.

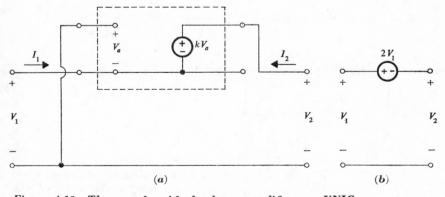

(a)   (b)

Figure 4.18 The use of an ideal voltage amplifier as a VNIC.

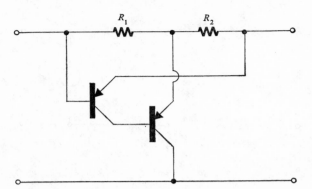

Figure 4.19 A practical INIC circuit.

A practical INIC circuit is shown in Fig. 4.19.[1] A simple small-signal equivalent circuit is shown in Fig. 4.20. In both figures, the biasing networks have been eliminated to emphasize the basic action of the circuit. For simplicity, we shall assume that the transistors are identical, i.e., $\alpha_a = \alpha_b = \alpha$. If we calculate the g parameters for the circuit of Fig. 4.20, we obtain, after some simplification,

$$\begin{bmatrix} 0 & \dfrac{R_1}{R_2} \\ 1 & 0 \end{bmatrix}$$

Thus we see that when $R_1 = R_2$, the conditions (5) of Sec. 4.3 are satisfied. Since the parameters g_{12} and g_{21} are both positive, the device is clearly an INIC. More accurate determinations of the g parameters can, of course, be obtained by using a more complicated model for the active devices; however, these would add little to the general theory that we are developing here, and they will be left as exercises.

[1] This circuit was presented by Larky in the paper previously referred to.

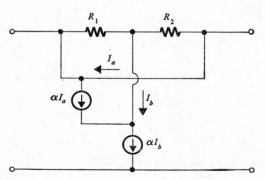

Figure 4.20 An equivalent circuit for the INIC of Fig. 4.19.

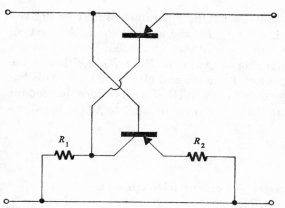

Figure 4.21 A practical VNIC circuit.

A practical VNIC circuit is shown in Fig. 4.21.[1] A simple small-signal equivalent circuit is shown in Fig. 4.22. The g parameters for the circuit are

$$\begin{bmatrix} \dfrac{1 - \alpha}{R_2} & -\alpha \\ -\dfrac{\alpha R_1}{R_2} & (1 - \alpha)R_1 \end{bmatrix}$$

As α approaches unity, the g parameters approach the following values:

$$\begin{bmatrix} 0 & -1 \\ -\dfrac{R_1}{R_2} & 0 \end{bmatrix}$$

Again we see that the product $g_{12}g_{21}$ is unity if the ratio R_1/R_2 is unity. Since g_{12} and g_{21} are negative, the device is a VNIC. As in the previous

[1] J. G. Linvill, Transistor Negative-impedance Converters, *Proc. IRE*, vol. 41, pp. 725–729, June, 1953.

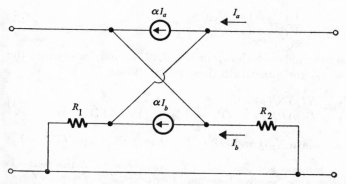

Figure 4.22 The equivalent circuit for the VNIC of Fig. 4.21

example, more detailed expressions for the g parameters may be derived if a more accurate model is selected for the active device. A practical aspect of the above circuits is the ease with which the value of the product $g_{12}g_{21}$ may be adjusted. Changing the value of R_1 or R_2 in either of the above circuits changes the value of k in (9) and (10) of Sec. 4.3. This k is sometimes referred to as the "gain" of the NIC, since it defines the amount of immittance multiplication that takes place in addition to the negative-conversion process.

4.5 *Synthesis of transfer functions with an NIC*

One important application of NICs is in synthesizing transfer functions of two-port networks. Specifically, let us consider the synthesis of *voltage* transfer functions.[1] We shall start with an arbitrary function defined as the ratio of two polynomials in the complex frequency variable p, and we shall require that the coefficients be real. We may write

$$\frac{V_2}{V_1} = \frac{N(p)}{D(p)} \tag{1}$$

If we specify that the output current of our two-port network is zero, then we may define the voltage transfer function in terms of the y parameters of the two-port network as

$$\frac{V_2}{V_1} = \frac{N(p)}{D(p)} = -\frac{y_{21}}{y_{22}} \tag{2}$$

Let us now divide both $N(p)$ and $D(p)$ by a polynomial $Q(p)$, having only negative real roots, of one degree lower order than the degree of $N(p)$ or $D(p)$ (whichever is the highest). Then

$$\frac{V_2}{V_1} = \frac{N(p)/Q(p)}{D(p)/Q(p)} = -\frac{y_{21}}{y_{22}} \tag{3}$$

If we now consider the network shown in Fig. 4.23, we may easily find the quantities y_{21} and y_{22} and substitute these in (3). Thus,

$$\frac{V_2}{V_1} = \frac{N(p)/Q(p)}{D(p)/Q(p)} = \frac{Y_a - Y_a'}{(Y_a - Y_a') + (Y_b - Y_b')} \tag{4}$$

Clearly, we can associate N/Q and $(D - N)/Q$ with the terms $(Y_a - Y_a')$

---

[1] The method given here was first presented in T. Yanagisawa, RC Active Networks using Current Inversion Type Negative Impedance Converters, *IRE Trans. on Circuit Theory*, vol. CT-4, no. 3, pp. 140–144, September, 1957.

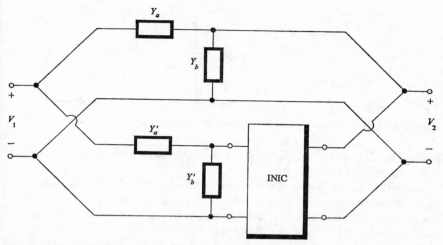

Figure 4.23   Using an INIC to synthesize voltage transfer functions.

and $(Y_b - Y_b')$, respectively. In addition, we may make partial-fraction expansions for N/Q and for $(D - N)/Q$ as follows:[1]

$$\frac{N(p)}{Q(p)} = \sum_i \frac{k_i^{(a)} p}{p + \sigma_i} + k_\infty^{(a)} p + k_o^{(a)} = Y_a - Y_a' \qquad (5)$$

$$\frac{D(p) - N(p)}{Q(p)} = \sum_i \frac{k_i^{(b)} p}{p + \sigma_i} + k_\infty^{(b)} p + k_o^{(b)} = Y_b - Y_b' \qquad (6)$$

In these expressions, the various k_i will be real and either positive or negative, depending on the choice of the zeros of $Q(p)$ and on the actual form of $N(p)$ and $D(p)$. If we associate the terms having positive k_i with Y_a and Y_b and the terms having negative k_i with $-Y_a'$ and $-Y_b'$, our network

[1] The usually accepted form of the partial-fraction expansion for a rational function $A(p)/B(p)$, where the degree of $A(p)$ is less than or equal to the degree of $B(p)$, is

$$\frac{A(p)}{B(p)} = \sum_i \frac{k_i'}{p + \sigma_i} + k_o'$$

To obtain the form of (5), we can obtain the partial-fraction expansion of $A(p)/pB(p)$. We obtain

$$\frac{A(p)}{pB(p)} = \sum_i \frac{k_i}{p + \sigma_i} + k_\infty$$

If both sides of the above equation are multiplied by p, we see that

$$\frac{A(p)}{B(p)} = \sum_i \frac{k_i p}{p + \sigma_i} + p k_\infty$$

This is equivalent to (5) if we let $\sigma_o = 0$.

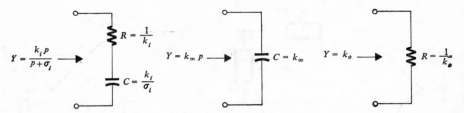

Figure 4.24   Driving-point admittances of simple RC networks.

realization is guaranteed, since the individual terms may be realized in the form shown in Fig. 4.24.

Note that there are no restrictions on the form of $N(p)$ and $D(p)$, but that the network realizations require only resistors and capacitors. Thus, we can realize complex-conjugate poles (which are normally only associated with combinations of resistance, capacitance, *and inductance*) by using only resistance and capacitance and an INIC. We could also have made our network realizations such that only resistance and inductance were required by specifying a slightly different form of partial-fraction expansion. This form of network, however, is usually of less interest. There are several advantages to eliminating inductors from network realizations. In general, they pose problems in weight, nonlinearity, presence of incidental dissipation, etc. These disadvantages are more acute at the lower frequencies. By comparison, the typical capacitor comes considerably closer to being the "ideal" element which we predicate in the models used in circuit realizations. Consequently, the use of resistance, capacitance, and active elements to achieve network realization is of considerable importance. This is referred to as *active RC synthesis.*

As an example of the above procedure, consider the transfer function

$$\frac{V_2}{V_1} = \frac{N(p)}{D(p)} = \frac{p^2 + 2p + 101}{p^2 + 2p + 81}$$

Several quite sophisticated techniques are available to guide one in choosing the location of the zeros of $Q(p)$. For cases in which $N(p)$ and $D(p)$ each have a single pair of complex-conjugate zeros, as a rule of thumb, we may choose the magnitude of σ_1 such that it is approximately equal to the magnitude of the natural frequency, i.e., the length of a vector from the origin of the complex frequency plane to a zero of $D(p)$. In this case, $\sigma_i = 10$ provides a reasonable approximation. The partial-fraction expansions are easily found to be

$$\frac{N(p)}{Q(p)} = \frac{p^2 + 2p + 101}{p + 10} = \frac{-18.1p}{p + 10} + p + 10.1$$

$$\frac{D(p) - N(p)}{Q(p)} = \frac{p^2 + 2p + 81 - (p^2 + 2p + 101)}{p + 10} = \frac{2p}{p + 10} - 2$$

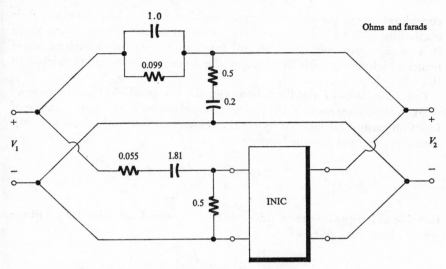

Figure 4.25   A network realization using an INIC.

The network realization is shown in Fig. 4.25. The component admittances have been found from Fig. 4.24. Naturally, any desired frequency or impedance normalization could be performed on this network to match desired specifications and to change the elements to more reasonable values.

Several other techniques are available which use NICs to accomplish various network realizations, including that of nonpositive-real driving-point functions. It is interesting to note that, although the technique of this section may, in theory, be applied to a transfer function with component polynomials of an arbitrarily high degree, in practice it is customary to limit the realization to polynomials of second degree. This limitation is due to sensitivity considerations.

4.6   *Synthesis of driving-point functions with NICs*

Let us now investigate some elementary properties of driving-point immittances. Consider the networks that can be formed from passive (i.e., positive-valued) resistors, capacitors, and inductors, and let us restrict ourselves to lumped linear finite elements.[1] It is well known that the driving-point immittances of such elements can only have poles and zeros in the left half of the complex frequency plane. This is easily seen from

---

[1] The abbreviation LLFPB is frequently used; the letters stand for "Lumped," "Linear," "Finite," "Passive," and "Bilateral."

considerations of the natural frequencies that result when the network is excited by either a voltage source or a current source. The network, since it is passive, can only have natural frequencies associated with response terms which decay with time. Thus, the poles and zeros are restricted to the left half plane.

Considerations of stability, however, do not preclude the presence of right-half-plane *zeros* in a driving-point function, even though this type of function cannot be realized by passive elements. For example, a network whose driving-point impedance is

$$Z(p) = \frac{\text{response}}{\text{excitation}} = \frac{V(p)}{I(p)} = \frac{p-1}{p}$$

is stable as long as it is excited by a current source. Excitation by a voltage source, however, gives us

$$Y(p) = \frac{\text{response}}{\text{excitation}} = \frac{I(p)}{V(p)} = \frac{p}{p-1}$$

and the resulting current exhibits the unstable characteristics of the network; i.e., it rises exponentially. We might describe a network with this driving-point immittance as being open-circuit stable (or short-circuit unstable), since excitation from an ideal current source of zero internal admittance corresponds with placing an open circuit across the input port of the network. In this section we shall see that we may synthesize driving-point functions which need have only the numerator *or* the denominator with left-half-plane zeros. The zeros of the other polynomial may be in the right half plane, the left half plane, or both. We shall, of course, require the coefficients of the component polynomials to be real so as to guarantee that their zeros are real or occur in complex-conjugate pairs. In addition, we shall require that the degree of the numerator polynomial be not more than one greater than the degree of the denominator polynomial. This requirement also follows from stability considerations. This type of driving-point function is frequently spoken of as being "nonpositive real."[1] Since the positive-real criterion is necessary and sufficient to guarantee realization of the function as a driving-point immittance using only passive elements, we shall see that the techniques of this section will allow us to realize driving-point functions that *cannot be realized by using passive components alone.* To do this we shall only require the use of resistors, capacitors, and NICs.

---

[1] "The requirement of left-half-plane poles and zeros is necessary but *not* sufficient for a given function to be positive real. See E. A. Guillemin, "Synthesis of Passive Networks," John Wiley & Sons, Inc., New York, 1957.

Let us consider a rational function $Y(p)$ as the ratio of current to voltage at the terminals of a one-port network. Let

$$Y(p) = \frac{I(p)}{V(p)} = \frac{N(p)}{D(p)} \tag{1}$$

The polynomials $N(p)$ and $D(p)$ must have real coefficients, and the zeros of $D(p)$ must lie in the left half plane. The degree of $N(p)$ can be no more than one greater than the degree of $D(p)$. It is easily shown that any arbitrary polynomial may be split into the difference of two polynomials such that each of these component polynomials has zeros only on the negative real axis or at the origin. To see this, consider what will happen if we assume that $N(p)$ is the arbitrary polynomial and we divide it by a polynomial $Q(p)$ which is one degree more than $N(p)$ and has only negative real zeros. We may write

$$Q(p) = K \prod_i (p + \sigma_i)$$

where the σ_i are positive real numbers. It is easy to see that we can express the function $N(p)/Q(p)$ as a partial-fraction expansion. Thus,

$$\frac{N(p)}{Q(p)} = \frac{N(p)}{K \prod_i (p + \sigma_i)} = \sum_r \frac{k_r}{p + \sigma_r} - \sum_j \frac{k_j}{p + \sigma_j}$$

In the above equation all the k_r and k_j are positive real constants. In effect, we have gathered all the negative residues of $N(p)/Q(p)$ in one group and all the positive residues in another group.[1] The final step in this process is to put the right side of the above equation over a common denominator. When this is done, we shall have $N(p)$ expressed as the difference of two polynomials, both of which have only negative real zeros. Although this technique is quite general, some sophistication may be observed in the choice of the zeros of $Q(p)$.[2]

Let us assume that this splitting procedure has been applied to the numerator polynomial of (1). Thus we shall let $N(p) = N_1(p) - N_2(p)$, where the polynomials $N_1(p)$ and $N_2(p)$ have only negative real zeros, i.e., zeros that lie on the negative real axis or at the origin. The zeros of $N(p)$

[1] The residue k_i is the coefficient a_{-1} in the Laurent series $N(p)/Q(p) = \sum_j a_j(p + \sigma_i)^j$.

[2] See I. M. Horowitz, Optimization of Negative-impedance Conversion Methods of Active RC Synthesis, *IRE Trans. on Circuit Theory*, vol. CT-6, pp. 296–303, September, 1959; see also R. E. Thomas, Polynomial Decomposition in Active Network Synthesis, *IRE Trans. on Circuit Theory*, vol. CT-8, pp. 270–274, September, 1961.

may lie anywhere on the complex frequency plane. Equation (1) becomes

$$Y(p) = \frac{N(p)}{D(p)} = \frac{N_1(p)}{D(p)} - \frac{N_2(p)}{D(p)}$$

We may now assume that the original one-port network is divided into two subnetworks with admittances $Y_1(p)$ and $Y_2(p)$ and which are connected in parallel. We may define

$$Y_1(p) = \frac{N_1(p)}{D(p)} \qquad Y_2(p) = \frac{-N_2(p)}{D(p)} \tag{2}$$

On an impedance basis, we may define

$$Z_1(p) = \frac{1}{Y_1(p)} = \frac{D(p)}{N_1(p)} \qquad Z_2(p) = \frac{1}{Y_2(p)} = \frac{-D(p)}{N_2(p)} \tag{3}$$

Since both $N_1(p)$ and $N_2(p)$ have only negative real zeros, the driving-point impedances $Z_1(p)$ and $Z_2(p)$ may be expressed as

$$Z_1(p) = \left(\frac{k_o{}^a}{p} + k_\infty{}^a + \sum_i \frac{k_i{}^a}{p + \sigma_i}\right) - \left(\frac{k_o{}^b}{p} + k_\infty{}^b + \sum_i \frac{k_i{}^b}{p + \sigma_i}\right)$$
$$Z_2(p) = \left(\frac{k_o{}^c}{p} + k_\infty{}^c + \sum_i \frac{k_i{}^c}{p + \sigma_i}\right) - \left(\frac{k_o{}^d}{p} + k_\infty{}^d + \sum_i \frac{k_i{}^d}{p + \sigma_i}\right) \tag{4}$$

The above expressions are simply partial-fraction expansions for $Z_1(p)$ and $Z_2(p)$ in terms of the residues at their poles and at infinity. The various k's given in the equation are all positive, but we have admitted the possibility of both positive and negative residues by the use of two parenthetical terms for both $Z_1(p)$ and $Z_2(p)$. Each of the parenthetical terms (without regard for the sign that precedes it) is realizable as a passive driving-point impedance. The forms of the various elements are shown in Fig. 4.26 (the reader should note the similarities and differences between these networks and those shown in Fig. 4.24). To affix the negative sign to the second parenthetical term of each of the equations (4) simply requires the use of an NIC. Thus, $Z_1(p)$ and $Z_2(p)$ will each consist of two networks in series, with an NIC connected in cascade with one of them. Thus, the original driving-point function can be realized with four component RC networks and two NICs. The general form of the realization is shown in Fig. 4.27. The designations $A, B, C,$ and D on the component networks refer to the superscripts a, b, c, and d, respectively, in the four parenthetical terms in (4).

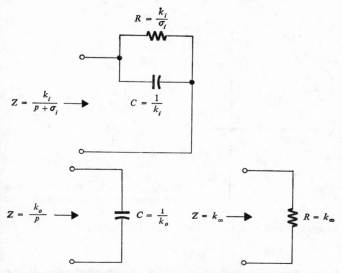

Figure 4.26   Driving-point impedances of simple RC networks.

As an example of the technique, let us consider a case in which $N(p)$ and $D(p)$ of (1) are second-order polynomials. Specifically, let

$$Y(p) = \frac{N(p)}{D(p)} = \frac{p^2 + p + 1}{p^2 + p + 2} \tag{5}$$

It is easy to show that for a polynomial $N(p)$ consisting of a pair of com-

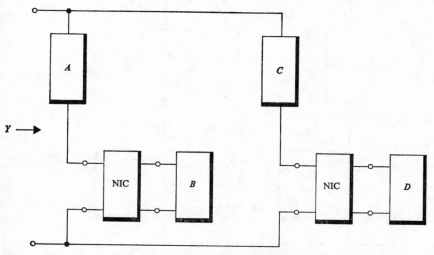

Figure 4.27   Using NICs to synthesize driving-point functions.

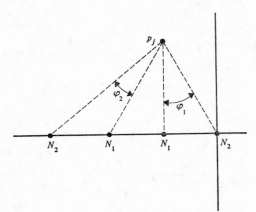

plex-conjugate zeros, the zeros of $N_1(p)$ and $N_2(p)$, where

$$N(p) = N_1(p) - N_2(p)$$

will have the relative positions shown in Fig. 4.28. Furthermore, if the
zeros of $N(p)$ are located at $p = p_j$ and $p = p_j{}^*$, as shown in the figure,
then the angles indicated as φ_1 and φ_2 in the figure are equal.[1] A reduction

[1] See L. P. Huelsman, Active RC Synthesis with Prescribed Sensitivities, *Proc. Natl.
Electronics Conf.*, vol. 16, pp. 412–426, 1960.

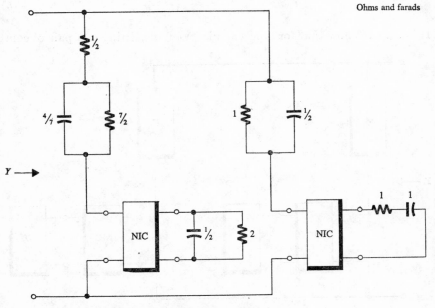

Figure 4.29 A driving-point-function realization.

in the total number of elements used in the network realization may be achieved by choosing one of the zeros of $N_2(p)$ at the origin. If we make this choice and select the zeros of $N_1(p)$ at $-\frac{1}{2}$ and -1, then the location of the other zero of $N_2(p)$ is fixed by the angle criterion indicated above. The location of this zero is easily found to be -2. Thus the $N(p)$ given in (5) may be split as follows:

$$\frac{p^2 + p + 1}{p^2 + p + 2} = \frac{2(p+1)(p+\frac{1}{2})}{p^2 + p + 2} - \frac{p(p+2)}{p^2 + p + 2} \tag{6}$$

The partial-fraction expansions of (6) for this example are

$$
\begin{aligned}
Z_1 &= \frac{p^2 + p + 2}{2(p+1)(p+\frac{1}{2})} = \frac{1}{2} + \frac{\frac{7}{4}}{p+\frac{1}{2}} - \frac{2}{p+1} \\
Z_2 &= \frac{p^2 + p + 2}{-p(p+2)} = \frac{2}{p+2} - \left(\frac{1}{p} + 1\right)
\end{aligned}
\tag{7}
$$

The final network realization is given in Fig. 4.29.

The procedure for realizing driving-point functions described in the above paragraphs is both straightforward and independent of the complexity of the polynomials which comprise the function. The mathematical techniques are simple, and the synthesis of the component networks follows easily. The realization, however, requires two NICs. Several techniques have been described in the literature for synthesizing arbitrary driving-point functions using a single NIC, and the interested reader is referred to them.[1] In general, the application of these techniques is very difficult. In addition, the network realizations that result may require more passive elements than the two-NIC realization. Thus, there may actually be a net increase in network complexity.

Two practical problems which occur in the actual use of NICs and RC elements in realizing network functions of any type are worth noting. These are (1) sensitivity considerations and (2) accuracy of elements. It is easy to see that in practically all procedures of this type a given function is realized as the difference between two other functions. The negative-component function is then, in general, realized as a positive function, the negative sign being provided by an NIC. As the conversion ratio or "gain" of the NIC changes even by a small amount, the resulting function may change by much more, i.e., the resulting function is *sensitive* to the NIC gain. It is possible to select the component functions so that the sensitivity of the result to the changes in NIC gain is minimized,[2] but even

---

[1] See, for example, B. K. Kinariwala, Synthesis of Active RC Networks, *Bell System Tech. J.*, vol. 38, pp. 1269–1316, September, 1959; J. M. Sipress, Synthesis of Active RC Networks, *IRE Trans. on Circuit Theory*, vol. CT-8, pp. 260–269, September, 1961.

[2] Horowitz, *op. cit.*

with this minimization, sensitivity remains a problem. The requirements
for accuracy in the values of the passive elements also result from the fact
that the fundamental mechanism in RC-NIC realizations is one of subtraction. The components in actual networks are frequently adjusted to
four-figure accuracy, and the circuit is quite intolerant of changes in their
values. Despite these objections, however, considerable interest is being
shown in active RC synthesis techniques.

4.7 *The gyrator*

In preceding sections we have seen how the matrix equations (6a) and
(6b) of Sec. 4.1 could be considered as the representations of ideal transformers when suitable restrictions were made on the coefficients a and b.
We also found that the transmission parameters defined by (6c) and (6d)
of Sec. 4.1 gave us the two types of negative-immittance converters. We
shall now explore the representations of (7) of Sec. 4.1 to see what devices
have the behavior defined by these equations.

First consider (7a) of Sec. 4.1. This matrix equation represents the
equations

$$V_1 = a(-I_2)$$
$$I_1 = bV_2 \tag{1}$$

If we divide equations (1), we obtain

$$\frac{V_1}{I_1} = \frac{a}{b}\frac{-I_2}{V_2} \tag{2}$$

Thus we see that the input impedance at port 1 of the two-port network
represented by (1) is a/b times the reciprocal of the impedance connected
to port 2. Similarly, we may write

$$\frac{V_2}{I_2} = \frac{a}{b}\frac{-I_1}{V_1} \tag{3}$$

This says that the input impedance at port 2 of the network is a/b times
the reciprocal of the impedance connected to port 1. The action of this
device is to "invert" the immittance connected to it. If $a = 1/b$, the
device is called a *gyrator*.[1]

---

[1] The gyrator as an ideal network element was first described in B. D. H. Tellegen, The
Gyrator, a New Electric Network Element, *Phillips Research Repts.*, vol. 3, pp. 81–101,
April, 1948. The name was chosen because of the correspondence between the form of the
equations describing a pair of LC circuits coupled by this device and the form of the equations describing frictionless mechanical systems with gyroscopic (or gyrostatic) coupling.
This effect also occurs in electromechanical transducers. Ferrites are well known for their
properties of gyration at microwave frequencies.

If we define an arbitrary two-port network by means of its y parameters and terminate it at port 2 in an admittance Y_L as shown in Fig. 4.30, we find that the input impedance at port 1 is given by the relation

$$Y_{IN} = \frac{I_1}{V_1} = y_{11} - \frac{y_{12}y_{21}}{y_{22} + Y_L} \tag{4}$$

Thus, the necessary and sufficient conditions that

$$Y_{IN} = G^2 Z_L \tag{5}$$

where $Z_L = 1/Y_L$, or, in other words, that the two-port device act as a gyrator, are

$$\begin{aligned} y_{11} = y_{22} = 0 \\ y_{12}y_{21} = -G^2 \end{aligned} \tag{6}$$

The dimensions of the quantities in (5) make it convenient to define a gyration conductance such that $y_{12} = G$ and $y_{21} = -G$. Thus, the defining equations for a gyrator become

$$\begin{aligned} I_1 = GV_2 \\ I_2 = -GV_1 \end{aligned} \tag{7}$$

If G is real, i.e., not a function of the complex frequency variable, we may write a set of equations in the time domain corresponding to (7). These are

$$\begin{aligned} i_1(t) = Gv_2(t) \\ i_2(t) = -Gv_1(t) \end{aligned}$$

From these equations we see that $v_1 i_1 + v_2 i_2 = 0$, i.e., that the gyrator is a lossless device. As such, it is usually considered as a passive device, although its physical realization, in general, requires external power supplies.

The equations (7) are the same as (1) if we define $b = 1/a = G$. The circuit symbol for a gyrator, together with the indicated direction of gyration, is shown in Fig. 4.31. In Appendix B it is shown that it is possible for a gyrator to have a gyration admittance which is a function of the complex frequency variable. Normally, however, G is considered as a constant.

Let us now consider the gyrator as a three-terminal device, as shown in Fig. 4.32. When terminal 3 is grounded, this device has the same y parame-

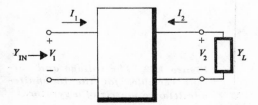

Figure 4.30   A two-port network terminated at port 2.

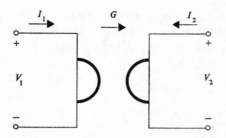

Figure 4.31   A gyrator.

ters as the device shown in Fig. 4.31. The indefinite-admittance matrix can be found by the method of Sec. 3.5. For the voltages and currents defined in Fig. 4.32, the indefinite-admittance matrix is

$$\begin{bmatrix} I_1 \\ I_2 \\ I_3 \end{bmatrix} = \begin{bmatrix} 0 & G & -G \\ -G & 0 & G \\ G & -G & 0 \end{bmatrix} \begin{bmatrix} V_1 \\ V_2 \\ V_3 \end{bmatrix} \tag{8}$$

From this we see that the y-parameter matrix of the resulting two-port network when terminal 1 is grounded is

$$\begin{bmatrix} I_2 \\ I_3 \end{bmatrix} = \begin{bmatrix} 0 & G \\ -G & 0 \end{bmatrix} \begin{bmatrix} V_2 \\ V_3 \end{bmatrix} \tag{9}$$

Similarly, when terminal 2 is grounded, the y-parameter matrix is

$$\begin{bmatrix} I_1 \\ I_3 \end{bmatrix} = \begin{bmatrix} 0 & -G \\ G & 0 \end{bmatrix} \begin{bmatrix} V_1 \\ V_3 \end{bmatrix} \tag{10}$$

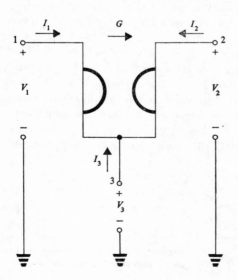

Figure 4.32   The voltage and current variables for the indefinite-admittance matrix of a gyrator.

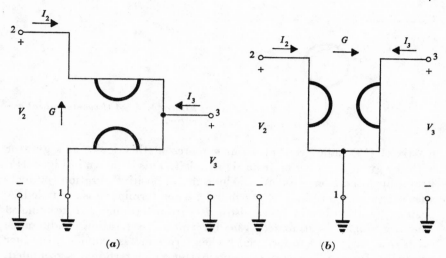

Figure 4.33   Two gyrator connections which have the same y-parameter matrix.

In Fig. 4.33*a* the original three-terminal gyrator is shown with terminal 1 grounded. An examination of the *y*-parameter matrix of (9) for this situation shows that this new device also has the properties of a gyrator. Therefore we may represent it as shown in Fig. 4.33*b*, i.e., as a gyrator in the usual position. Similarly, when terminal 2 is grounded, as shown in Fig. 4.34*a* (note the downward direction of the arrow), the *y*-parameter

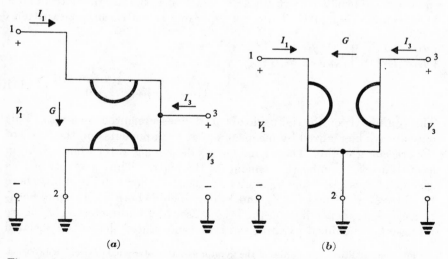

Figure 4.34   Two gyrator connections which have the same y-parameter matrix.

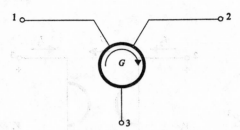

Figure 4.35   A three-terminal gyrator.

matrix of (10) indicates that we may represent this device as a gyrator with the gyration direction from right to left. This is shown in Fig. 4.34b. From this discussion, we may conclude that a positive gyration conductance exists from terminal 1 to terminal 2 when terminal 3 is grounded. A positive gyration conductance also exists from terminal 2 to terminal 3 when terminal 1 is grounded. Finally, a positive gyration conductance exists from terminal 3 to terminal 1 when terminal 2 is grounded. In other words the device acts as a gyrator no matter which terminal is grounded. This is indicated by the symbol in Fig. 4.35, frequently used to represent the gyrator, which indicates the correct polarity or direction for the gyration conductance between all terminals.[1]

The material of the previous section, with its discussion of NICs, has opened the possibility of using negative immittances in a network realization. This additional flexibility makes possible a general procedure for developing circuit configurations for gyrators. Consider a two-port network as defined by its y parameters. In Sec. 2.9 it was shown that any square matrix may be written as the sum of a symmetric matrix and a skew-symmetric matrix. Thus, our y-parameter matrix may be written

$$\begin{bmatrix} y_{11} & y_{12} \\ y_{21} & y_{22} \end{bmatrix} = \begin{bmatrix} y_{11} & \frac{1}{2}(y_{12} + y_{21}) \\ \frac{1}{2}(y_{12} + y_{21}) & y_{22} \end{bmatrix}$$
$$+ \begin{bmatrix} 0 & \frac{1}{2}(y_{12} - y_{21}) \\ -\frac{1}{2}(y_{12} - y_{21}) & 0 \end{bmatrix} \quad (11)$$

The first matrix on the right side of (11) defines a reciprocal network. This may always be realized by means of passive components and the NICs of the preceding section. The second matrix defines a gyrator whose gyration admittance is given by the elements of the matrix. Thus, the network, as specified by its y parameters, may be realized as shown in Fig. 4.36, where the three admittances Y_a, Y_b, and Y_c may include both positive and negative elements, depending on the original set of y parameters. This figure represents a nonideal gyrator, since it has unwanted elements associated

[1] For some additional properties of the gyrator as a three-terminal device, see J. Shekel, The Gyrator as a Three Terminal Element, *Proc. IRE*, vol. 41, pp. 1014–1016, August, 1953.

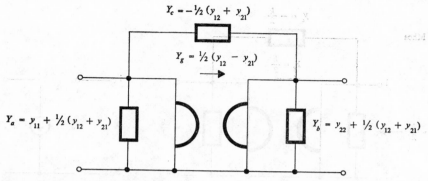

Figure 4.36 *A nonideal gyrator.*

with it. If we desire to synthesize an ideal gyrator with gyration admittance Y_g, then these elements may be eliminated by shunting them with other elements of the opposite sign, as indicated in Fig. 4.37.

For example, consider an ideal voltage-controlled current generator. The y-parameter matrix for such a device, and the separation of this matrix into the sum of a symmetric matrix and a skew-symmetric matrix, is

$$\begin{bmatrix} 0 & 0 \\ k & 0 \end{bmatrix} = \begin{bmatrix} 0 & \dfrac{k}{2} \\ \dfrac{k}{2} & 0 \end{bmatrix} + \begin{bmatrix} 0 & -\dfrac{k}{2} \\ \dfrac{k}{2} & 0 \end{bmatrix} \tag{12}$$

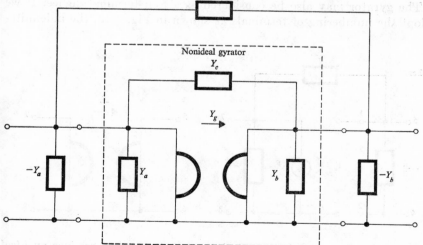

Figure 4.37 *Compensating the nonideal gyrator.*

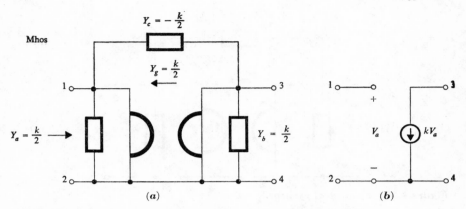

Figure 4.38   Two networks which have the same y-parameter matrix.

The nonideal gyrator equivalent to this controlled source is shown in Fig. 4.38. Both circuits shown in this figure have the y-parameter matrix given in (12). Therefore they are equivalent networks. The compensation necessary to produce an ideal gyrator is easily seen from this figure. The resulting ideal gyrator is shown in Fig. 4.39, together with the values of admittance required for compensation. Both circuits in this figure have the same y-parameter matrix; i.e., they will perform as ideal gyrators. The same terminal numbering has been preserved between the two figures to aid in the identification of the results. The important conclusion of this development is that an ideal gyrator may always be realized if we have available a nonreciprocal device and positive and negative immittances.

The gyrator may also be considered as a four-terminal device. If we adopt the numbering of terminals as shown in Fig. 4.40, the indefinite-

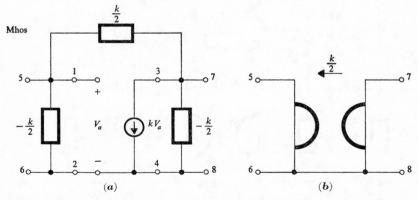

Figure 4.39   Compensating an ideal controlled source to produce an ideal gyrator.

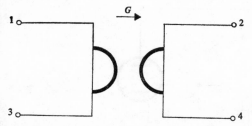

Figure 4.40   A four-terminal
gyrator.

admittance matrix is

$$
\begin{bmatrix}
0 & G & 0 & -G \\
-G & 0 & G & 0 \\
0 & -G & 0 & G \\
G & 0 & -G & 0
\end{bmatrix}
\tag{13}
$$

In the example of Fig. 3.46, the indefinite-admittance matrix for a pair of pentodes connected together at their cathodes was derived. The indefinite-admittance matrices for two cases of this connection are given in Fig. 4.41.

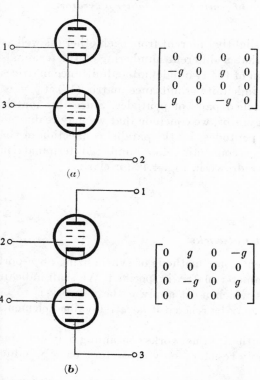

$$
\begin{bmatrix}
0 & 0 & 0 & 0 \\
-g & 0 & g & 0 \\
0 & 0 & 0 & 0 \\
g & 0 & -g & 0
\end{bmatrix}
$$

(a)

$$
\begin{bmatrix}
0 & g & 0 & -g \\
0 & 0 & 0 & 0 \\
0 & -g & 0 & g \\
0 & 0 & 0 & 0
\end{bmatrix}
$$

(b)

Figure 4.41   Two pentode connections and their indefinite-admittance matrices.

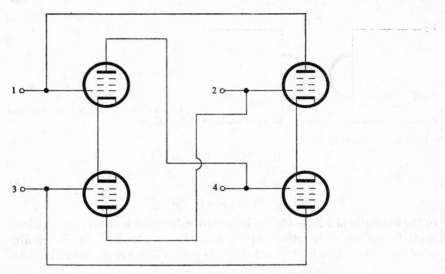

Figure 4.42   An interconnection of pentodes to produce a gyrator.

The circuits of this figure are slightly different from each other (as well as different from Fig. 3.46) in that a different numbering of the terminals has been used. The summation of the two indefinite-admittance matrices shown in Fig. 4.41 yields the indefinite-admittance matrix (13) if $g = G$. This, of course, requires matched pairs of pentodes. Since this matrix represents the four-terminal gyrator, we conclude that we may realize an ideal gyrator (if we use ideal pentodes) by the parallel connection of the two pentode pairs formed by connecting like-numbered terminals in Fig. 4.41.[1] The connection is redrawn in Fig. 4.42 for clarity.

4.8 *Synthesis of n-port networks*

In this section we shall present some methods of synthesizing an n-port network for which the y-parameter matrix is specified. We shall indicate how some of the restrictions which must apply if the network is to be realized by passive elements may be relaxed if negative-valued elements and gyrators are allowed.

First let us consider the synthesis of networks containing only one kind of element, i.e., containing only resistors, only capacitors, or only induc-

[1] G. E. Sharpe, The Pentode Gyrator, *IRE Trans. on Circuit Theory*, vol. CT-4, no. 4, pp. 322–323, December, 1957.

tors. For this case, the y-parameter matrix will have one of the three following forms:

$$Y = \begin{bmatrix} a_{11} & \cdots & a_{1n} \\ \cdot & \cdots & \cdot \\ a_{n1} & \cdots & a_{nn} \end{bmatrix} \tag{1a}$$

$$Y = p \begin{bmatrix} a_{11} & \cdots & a_{1n} \\ \cdot & \cdots & \cdot \\ a_{n1} & \cdots & a_{nn} \end{bmatrix} \tag{1b}$$

$$Y = \frac{1}{p} \begin{bmatrix} a_{11} & \cdots & a_{1n} \\ \cdot & \cdots & \cdot \\ a_{n1} & \cdots & a_{nn} \end{bmatrix} \tag{1c}$$

where the a_{ij} are real. Let us consider the y-parameter matrix of $(1a)$. The realization of this will require only resistive elements. If we restrict ourselves to the passive case and specify that all our ports have one common terminal [the network in this case can be considered as an $(n + 1)$-terminal network], then all the diagonal elements will be positive, and all the off-diagonal elements will be negative (this assumes that we have defined all the port voltages as positive with respect to the common terminal). Since the total admittance at any port must be equal to or greater than the sum of the mutual admittances, we see that

$$a_{ii} \geq \sum_k |a_{ik}| \qquad k = 1, \ldots, i - 1, i + 1, \ldots, n \tag{2}$$

This is the condition which defines a dominant matrix (see Sec. 2.8). Therefore we see that for a symmetric y-parameter matrix with real positive diagonal elements and real negative off-diagonal elements to be realized by an $(n + 1)$-terminal network consisting of positive-valued resistors, it is necessary and sufficient that the y-parameter matrix be dominant. An example of such a y-parameter matrix and the resulting network realization is shown in Fig. 4.43. The same conditions apply to the matrices $(1b)$ and $(1c)$, with the obvious difference that the elements will be capacitors or inductors, rather than resistors.

The restriction that the off-diagonal elements of the y-parameter matrix be negative may be removed if we permit the n-port network to have $2n$ terminals, i.e., if we do not require that all the ports have a common terminal. In this case, the off-diagonal elements may be either positive or negative, while the diagonal elements must, of course, be positive. Then dominance is a sufficient, but not necessary, condition for realization.[1] To see the sufficiency, consider the network shown in Fig. 4.44.

[1] For a discussion of this and other network situations see P. Slepian and L. Weinberg, *Synthesis Applications of Paramount and Dominant Matrices, Proc. Natl. Electronics Conf.*, vol. 14, pp. 611–630, 1958.

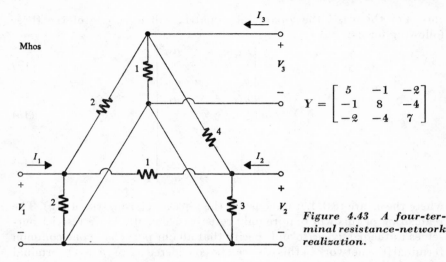

$$Y = \begin{bmatrix} 5 & -1 & -2 \\ -1 & 8 & -4 \\ -2 & -4 & 7 \end{bmatrix}$$

Figure 4.43 A four-ter-
minal resistance-network
realization.

This shows the resistors that will appear between the ith and jth ports of
a given network when it is realized from a dominant y-parameter matrix.
The values of the components are given by the relationships

$$G_i = a_{ii} - \sum_k |a_{ik}| \qquad k \neq i$$

$$G_j = a_{jj} - \sum_k |a_{jk}| \qquad k \neq j \tag{3}$$

$$G_1 = |a_{ij}| - a_{ij}$$
$$G_2 = |a_{ij}| + a_{ij}$$

where the a_{ij} are the elements of the y-parameter matrix. G_1 and G_2 will
have different values among the different ports. G_i and G_j are specified as
the total required shunt admittance at the ith and jth ports. If the off-
diagonal elements a_{ij} are negative, the cross arms in Fig. 4.44 will be absent. If the off-diagonal elements a_{ij} are positive, the horizontal series arms
will be absent. All the elements are specified on an admittance basis. A
y-parameter matrix with all positive elements and its realization is shown

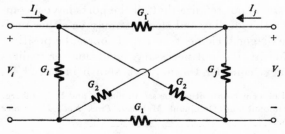

Figure 4.44 The inter-
port resistance network.

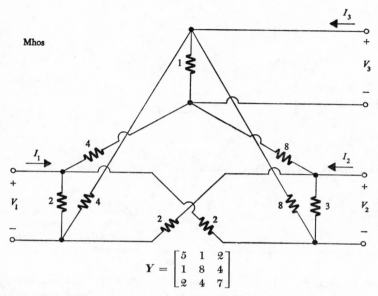

$$Y = \begin{bmatrix} 5 & 1 & 2 \\ 1 & 8 & 4 \\ 2 & 4 & 7 \end{bmatrix}$$

Figure 4.45 A three-port resistance-network realization.

in Fig. 4.45. The magnitudes of the elements in this matrix are the same as those of the matrix which was realized in Fig. 4.43. Identical realization techniques may be applied to the y-parameter matrices representing purely capacitive and purely inductive networks.

If a nondominant symmetric matrix with all real elements is to be realized as an $(n + 1)$-terminal resistive network, negative-valued resistors must be used. These can, of course, be realized by means of NICs. Similarly, since a nonsymmetric matrix with all real elements can be written as the sum of a symmetric matrix and a skew-symmetric matrix, both of which have real elements, a nonsymmetric matrix may also be realized as an $(n + 1)$-terminal network. It will consist of the parallel connection of the realization of the symmetric matrix and the realization of the skew-symmetric matrix. The skew-symmetric matrix may be realized by means of gyrators, and the symmetric matrix by positive- or negative-valued elements, depending on its form. Thus, by means of the concepts of negative-valued components and gyrators, we can remove many of the restrictions from passive synthesis.

As an example, consider the following y-parameter matrix and its symmetric and skew-symmetric components:

$$\begin{bmatrix} 4 & -2 & 0 \\ -2 & 5 & -2 \\ -2 & -2 & 1 \end{bmatrix} = \begin{bmatrix} 0 & 0 & 1 \\ 0 & 0 & 0 \\ -1 & 0 & 0 \end{bmatrix} + \begin{bmatrix} 4 & -2 & -1 \\ -2 & 5 & -2 \\ -1 & -2 & 1 \end{bmatrix}$$

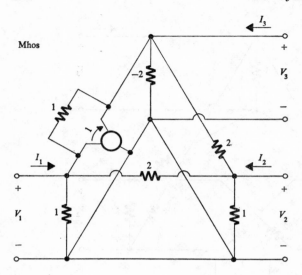

Mhos

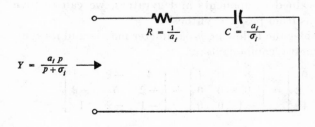

Figure 4.46 A realization for a nondominant nonsymmetric y-parameter matrix.

We see that a gyrator will be required between ports 1 and 3, and a negative resistance (due to the nondominance of the third row and column of the symmetric matrix) will be required at port 3. The $(n + 1)$-terminal realization is shown in Fig. 4.46.

A similar treatment can be made for networks which are realizable as two-type-element networks: RC, RL, or LC networks. In these cases, each element of the y-parameter matrix can be expressed as a partial-fraction expansion. The matrix can then be expressed as a sum of residue matrices. For example, for an RC realization, we may write

$$
\mathbf{Y} = \begin{bmatrix} y_{11} & \cdots & y_{1n} \\ \cdots\cdots\cdots\cdots \\ y_{n1} & \cdots & y_{nn} \end{bmatrix} = \sum_k \frac{p}{p + \sigma_k} \begin{bmatrix} a_{11}^{(k)} & \cdots & a_{1n}^{(k)} \\ \cdots\cdots\cdots\cdots \\ a_{n1}^{(k)} & \cdots & a_{nn}^{(k)} \end{bmatrix}
$$
$$
+ \begin{bmatrix} a_{11}^{(0)} & \cdots & a_{1n}^{(0)} \\ \cdots\cdots\cdots\cdots \\ a_{n1}^{(0)} & \cdots & a_{nn}^{(0)} \end{bmatrix} + p \begin{bmatrix} a_{11}^{(\infty)} & \cdots & a_{1n}^{(\infty)} \\ \cdots\cdots\cdots\cdots \\ a_{n1}^{(\infty)} & \cdots & a_{nn}^{(\infty)} \end{bmatrix} \quad (4)
$$

The one-type-element treatment described in the above paragraphs may

$Y = \frac{a_i p}{p + \sigma_i} \longrightarrow$ $R = \frac{1}{a_i}$ $C = \frac{a_i}{\sigma_i}$

Figure 4.47 The driving-point admittance of an RC network.

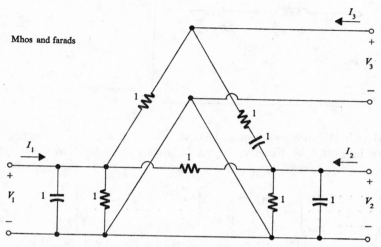

Figure. 4.48 *An RC-network realization.*

be applied to the last two matrices in (4). The elements of the residue matrices in the summation may be realized by the configuration shown in Fig. 4.47. The same criterion may be applied to the residue matrices as was applied to the matrices of the one-type-element networks to determine if these are realizable by passive components. As an example, consider the following y-parameter matrix and its residue matrices:

$$\begin{bmatrix} 3+p & -1 & -1 \\ -1 & \dfrac{p^2+4p+2}{p+1} & \dfrac{-p}{p+1} \\ -1 & \dfrac{-p}{p+1} & \dfrac{2p+1}{p+1} \end{bmatrix} = \dfrac{p}{p+1}\begin{bmatrix} 0 & 0 & 0 \\ 0 & 1 & -1 \\ 0 & -1 & 1 \end{bmatrix}$$

$$+ p\begin{bmatrix} 1 & 0 & 0 \\ 0 & 1 & 0 \\ 0 & 0 & 0 \end{bmatrix} + \begin{bmatrix} 3 & -1 & -1 \\ -1 & 2 & 0 \\ -1 & 0 & 1 \end{bmatrix}$$

The realization is shown in Fig. 4.48. Similarly, for an RL realization we may write

$$Y = \begin{bmatrix} y_{11} & \cdots & y_{1n} \\ \cdots\cdots\cdots\cdots \\ y_{n1} & \cdots & y_{nn} \end{bmatrix} = \sum_k \dfrac{1}{p+\sigma_k}\begin{bmatrix} a_{11}^{(k)} & \cdots & a_{1n}^{(k)} \\ \cdots\cdots\cdots\cdots\cdots \\ a_{n1}^{(k)} & \cdots & a_{nn}^{(k)} \end{bmatrix}$$

$$+ \begin{bmatrix} a_{11}^{(\infty)} & \cdots & a_{1n}^{(\infty)} \\ \cdots\cdots\cdots\cdots\cdots \\ a_{n1}^{(\infty)} & \cdots & a_{nn}^{(\infty)} \end{bmatrix} + \dfrac{1}{p}\begin{bmatrix} a_{11}^{(0)} & \cdots & a_{1n}^{(0)} \\ \cdots\cdots\cdots\cdots\cdots \\ a_{n1}^{(0)} & \cdots & a_{nn}^{(0)} \end{bmatrix} \quad (5)$$

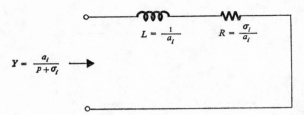

Figure 4.49 The driv-
ing-point admittance of
an RL network.

The matrices in the summation may be realized by the network configuration shown in Fig. 4.49. Finally, for an *LC* network realization we may
write

$$
\mathbf{Y} = \begin{bmatrix} y_{11} & \cdots & y_{1n} \\ \cdots & \cdots & \cdots \\ y_{n1} & \cdots & y_{nn} \end{bmatrix} = \sum_k \frac{p}{p^2 + \omega_k{}^2} \begin{bmatrix} a_{11}{}^{(k)} & \cdots & a_{1n}{}^{(k)} \\ \cdots & \cdots & \cdots \\ a_{n1}{}^{(k)} & \cdots & a_{nn}{}^{(k)} \end{bmatrix}
$$
$$
+ p \begin{bmatrix} a_{11}{}^{(\infty)} & \cdots & a_{1n}{}^{(\infty)} \\ \cdots & \cdots & \cdots \\ a_{n1}{}^{(\infty)} & \cdots & a_{nn}{}^{(\infty)} \end{bmatrix} + \frac{1}{p} \begin{bmatrix} a_{11}{}^{(0)} & \cdots & a_{1n}{}^{(0)} \\ \cdots & \cdots & \cdots \\ a_{n1}{}^{(0)} & \cdots & a_{nn}{}^{(0)} \end{bmatrix} \quad (6)
$$

The matrices in the summation may be realized by the network configuration shown in Fig. 4.50. It should be noted that if the residue matrices are
nonsymmetric, we may, in theory, postulate gyrators with complex gyration admittances to provide the necessary realization. The details are
given in Appendix B.

In this section we have illustrated some of the methods and the criteria
that may be applied to the realization of one-type-element and two-type-
element networks. It has been shown that some of the conditions for
realization may be relaxed if negative-valued elements and gyrators are
permitted. It should be pointed out, however, that although in theory
these operations are permitted, the actual construction of circuits with
large numbers of devices such as gyrators and NICs is usually avoided.
Such "paper" realizations, however, have a very important purpose in
that they serve to emphasize some of the significant characteristics of a
given network, and thus aid the designer in gaining a greater over-all
perspective of his problem and its possible solutions.

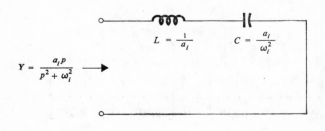

Figure 4.50 The
driving-point admit-
tance of an LC net-
work.

4.9 *Other two-port networks*

Three other sets of transmission parameters listed in (6) and (7) of Sec. 4.1 have not been discussed. The first of these is (7*b*) of Sec. 4.1. The equations to be considered are

$$I_2 = \frac{1}{a} V_1 \tag{1}$$
$$I_1 = -bV_2$$

If we define $b = 1/a = G$ and compare the result with (7) of Sec. 4.7, we see that this case is simply the gyrator of Fig. 4.31 with a negative gyration conductance, i.e., with a gyration conductance in the direction opposite that indicated.

The second case still undiscussed is that of (7*c*) of Sec. 4.1. The transmission matrix of this equation may be expressed as a product:

$$\begin{bmatrix} 0 & -a \\ b & 0 \end{bmatrix} = \begin{bmatrix} 0 & a \\ b & 0 \end{bmatrix} \begin{bmatrix} 1 & 0 \\ 0 & -1 \end{bmatrix}$$

If we define $b = 1/a = G$, we may consider this case as the cascade connection of a gyrator of gyration conductance G and an INIC of unity gain. There are, of course, other possible representations. This case, however, seems to imply no new basic properties and will not be discussed further.

The third and final case (7*d*) of Sec. 4.1 may be viewed as a similar cascade. Since

$$\begin{bmatrix} 0 & a \\ -b & 0 \end{bmatrix} = \begin{bmatrix} 0 & a \\ b & 0 \end{bmatrix} \begin{bmatrix} -1 & 0 \\ 0 & 1 \end{bmatrix}$$

this may be considered as the cascade connection of a gyrator and a VNIC of unity gain. Again, other representations are possible, but the case is of little fundamental interest.

A summary of the representations of various two-port devices is given in Table 4.1. A careful study of the table is recommended at this time.

PROBLEMS

4.1 Find all possible sets of network parameters for the following two-port networks: (*a*) an ideal transformer with turns ratio 1 :*n*; (*b*) an INIC; (*c*) a VNIC; (*d*) a gyrator.

4.2 Express the condition that a two-port device act as an NIC in terms of the elements of the following matrices: (*a*) the *h*-parameter matrix; (*b*) the $ABCD$-parameter matrix; (c) the $\mathcal{ABCD}$-parameter matrix. Distinguish between an INIC and a VNIC in each case.

4.3 Is it possible to compensate an NIC which is nonideal in the sense that both g_{11} and g_{22} are not equal to zero? Explain.

4.4 Find networks which are equivalent to the following cascade connections of two-port networks: (a) two INICs; (b) two VNICs; (c) two gyrators; (d) a VNIC and an INIC.

4.5 Find the z parameters of the network resulting if a given network (described by its z parameters) has the following connected to port 2: (a) an INIC; (b) a VNIC; (c) a gyrator.

4.6 Find the y parameters of the network resulting if a given network (described by its y parameters) has the following connected to port 2: (a) an INIC; (b) a VNIC; (c) a gyrator.

4.7 Find the g parameters for the circuit shown in Fig. 4.20.

4.8 Find the g parameters for the circuit shown in Fig. 4.22.

4.9 Find the compensating circuit necessary to convert the device shown in Fig. P4.9 to an ideal gyrator.

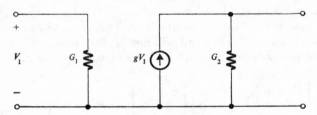

Figure P4.9

4.10 Derive the indefinite-admittance matrix (13) of Sec. 4.7 for the circuit shown in Fig. 4.40.

4.11 An arbitrary reciprocal network with four ports is made into a two-port network by connecting an NIC between ports 3 and 4. Show that the driving-point admittances y_{11} and y_{22} of the resulting two-port network are independent of the type of NIC that is used.

4.12 An arbitrary reciprocal four-port network is made into a two-port network by connecting an NIC between ports 3 and 4. Show that the transfer admittances of the resulting two-port network will be interchanged if the type of NIC is changed.

4.13 Develop a method of voltage transfer-function realization similar to that of Sec. 4.5, but based on z parameters rather than y parameters.

4.14 Find a realization for a 1-henry inductor using only positive and/or negative resistors and capacitors.

4.15 Show that the effect of connecting an admittance Y in series with one terminal of a three-terminal gyrator of gyration conductance G is the same as connecting an admittance G^2/Y between the other two terminals of the gyrator.

4.16 Find an expression for the input impedance of the circuit shown in Fig. P4.16. Under what conditions will it function as an NIC? Is it a VNIC or an INIC?

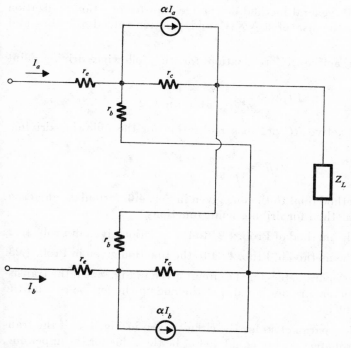

Figure P4.16

4.17 If a passive reciprocal three-port network has an NIC connected between two of its ports, find the input immittance at the third port for the case of (*a*) an INIC; (*b*) a VNIC.

4.18 Find a network realization for the following bandpass voltage transfer function. Use only positive-valued resistors and capacitors and an INIC.

$$\frac{V_2}{V_1} = \frac{p}{p^2 + 0.2p + 1}$$

4.19 Find a network realization for the low-pass voltage transfer function given below. Use only positive-valued resistors and capacitors and an INIC.

$$\frac{V_2}{V_1} = \frac{5}{p^2 + 2p + 5}$$

4.20 Find a network realization for the voltage transfer function given below. Use only positive-valued resistors and capacitors and an INIC.

$$\frac{V_2}{V_1} = \frac{p^2 + 64}{p^3 + 2p^2 + 37p}$$

4.21 Develop a general method of voltage transfer-function realization which requires the use of a VNIC and positive-valued resistors and capacitors.

4.22 Find an active RC realization for the following driving-point function:

$$Y(p) = \frac{p^2 + 1}{p^3 + 4p^2 + 5p + 2}$$

4.23 Find an active RC network realization for the following driving-point function:

$$Z(p) = \frac{p^2 - 1}{p(p^2 + p + 2)}$$

4.24 By a method dual to the one given in Sec. 4.6, formulate an active RC synthesis method for driving-point functions.

4.25 Apply the method of Prob. 4.24 to the function given in Prob. 4.22.

4.26 Apply the method of Prob. 4.24 to the function given in Prob. 4.23.

4.27 Find the g parameters for the circuit given in Fig. 4.20 if the transistor gain parameters are not equal. Let the one on the left be α_a, and the one on the right be α_b.

4.28 Find the g parameters for the circuit given in Fig. 4.22 if the transistor gain parameters are not equal. Let α_a be the value for the upper one, and α_b be the value for the lower one.

4.29 Show that a voltage transfer function may be realized (within a constant multiplier) by realizing an appropriate driving-point immittance function. Thus we may use the techniques of Sec. 4.6 to realize voltage transfer functions.

4.30 With port 2 open-circuited, the input impedance and the voltage transfer function of a given two-port network are specified as

$$Z_{\text{IN}} = \frac{p + 1}{p^2 + 4} \qquad \frac{V_2}{V_1} = \frac{2p}{p^2 + 1}$$

If it is also desired to have short-circuit transfer admittances with the values

$$y_{12} = 0 \qquad y_{21} = \frac{-p}{p+1}$$

find a realization for the network using only positive- and negative-valued resistors and capacitors and gyrators.

4.31 Find a network realization for the following y-parameter matrix. The realization should be in the form of a four-terminal network using positive- and negative-valued R and C elements.

$$\begin{bmatrix} \dfrac{p^2+1}{p+1} & \dfrac{p+4}{p+1} & \dfrac{2}{p+1} \\[2ex] \dfrac{-p+2}{p+1} & \dfrac{3p}{p+1} & 0 \\[2ex] \dfrac{2}{p+1} & 0 & \dfrac{p^2}{p+1} \end{bmatrix}$$

Chapter 5 *Linear vector spaces*

5.1 *Introduction*

The network studies made in previous chapters in terms of matrix notation can be given a powerful additional significance through the use of the concepts of linear vector spaces. In plane geometry, we think of a vector as a line of a certain magnitude having a specified orientation or direction. This viewpoint is helpful in studies of functions of two real variables, such as complex-variable theory, where, in addition to defining a number by the magnitude of its real and imaginary portions, we also find it convenient to visualize it as a vector starting from the origin of a two-dimensional geometrical structure: a plane. Similarly, a point located in a three-dimensional coordinate system can be represented by a vector from the origin of that system to the point in question. Thus, we can work with a set of three real variables whose values specify a unique point in a three-dimensional space. In the actual physical world that we deal with, there are many quite general situations which cannot conveniently be subjected to the limitation that they be expressed only by a maximum of three real variables (or three complex variables, for that matter). For example, we might consider a resistance network excited by fixed d-c potentials. Suppose that there are three nodes in the network, as shown in Fig. 5.1. If we define one

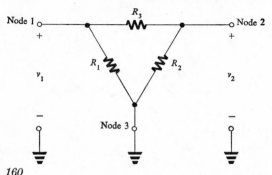

Figure 5.1 A network with two nodal voltages.

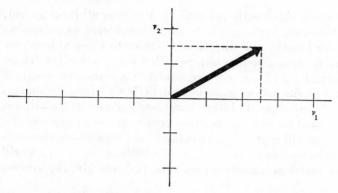

Figure 5.2   The two-dimensional representation of two voltages.

of these as the reference node, then there are two nodal voltages which enter into the equations for the network. Suppose that we set up a two-dimensional cartesian-coordinate system as shown in Fig. 5.2. If we label the rectangular axes with units of v_1 and v_2, then a single vector on the plane serves to completely specify the state of the network in terms of its nodal voltages at a given instant of time. If there were $n + 1$ nodes in this network, then the specification of n nodal voltages would serve to completely define the condition of the network. If we extend the geometrical concept, we can then speak of a "vector" in an "n-dimensional space" as defining the state of the system with respect to its nodal voltages at a given instant of time. Actually, all we are saying is that if the n nodal voltages are specified, then everything is known about some quantity which we might call the over-all voltage vector of the network. We can also take the opposite viewpoint and say that a single vector in an n-dimensional space specifies the n nodal voltages of the network. The most difficult aspect of this concept is ridding oneself of the geometrical limitations so carefully acquired through many years. We live in a three-dimensional world, and n dimensions are difficult to visualize. Nevertheless, we shall find that all the usual geometrical ideas of a two- or three-dimensional coordinate system, e.g., length and scalar products, can be extended to n dimensions. Thus, we find that we can adopt the concept of a "vector in an n-dimensional space." The usefulness of this concept will become readily apparent in the material which follows.

5.2   *Linear vector spaces*

In mathematical language we may use the word *space* to define a collection or assembly of objects. These may be numbers, functions, etc. In the case of a *linear vector space* (frequently referred to simply as a vector space), the objects of interest are vectors, which can be considered as possessing both magnitude (or length) and direction. To refer to these objects, we shall use lightface lowercase roman letters with a *single* subscript. Thus, quantities such as a_i, b_i, . . . , x_i will be considered vectors. Frequently it will be necessary to write sets of equations involving vectors. To do this we shall use matrix notation. Boldface lowercase roman letters without subscripts will be used for column matrices whose elements are vectors. Thus, a, b, . . . , x will represent the column matrices whose elements are, respectively, the vectors a_i, b_i, . . . , x_i. Similarly, a^t, b^t, . . . , x^t will represent the row matrices whose elements are, respectively, the vectors a_i, b_i, . . . , x_i.

In addition to the vectors, we shall also discuss *scalars*. These may be thought of as real or complex numbers which obey the usual algebraic rules for real and complex numbers. We shall find it convenient to represent them in two ways. One of the representations will be by lowercase lightface Greek letters with a single subscript. Thus, α_i, β_i, . . . , ζ_i will represent scalars. Boldface lowercase Greek letters without subscript such as α, β, . . . , ζ will be used for column matrices whose elements are the scalars α_i, β_i, . . . , ζ_i. The second representation for scalars will be lightface lowercase roman letters with a *double* subscript. Thus, quantities such as a_{ij}, b_{ij}, . . . , f_{ij}, etc., will be considered as scalars. These elements may be arranged in the form of column matrices or square matrices. A group of elements a_{ij} ($i = 1, 2, . . . , n$), arranged as the elements of a column matrix, will be referred to by the matrix notation A_j, i.e., by a boldface uppercase roman letter with a single subscript. A group of scalars a_{ij}, arranged as the elements of a square matrix, will be referred to by the matrix notation A, i.e., by a boldface uppercase roman letter with no subscript. Several examples of vector and scalar notation are given in Table 5.1.

We may now define a linear vector space in terms of two fundamental operations on the objects of which it is composed. These objects are, of course, the vectors of the collection. The first of these operations is the addition of two vectors; the second is the multiplication of a vector by a scalar. The description of these operations follows:

Addition of two vectors If a_1 and a_2 are two vectors belonging to the collection, then there exists a unique operation called addition which may be applied to these vectors. The object produced by this operation is also a vector belonging to the collection. If we call this resulting vector a_3, the operation may be indicated by the symbolism $a_1 + a_2 = a_3$. The properties of the operation are:

1. It is commutative; i.e.,

$$a_1 + a_2 = a_2 + a_1$$

Table 5.1   Text notation for vectors and scalars

Elements	Description of notation	Examples	Column-matrix notation	Square-matrix notation
Vectors	Lightface, lower-case roman letters with a single subscript	$a_1, \ldots, a_i$ $b_1, \ldots, b_i$ $u_1, \ldots, u_i$ $x_1, \ldots, x_i$	$a = \begin{bmatrix} a_1 \\ \cdot\cdot \\ a_n \end{bmatrix}$	
Scalars	Lightface, lower-case Greek letters with a single subscript	$\alpha_1, \ldots, \alpha_i$ $\beta_1, \ldots, \beta_i$ $\gamma_1, \ldots, \gamma_i$ $\varphi_1, \ldots, \varphi_i$	$\alpha = \begin{bmatrix} \alpha_1 \\ \cdot\cdot \\ \alpha_n \end{bmatrix}$	
	Lightface, lower-case roman letters with a double subscript	$a_{11}, \ldots, a_{ij}$ $b_{11}, \ldots, b_{ij}$ $f_{11}, \ldots, f_{ij}$ $g_{11}, \ldots, g_{ij}$	$A_j = \begin{bmatrix} a_{1j} \\ \cdot\cdot \\ a_{nj} \end{bmatrix}$	$A = \begin{bmatrix} a_{11} \cdots a_{1n} \\ \cdots\cdots\cdots \\ a_{n1} \cdots a_{nn} \end{bmatrix}$

2. It is associative; i.e.,

$$(a_1 + a_2) + a_3 = a_1 + (a_2 + a_3)$$

3. A unique vector 0 exists with the property

$$0 + a_1 = a_1 + 0 = a_1$$

Multiplication of a vector by a scalar   If a_1 is a vector belonging to the collection, and α_1 is a scalar, then there exists a unique operation called multiplication which may be applied to these objects. The result is a vector belonging to the collection. If we call this resulting vector a_2, the operation may be indicated by the symbolism $\alpha_1 a_1 = a_2$. If we also consider a second scalar α_2, then the properties of the operation are:

1. It is commutative with respect to the scalars; i.e.,

$$(\alpha_1 \alpha_2)a_1 = (\alpha_2 \alpha_1)a_1$$

2. It is associative with respect to the scalars; i.e.,

$$(\alpha_1 \alpha_2)a_1 = \alpha_1(\alpha_2 a_1)$$

3. It is distributive with respect to addition; i.e.,

$$\alpha_1(a_1 + a_2) = \alpha_1 a_1 + \alpha_1 a_2$$

4. A unique scalar 1 exists with the property $1a_1 = a_1$.

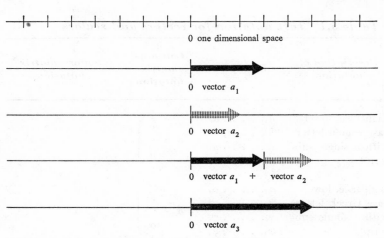

Figure 5.3   A one-dimensional linear vector space.

The above operations define a linear vector space in terms of the properties of the objects of which it is comprised. Some examples of specific linear vector spaces are given in the following paragraphs.

A one-dimensional linear vector space   Consider the set of all collinear vectors as shown in Fig. 5.3. The addition of any two vectors such as a_1 and a_2 produces a third vector a_3 which is certainly a member of the one-dimensional space. Similarly, multiplication of any vector by a scalar produces a vector which is a member of the one-dimensional space. Since the defining operations are satisfied, the result is a linear vector space. It is important to note two things concerning this space:

1. If we define a reference vector of a certain magnitude, then any vector in the space may be defined in terms of this reference vector. For example, if we let a_1 in Fig. 5.3 be the reference vector, we may express any other vector as $\alpha_1 a_1$ by giving an appropriate value to the scalar α_1.

2. If there exist any two vectors a_1 and a_2 in this one-dimensional vector space, then there exist nonzero constants α_1 and α_2 such that we may write

$$\alpha_1 a_1 + \alpha_2 a_2 = 0 \tag{1}$$

For example, if a_1 is a vector six units in length in the positive direction, and a_2 is a vector three units in length in the positive direction, we need only choose the ratio α_2/α_1 as -2 to satisfy (1).

A two-dimensional linear vector space   Consider the set of all coplanar vectors of the type shown in Fig. 5.4a. It is easy to show that the operations of addition and multiplication by a scalar are satisfied by the vectors in this space; therefore we may designate it as a two-dimensional linear vector space. The same points that we noted with respect to the first example may be repeated here:

1. Any vector in the space may be expressed as the vector sum of two arbitrary vectors, as long as these vectors are not collinear. This may be done by multiplying the arbitrary vectors by appropriate scalars. Thus, in Fig. 5.4b, the vector b_1 is represented as $3a_1 + 2a_2$, where the vectors a_1 and a_2 are not collinear. Consider for a moment what would happen if a_1 and a_2 were collinear. Then we could find constants α_1 and α_2 such that $\alpha_1 a_1 + \alpha_2 a_2 = 0$. Obviously, this is a condition to be avoided if a_1 and a_2 are to form a means by which all other vectors in the two-dimensional linear vector space can be represented. Note also that there are an infinite number of ways of choosing a_1 and a_2. The only restriction is that they are *not* collinear. Thus, in Fig. 5.4c, the same vector b_1 can be represented by $-5a_3 + 2a_4$.

2. If there exist any three vectors a_1, a_2, and a_3 in this two-dimensional

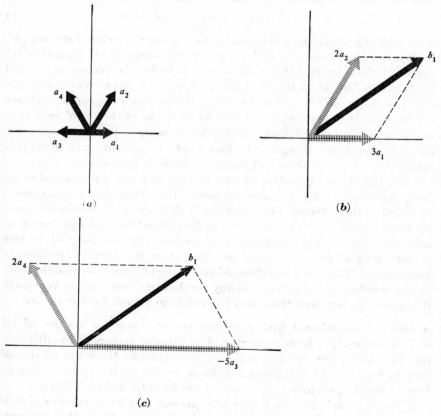

Figure 5.4 *A two-dimensional linear vector space.*

space, then there exist constants α_1, α_2, and α_3, all of which are not zero, such that

$$\alpha_1 a_1 + \alpha_2 a_2 + \alpha_3 a_3 = 0 \tag{2}$$

To see this, consider that either a_1 and a_2 are collinear, or they are not collinear. If they are, then we may choose $\alpha_3 = 0$ and choose the appropriate values of α_1 and α_2 to express the collinearity. This satisfies the conditions of (2). On the other hand, if a_1 and a_2 are not collinear, then by point 1 above, we may express a_3 as a linear combination of the two. Let this combination be $a_3 = -\beta_1 a_1 - \beta_2 b_2$. Then (2) becomes

$$(\alpha_1 - \alpha_3\beta_1)a_1 + (\alpha_2 - \alpha_3\beta_2)a_2 = 0 \tag{3}$$

and, if β_1 and β_2 are specified, we need only choose $\alpha_1 = \alpha_3\beta_1$ and $\alpha_2 = \alpha_3\beta_2$ to satisfy (2).

At this point, let us define certain ideas which have been indicated by the above examples: If a set of vectors a_i are such that a set of constants α_i may be found, not all of which are zero, such that the relation

$$\alpha_1 a_1 + \alpha_2 a_2 + \cdots + \alpha_n a_n = 0 \tag{4}$$

is satisfied, these vectors will be said to be *linearly dependent*. For example, in Fig. 5.3 the vectors a_1 and a_2 are linearly dependent. Equation (1) expresses the relation (4) for this case. Similarly, the vectors a_1, a_2, and b_1 as shown in Fig. 5.4*b* are linearly dependent, for we can write the equation $3a_1 + 2a_2 - b_1 = 0$. Note that the concept of linear dependence carries with it the factual result that at least one of the set of vectors a_i can be expressed as a linear combination of some of the remaining ones. On the other hand, if we cannot find a set of constants such that (4) is satisfied, we say that the set of vectors is *linearly independent*.

From the above examples, we can see that in a one-dimensional space every set of two vectors is linearly dependent. In a two-dimensional space, every set of three vectors must be linearly dependent. In this latter space we have shown that any vector may be defined in terms of two non-collinear vectors. The property of noncollinearity, as assigned to two vectors, may be restated as the fact that these two vectors are linearly independent. Thus, in a two-dimensional space we may conclude that any vector may be defined in terms of any two linearly independent vectors in the space. We say that these two vectors form a *basis* for the space.

A three-dimensional linear vector space   Consider the set of all spatial vectors. The basic properties of addition of vectors and multiplication by a scalar are certainly satisfied, and therefore the set of all spatial vectors forms a three-dimensional linear vector space. The conclusions formed for the previous two examples can be extended as follows:

1. Any vector in the space may be expressed as a linear combination of any three linearly independent vectors in the space. We could also word

this as follows: Any set of three linearly independent vectors in a three-dimensional space forms a basis for the space.

2. Any four vectors in this three-dimensional space are linearly dependent; i.e., we may always find scalars α_i, not all of which are zero, such that

$$\alpha_1 a_1 + \alpha_2 a_2 + \alpha_3 a_3 + \alpha_4 a_4 = 0$$

where the a_i are any four vectors in the space.

An n-dimensional linear vector space Suppose a set of n "vectors" exists such that no nonzero scalars can be found satisfying (4). These vectors then form a basis for an n-dimensional space since, by definition, they are linearly independent. In this space, it must always be true that any set of $n + 1$ vectors is linearly dependent. As long as the operations of addition of vectors and multiplication by a scalar are defined, we may apply all the techniques which are applicable to any linear vector space to this one, despite its n-dimensionality. The only "operation" that is to be avoided is the attempt to geometrically visualize the space!

Because of the fundamental importance of the above concepts, at this point let us review the above material and define the salient terms:

Linear vector space A collection of vectors such that operations of addition of vectors and multiplication by a scalar produce only members of the collection.

Linear dependence A set of vectors a_i are linearly dependent if scalars α_i exist, all of which are not zero, satisfying (4).

Linear independence A set of vectors a_i are linearly independent if no set of scalars α_i (not all zero) exists such that (4) is satisfied.

Basis A set of vectors forms a basis for a linear vector space if the vectors are linearly independent and if every vector in the space can be expressed in terms of the set.

Properties of an n-dimensional space (1) Any set of n linearly independent vectors forms a basis for the space; (2) any set of $n + 1$ vectors is linearly dependent; (3) any vector in the space may be expressed as a linear combination of the basis vectors.

5.3 *Orthonormal bases*

In a one-dimensional vector space, it is frequently convenient to take a vector of unit length as the basis vector. If we call this vector x_1, then any arbitrary vector a_1 may be expressed as $a_1 = \alpha_1 x_1$, where α_1 is, of course, a scalar. Frequently, α_1 is also referred to as a *measure number*, since it indicates the number of unit lengths of x_1 of which a_1 consists. We can also easily compute the length of the arbitrary vector a_1. It is simply the magnitude of α_1. A convenient way of writing this is to use a pair of vertical lines to indicate magnitude; thus,

$$|a_1| = |\alpha_1|$$

(for the case in which $a_1 = \alpha_1 x_1$, and x_1 is of unit length).

In two-dimensional and higher-order spaces, it is frequently important to define a *scalar product*. This is a function of two vectors which produces a scalar. Functions of this general type are frequently referred to as functionals. They will be discussed in more detail in Sec. 5.7. The scalar product of two vectors a_1 and a_2 in a two-dimensional space is defined by the relation

$$a_1 \cdot a_2 = |a_1||a_2| \cos \varphi \tag{1}$$

where $a_1 \cdot a_2$ is the usual symbolism for the scalar product, and φ is the angle between the vectors. Another definition of the scalar product is the following: Let the vector a_1 be replaced by the sum of two vectors b_1 and b_2, where b_2 is parallel to a_2, and b_1 is perpendicular to a_2. Then, if a_2 and b_2 are in the same direction, $a_1 \cdot a_2 = |b_2||a_2|$. This is illustrated in Fig. 5.5. If a_2 and b_2 are in opposite directions, then $a_1 \cdot a_2 = -|b_2||a_2|$. The scalar product is also sometimes referred to as a *dot product*. The following properties of the scalar product are easily established:

$$\begin{aligned}
a_1 \cdot a_2 &= a_2 \cdot a_1 \\
(\alpha_1 a_1) \cdot (\alpha_2 a_2) &= (\alpha_1 \alpha_2)(a_1 \cdot a_2) \\
a_1 \cdot (a_2 + a_3) &= (a_1 \cdot a_2) + (a_1 \cdot a_3) \\
a_1 \cdot a_1 &= |a_1|^2
\end{aligned} \tag{2}$$

It is desirable to formulate a general method of expressing the scalar product which is applicable to spaces of higher dimension. This is most easily done by specifying all vectors in terms of measure numbers referred

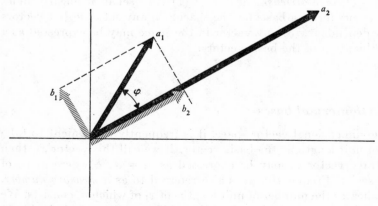

Figure 5.5   *The scalar product* $a_1 \cdot a_2$.

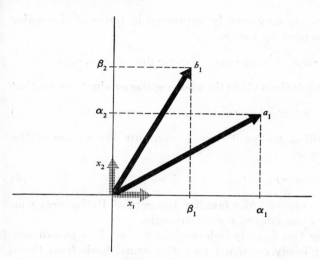

Figure 5.6   The scalar product defined on an orthonormal basis.

to an orthonormal basis. We may define two vectors x_1 and x_2 as forming
an *orthonormal basis* for a two-dimensional vector space by the following
relations:

$$x_1 \cdot x_2 = 0$$
$$x_1 \cdot x_1 = 1 \tag{3}$$
$$x_2 \cdot x_2 = 1$$

The first of the above relations expresses the property of *orthogonality*.
We may define two vectors as *orthogonal* to each other if their scalar product is zero. The other relations above indicate normalizations, i.e., the
fact that the length of the basis vectors is taken as unity. Since the two
vectors are not collinear, they are linearly independent, and thus they
form a basis for the space. We may summarize all the above by saying
that x_1 and x_2 form an orthonormal basis for the two-dimensional space.
In this space, we may use a geometrical interpretation of orthogonality to
point out that x_1 and x_2 are simply a pair of vectors of unit length at right
angles to each other. For convenience these are frequently drawn as the
horizontal and vertical axes of a two-dimensional rectangular or cartesian
coordinate system.

Let us now express a pair of arbitrary vectors a_1 and b_1 in terms of their
measure numbers as referred to an orthonormal basis. This is shown in
Fig. 5.6. We may express the measure numbers as α_i and β_i; thus, our
vectors may be written

$$a_1 = \alpha_1 x_1 + \alpha_2 x_2$$
$$b_1 = \beta_1 x_1 + \beta_2 x_2 \tag{4}$$

The scalar product $a_1 \cdot b_1$ may now be expressed in terms of the scalar products of the component vectors as

$$a_1 \cdot b_1 = \alpha_1 x_1 \cdot \beta_1 x_1 + \alpha_1 x_1 \cdot \beta_2 x_2 + \alpha_2 x_2 \cdot \beta_1 x_1 + \alpha_2 x_2 \cdot \beta_2 x_2$$

Substituting from the relations (3) in the above scalar product, we see that

$$a_1 \cdot b_1 = \alpha_1 \beta_1 + \alpha_2 \beta_2 \tag{5}$$

Note that this definition makes it easy to compute the square of the length of a single vector:

$$a_1 \cdot a_1 = |a_1|^2 = \alpha_1{}^2 + \alpha_2{}^2 \tag{6}$$

This relation simply expresses the familiar theorem of Pythagoras concerning the lengths of the sides of a right triangle.

If we are given any two linearly independent vectors in a two-dimensional space, we may easily construct an orthonormal basis from them. Suppose, for example, that two vectors a_1 and a_2 are linearly independent and not necessarily of unit length. We will take a normalized version of a_1 as the first vector of our orthonormal basis. We define

$$x_1 = \frac{a_1}{|a_1|}$$

Clearly, x_1 is of unit length. We may now construct a vector w_2 (not necessarily of unit length) orthogonal to x_1 as follows:

$$w_2 = a_2 - (a_2 \cdot x_1)x_1 \tag{7}$$

To prove that w_2 is orthogonal to x_1, take the scalar product of the two vectors:

$$x_1 \cdot w_2 = x_1 \cdot a_2 - x_1 \cdot (a_2 \cdot x_1)x_1$$

But $a_2 \cdot x_1$ is a scalar; therefore we may rewrite the above as

$$x_1 \cdot w_2 = x_1 \cdot a_2 - (a_2 \cdot x_1)(x_1 \cdot x_1) = 0$$

Since x_1 is of unit length, its scalar product with itself is unity; thus the above scalar product of x_1 and w_2 is zero, and the vectors are orthogonal. The final step is to normalize the length of w_2. To do this we define x_2 as follows:

$$x_2 = \frac{w_2}{|w_2|}$$

The vectors x_1 and x_2 as produced by the above process form an orthonormal basis for the two-dimensional space.

It may be helpful to illustrate this process. In Fig. 5.7*a* we have shown

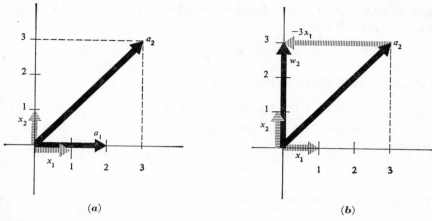

Figure 5.7 *Constructing an orthonormal basis.*

two vectors a_1 and a_2. The magnitude of a_1 is 2, and thus, by normalization, we produce x_1 (of unit length) as indicated. The scalar product $a_2 \cdot x_1$ is easily seen to be 3. In Fig. 5.7b, the relation (7) has been applied to illustrate $w_2 = a_2 - 3x_1$. Since the magnitude of w_2 is 3, we simply divide this vector by 3 to produce x_2. Clearly, the resulting x_1 and x_2 form an orthonormal basis for the two-dimensional space.

Let us now consider a three-dimensional vector space. Three linearly independent vectors are needed to form a basis for the space. If the vectors x_1, x_2, x_3 are to form an orthonormal basis, they must satisfy the following relationships:

$$\begin{aligned}
x_1 \cdot x_2 &= 0 & x_1 \cdot x_1 &= 1 \\
x_2 \cdot x_3 &= 0 & x_2 \cdot x_2 &= 1 \\
x_3 \cdot x_1 &= 0 & x_3 \cdot x_3 &= 1
\end{aligned} \tag{8}$$

The relations in the left-hand column may be thought of as taking care of the orthogonality relationship, while those in the right-hand column are the conditions for normalization. We may summarize the above conditions in a single mathematical statement by the use of the Kronecker delta δ_{ij}. We define this symbol as follows:

$$\delta_{ij} = \begin{cases} 1 & i = j \\ 0 & i \neq j \end{cases} \tag{9}$$

The relations of (8) may now be expressed as

$$x_i \cdot x_j = \delta_{ij} \qquad i, j = 1, 2, 3 \tag{10}$$

Just as in the two-dimensional case, we may construct an orthonormal set of basis vectors starting with any set of linearly independent vectors

a_i $(i = 1,2,3)$. Let the desired orthonormal basis vectors be x_i $(i = 1,2,3)$. Then we may choose

$$x_1 = \frac{a_1}{|a_1|}$$

Proceeding as in the two-dimensional case, let

$$w_2 = a_2 - (a_2 \cdot x_1)x_1$$

As was shown, this is clearly orthogonal to x_1 and may be normalized by defining

$$x_2 = \frac{w_2}{|w_2|}$$

To find the third vector, consider

$$w_3 = a_3 - (a_3 \cdot x_1)x_1 - (a_3 \cdot x_2)x_2 \tag{11}$$

It is easily established that this vector is orthogonal to x_1, since

$$
\begin{aligned}
x_1 \cdot w_3 &= (x_1 \cdot a_3) - (a_3 \cdot x_1)(x_1 \cdot x_1) - (a_3 \cdot x_2)(x_1 \cdot x_2)\\
&= (x_1 \cdot a_3) - (a_3 \cdot x_1)1 - (a_3 \cdot x_2)0\\
&= (x_1 \cdot a_3) - (a_3 \cdot x_1) = 0
\end{aligned}
$$

In exactly the same manner it may be shown that

$$x_2 \cdot w_3 = (x_2 \cdot a_3) - (a_3 \cdot x_1)(x_2 \cdot x_1) - (a_3 \cdot x_2)(x_2 \cdot x_2) = 0$$

Thus, w_3 is also orthogonal to x_2. If we define

$$x_3 = \frac{w_3}{|w_3|}$$

then we have produced a set of three vectors x_i which are all of unit length, and which are mutually orthogonal.

If two arbitrary vectors a_1 and b_1 in a three-dimensional vector space are defined on an orthonormal basis with vectors x_i, the same advantages accrue as did in the two-dimensional case. Let us define the vectors as

$$
\begin{aligned}
a_1 &= \alpha_1 x_1 + \alpha_2 x_2 + \alpha_3 x_3\\
b_1 &= \beta_1 x_1 + \beta_2 x_2 + \beta_3 x_3
\end{aligned}
$$

The scalar product $a_1 \cdot b_1$ may be found in the same manner as (5) was found for the two-dimensional case. Thus we see that for the three-dimensional case,

$$a_1 \cdot b_1 = \alpha_1 \beta_1 + \alpha_2 \beta_2 + \alpha_3 \beta_3 \tag{12}$$

Similarly, we can determine the square of the length of an arbitrary vector a_1 as

$$a_1 \cdot a_1 = |a_1|^2 = \alpha_1{}^2 + \alpha_2{}^2 + \alpha_3{}^2 \tag{13}$$

The extension of the concept of an orthonormal set of basis vectors to spaces with a dimensionality greater than three is very straightforward from a mathematical viewpoint. In the two-dimensional case we started with an arbitrary vector, normalized its length to unity, and then established a process by which a second vector was created at right angles to the first. We finished the process with a final normalization. In the three-dimensional case we followed the same procedure to establish two orthonormal vectors, then created a vector which was perpendicular to the plane formed by the other two. Again, the final step was normalization. In higher-dimensional spaces (for example, a four-dimensional space), we may conceive of the three orthonormal vectors as creating a *hyperplane*, and thus we are required to find a vector "perpendicular" to this hyperplane. The concept in terms of geometrical thinking is naturally somewhat vague, but the mathematics follows easily.

Let us consider an n-dimensional space. We shall assume that we have a set of linearly independent basis vectors a_i $(i = 1,2, \ldots , n)$ and we desire to find a set of orthonormal basis vectors x_i. The procedure of the preceding paragraphs is clearly satisfactory to find the first three of these x_i. For x_4 we first find a vector w_4 which may be defined as

$$w_4 = a_4 - (a_4 \cdot x_1)x_1 - (a_4 \cdot x_2)x_2 - (a_4 \cdot x_3)x_3$$

Then we normalize this vector to produce x_4, where

$$x_4 = \frac{w_4}{|w_4|}$$

This process may be continued by a fairly obvious extension to find the other desired vectors. In general, we may write

$$w_i = a_i - \sum_{k=1}^{i-1} (a_i \cdot x_k)x_k \tag{14}$$

$$x_i = \frac{w_i}{|w_i|}$$

These relations provide the means for finding the ith orthonormal basis vector of a set of n such vectors. We must, of course, find the vectors in numerical order to use relation (14).

The use of an orthonormal basis for an n-dimensional vector space provides a simple formulation for the scalar product of two vectors in the space, which is merely an extension of the two- and three-dimensional cases. If we define two vectors a_1 and b_1 on such a basis,

$$a_1 = \sum_{i=1}^{n} \alpha_i x_i$$

$$b_1 = \sum_{i=1}^{n} \beta_i x_i \tag{15}$$

then we may define the scalar product of these two vectors as

$$a_1 \cdot b_1 = \sum_{i=1}^{n} \alpha_i \beta_i \tag{16}$$

Similarly, the formula for the square of the length of a given vector a_1 is

$$a_1 \cdot a_1 = |a_1|^2 = \sum_{i=1}^{n} \alpha_i{}^2 \tag{17}$$

5.4   *Transformations of basis vectors*

Suppose we have a set of n linearly independent vectors u_i which forms a basis for an n-dimensional linear vector space. We shall not restrict ourselves to the case in which this basis is orthonormal, or even orthogonal. Suppose we are also interested in some other set of linearly independent vectors w_i which also forms a basis for the space. Since the original u_i vectors form a basis, each of the new vectors w_i may be expressed as a linear combination of the original basis vectors. For example, we may write

$$
\begin{aligned}
w_1 &= f_{11}u_1 + f_{12}u_2 + \cdots + f_{1n}u_n \\
w_2 &= f_{21}u_1 + f_{22}u_2 + \cdots + f_{2n}u_n \\
&\cdots \cdots \cdots \cdots \cdots \cdots \cdots \cdots \cdots \\
w_n &= f_{n1}u_1 + f_{n2}u_2 + \cdots + f_{nn}u_n
\end{aligned}
\tag{1}
$$

Clearly, the above relation may be expressed in matrix form; i.e.,

$$w = Fu \tag{2}$$

where $\quad w = \begin{bmatrix} w_1 \\ \cdots \\ w_n \end{bmatrix} \quad F = \begin{bmatrix} f_{11} & \cdots & f_{1n} \\ \cdots & \cdots & \cdots \\ f_{n1} & \cdots & f_{nn} \end{bmatrix} \quad u = \begin{bmatrix} u_1 \\ \cdots \\ u_n \end{bmatrix}$

Thus we see that the relations between any two sets of vectors, both of which form bases for an n-dimensional linear vector space, may be expressed by means of an $n \times n$ matrix.

Let us now assume that a vector a_1 is defined in the n-dimensional space. In terms of the basis vectors u_i we may write

$$a_1 = \sum_{i=1}^{n} \alpha_i{}^{(u)} u_i \tag{3}$$

This may also be expressed by the matrix equation

$$a_1 = (\alpha^{(u)})^t u = u^t \alpha^{(u)} \tag{4}$$

In the above equations the superscript (u) indicates that the quantities $\alpha_i^{(u)}$ are measure numbers referred to the basis vectors u_i. The matrix $\boldsymbol{\alpha}^{(u)}$ is defined as

$$\boldsymbol{\alpha}^{(u)} = \begin{bmatrix} \alpha_1^{(u)} \\ \cdots \\ \alpha_n^{(u)} \end{bmatrix}$$

If we desire to express the vector a_1 in terms of some other basis vectors w_i, we must find the relation between the $\alpha_i^{(u)}$ as defined above and another set of scalars $\alpha_i^{(w)}$ defined by the relation

$$a_1 = \sum_{i=1}^{n} \alpha_i^{(w)} w_i = (\boldsymbol{\alpha}^{(w)})^t \boldsymbol{w} \tag{5}$$

where

$$\boldsymbol{\alpha}^{(w)} = \begin{bmatrix} \alpha_1^{(w)} \\ \cdots \\ \alpha_n^{(w)} \end{bmatrix}$$

This is easily done if we have a relation between the u_i and the w_i such as (1). We may proceed as follows:

$$a_1 = (\boldsymbol{\alpha}^{(u)})^t \boldsymbol{u} = (\boldsymbol{\alpha}^{(w)})^t \boldsymbol{w} = (\boldsymbol{\alpha}^{(w)})^t \boldsymbol{Fu}$$

from which it follows that

$$\begin{aligned} (\boldsymbol{\alpha}^{(u)})^t &= (\boldsymbol{\alpha}^{(w)})^t \boldsymbol{F} \\ \boldsymbol{\alpha}^{(u)} &= \boldsymbol{F}^t \boldsymbol{\alpha}^{(w)} \\ \boldsymbol{\alpha}^{(w)} &= (\boldsymbol{F}^t)^{-1} \boldsymbol{\alpha}^{(u)} \end{aligned} \tag{6}$$

The conclusion of the above is that if F is the matrix relating the basis vectors u_i and w_i, i.e., if $w = Fu$, then the components of an arbitrary vector defined on the two bases are related by the expression $\boldsymbol{\alpha}^{(w)} = (\boldsymbol{F}^t)^{-1} \boldsymbol{\alpha}^{(u)}$, where the $\alpha_i^{(w)}$ are the measure numbers defined on the new w_i basis, and the $\alpha_i^{(u)}$ are the measure numbers defined on the original u_i basis.

As an example of the above procedure, consider a two-dimensional space. Let x_i be an orthonormal basis, and let the w_i be defined as follows:

$$\begin{bmatrix} w_1 \\ w_2 \end{bmatrix} = \begin{bmatrix} 2 & 0 \\ (\tfrac{1}{2})^{\frac{1}{2}} & (\tfrac{1}{2})^{\frac{1}{2}} \end{bmatrix} \begin{bmatrix} x_1 \\ x_2 \end{bmatrix} \tag{7}$$

These two bases are shown in Fig. 5.8. The inverse of the transpose of the square matrix relating the two sets of basis vectors is

$$\begin{bmatrix} \tfrac{1}{2} & -\tfrac{1}{2} \\ 0 & 2^{\frac{1}{2}} \end{bmatrix}$$

Now let us consider the vector $a_1 = 2x_1 + 0x_1$. In other words, a_1 is a vector collinear with the x_1 basis vector. The components of a_1 in terms of the

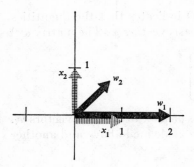

Figure 5.8   *The bases x_i and w_i.*

w_i basis are easily found from (6) to be

$$\left.\begin{matrix}\alpha_1{}^{(w)} \\ \alpha_2{}^{(w)}\end{matrix}\right] = \begin{bmatrix} \frac{1}{2} & -\frac{1}{2} \\ 0 & 2^{\frac{1}{2}} \end{bmatrix} \left.\begin{matrix}2 \\ 0\end{matrix}\right] = \left.\begin{matrix}1 \\ 0\end{matrix}\right]$$

Thus, we may write $a_1 = 1w_1 + 0w_2$. The vector is shown in Fig. 5.9. In Fig. 5.9 we have also indicated a second example, the vector

$$b_1 = -1x_1 + 1x_2$$

If we apply (6), we see that

$$\left.\begin{matrix}\beta_1{}^{(w)} \\ \beta_2{}^{(w)}\end{matrix}\right] = \begin{bmatrix} \frac{1}{2} & -\frac{1}{2} \\ 0 & 2^{\frac{1}{2}} \end{bmatrix} \left.\begin{matrix}-1 \\ 1\end{matrix}\right] = \left.\begin{matrix}-1 \\ 2^{\frac{1}{2}}\end{matrix}\right]$$

In other words, b_1 may also be expressed as $b_1 = -1w_1 + 2^{\frac{1}{2}}w_2$.

So far, in this section, we have discussed the manner in which an arbitrary vector may be expressed in terms of different bases and the relations that exist between the measure numbers for the *same vector* in the two different reference systems. Now, let us consider the relations that must exist *between two vectors*, both of which are defined on the same basis. As before, we shall *not* require that the basis be orthonormal. Let the vectors

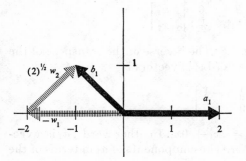

Figure 5.9   *The vectors a_1 and b_1 defined on the w_i basis.*

be a_1 and b_1, and let the basis vectors be u_i. We may write

$$a_1 = \sum_i \alpha_i{}^{(u)} u_i = (\boldsymbol{\alpha}^{(u)})^t \boldsymbol{u}$$

$$b_1 = \sum_i \beta_i{}^{(u)} u_i = (\boldsymbol{\beta}^{(u)})^t \boldsymbol{u}$$

We may view the vector b_1 as being derived from the vector a_1 by means of a linear transformation. By this we mean that each of the measure numbers $\beta_i{}^{(u)}$ is related to some or all of the measure numbers $\alpha_i{}^{(u)}$ and that the relation is linear; i.e., it does not involve higher-order powers of the $\alpha_i{}^{(u)}$ terms. Thus, we may write

$$\beta_1{}^{(u)} = g_{11}{}^{(u)} \alpha_1{}^{(u)} + \cdots + g_{1n}{}^{(u)} \alpha_n{}^{(u)}$$
$$\cdots \cdots \cdots \cdots \cdots \cdots \cdots \cdots \cdots$$
$$\beta_n{}^{(u)} = g_{n1}{}^{(u)} \alpha_1{}^{(u)} + \cdots + g_{nn}{}^{(u)} \alpha_n{}^{(u)}$$

This is clearly a set of simultaneous equations which may be expressed in the form of a matrix equation as

$$\boldsymbol{\beta}^{(u)} = \boldsymbol{G}^{(u)} \boldsymbol{\alpha}^{(u)} \tag{8}$$

where $\boldsymbol{G}^{(u)}$ is an $n \times n$ square matrix. $\boldsymbol{G}^{(u)}$ is frequently referred to as a *linear operator* or a *linear transformation*.

As an example of this type of transformation, consider a two-dimensional space. If we choose orthonormal basis vectors x_1 and x_2, and if we desire to rotate a vector a_1 through a counterclockwise angle φ to produce a vector b_1, then, in terms of the angles shown in Fig. 5.10, we may write

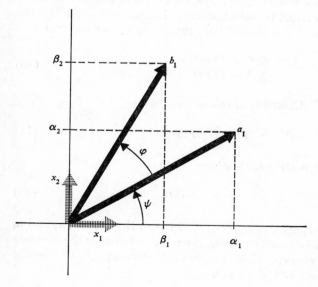

Figure 5.10 An ex-
ample of a linear
transformation.

the equations for the measure numbers β_i as

$$\beta_1 = |b_1| \, (\cos \psi \cos \varphi - \sin \psi \sin \varphi)$$
$$\beta_2 = |b_1| \, (\cos \psi \sin \varphi + \sin \psi \cos \varphi) \tag{9}$$

Similarly, for the α_i we have

$$\alpha_1 = |a_1| \cos \psi$$
$$\alpha_2 = |a_1| \sin \psi \tag{10}$$

Substituting in (9) leads to the following expression for the relations between the measure numbers of the two vectors:

$$\begin{bmatrix} \beta_1 \\ \beta_2 \end{bmatrix} = \frac{|b_1|}{|a_1|} \begin{bmatrix} \cos \varphi & -\sin \varphi \\ \sin \varphi & \cos \varphi \end{bmatrix} \begin{bmatrix} \alpha_1 \\ \alpha_2 \end{bmatrix} \tag{11}$$

A most important problem in the study of vector spaces is determining what happens to a transformation such as (8) when we change to some new basis. For example, if we redefine the vectors a_1 and b_1 in terms of some new basis vectors w_i, such that

$$a_1 = \sum_i \alpha_i^{(w)} w_i = (\boldsymbol{\alpha}^{(w)})^t \boldsymbol{w}$$
$$b_1 = \sum_i \beta_i^{(w)} w_i = (\boldsymbol{\beta}^{(w)})^t \boldsymbol{w} \tag{12}$$

and if the two bases are related by (2), i.e., $\boldsymbol{w} = \boldsymbol{Fu}$, we desire to know what the form of the original transformation is, i.e., we desire to know the relation between the $\alpha_i^{(w)}$ and the $\beta_i^{(w)}$ of (12). From (6) we see that

$$\boldsymbol{\alpha}^{(u)} = \boldsymbol{F}^t \boldsymbol{\alpha}^{(w)}$$
$$\boldsymbol{\beta}^{(u)} = \boldsymbol{F}^t \boldsymbol{\beta}^{(w)} \tag{13}$$

If these results are substituted into (8), we see that

$$\boldsymbol{\beta}^{(w)} = (\boldsymbol{F}^t)^{-1} \boldsymbol{G}^{(u)} \boldsymbol{F}^t \boldsymbol{\alpha}^{(w)} \tag{14}$$

Thus we may define a matrix $\boldsymbol{G}^{(w)}$, where

$$\boldsymbol{G}^{(w)} = (\boldsymbol{F}^t)^{-1} \boldsymbol{G}^{(u)} \boldsymbol{F}^t \tag{15}$$

Thus the matrix $\boldsymbol{G}^{(w)}$ specifies the relation between the vectors a_1 and b_1 as defined on the w_i basis. In other words, the relation between the measure numbers of the two vectors previously expressed by the matrix $\boldsymbol{G}^{(u)}$ is now expressed by the matrix $\boldsymbol{G}^{(w)}$ defined by (15).

As an example of the above development, consider the vectors a_1 and b_1 which were used in the previous example and which are shown in Fig. 5.9. If we use the x_i vectors shown in Fig. 5.8 as a basis, then (11) (where φ is the angle between the two vectors a_1 and b_1) becomes the matrix $G^{(x)}$. Thus,

$$G^{(x)} = \begin{bmatrix} -\frac{1}{2} & -\frac{1}{2} \\ \frac{1}{2} & -\frac{1}{2} \end{bmatrix}$$

This 2×2 matrix specifies the relation between the measure numbers of the two vectors as they are defined on the x_i basis. The F matrix relating the basis x_i and the basis w_i has already been found in (7). Therefore we may substitute directly in (15) as follows:

$$\begin{aligned}
G^{(w)} &= (F^t)^{-1} G^{(x)} F^t \\
&= \begin{bmatrix} \frac{1}{2} & -\frac{1}{2} \\ 0 & 2^{\frac{1}{2}} \end{bmatrix} \begin{bmatrix} -\frac{1}{2} & -\frac{1}{2} \\ \frac{1}{2} & -\frac{1}{2} \end{bmatrix} \begin{bmatrix} 2 & (\frac{1}{2})^{\frac{1}{2}} \\ 0 & (\frac{1}{2})^{\frac{1}{2}} \end{bmatrix} \\
G^{(w)} &= \begin{bmatrix} -1 & -\frac{2^{\frac{1}{2}}}{4} \\ 2^{\frac{1}{2}} & 0 \end{bmatrix}
\end{aligned}$$

In this section two very important ideas have been presented. They are: (1) the relations among the various components of a particular vector when this vector is expressed in terms of different bases and (2) the relations between the measure numbers of two vectors when the basis on which this relation is specified is changed to some other basis. To emphasize these concepts, Table 5.2, on page 180, presents the general relations derived in this section. Table 5.3 follows the general format of Table 5.2, but gives the specific numbers relating to the examples and the illustrations of Figs. 5.8 and 5.9. A careful study of the tables is strongly recommended at this point, since future sections of this chapter will build heavily on this material.

5.5 *Linear transformations*

In the last section we introduced the concept of a linear transformation. We pointed out that this may be viewed as an operation in which an arbitrary vector, defined by means of its measure numbers on a certain set of basis vectors, is transformed into some other vector. In addition, we noted that this type of operation, which can be expressed by a set of simultaneous equations, can be represented by a matrix. In general, we will be mainly concerned with nonsingular transformations, i.e., transformations whose matrices are nonsingular.

Table 5.2   Transformations between vectors on two bases

Relations on the w_i basis	Relations between the two bases	Relations on the x_i basis
	$w = Fx$	
$a_1 = (\alpha^{(w)})^t w$	$\alpha^{(w)} = (F^t)^{-1}\alpha^{(x)}$	$a_1 = (\alpha^{(x)})^t x$
$b_1 = (\beta^{(w)})^t w$	$\beta^{(w)} = (F^t)^{-1}\beta^{(x)}$	$b_1 = (\beta^{(x)})^t x$
$\beta^{(w)} = G^{(w)}\alpha^{(w)}$	$G^{(w)} = (F^t)^{-1}G^{(x)}F^t$	$\beta^{(x)} = G^{(x)}\alpha^{(x)}$

It is easily shown that a linear transformation which is characterized by a nonsingular matrix is unique; i.e., if a vector a_1 is transformed by the matrix F into a vector g_1, then there is no possibility of g_1 being the result of the transform F operating on any vector other than a_1. To see this, let

$$a_1 = \alpha^t x \qquad g_1 = \gamma^t x$$

where α is the column matrix whose elements are the measure numbers α_i of the vector a_1, and γ is the column matrix whose elements are the measure numbers γ_i of the vector g_1. The transformation may be written

$$\gamma = F\alpha$$

Assume that a vector b_1 with measure numbers β_i is also transformed by the matrix F into the vector g_1. If this is true we may write

$$\gamma = F\beta$$

Then, by subtraction,

$$F(\alpha - \beta) = 0$$

This matrix equation simply represents a set of homogeneous equations, and Sec. 2.6 tells us that if the matrix equation is to be satisfied, either the vector whose measure numbers are $(\gamma - \beta)$ must equal zero, or det F must equal zero. Since F is nonsingular, det $F \neq 0$; therefore we conclude that b_1 can only be equal to a_1, and thus the transformation must be unique. In the remainder of this section we shall discuss some specific types of linear transformations and their properties.

Of special interest in the theory of linear transformations is a matrix H whose elements are real, and which is defined by the relation

$$H^t = H^{-1} \tag{1}$$

A matrix of this type, i.e., one whose transpose is equal to its inverse, is called an *orthogonal matrix*. Similarly, a transformation represented by such a matrix is called an *orthogonal transformation*. Let us investigate some properties of the orthogonal matrix and of the transformation char-

Table 5.3 An example of transformations between two vectors on two bases

Relations on the w_i basis	Relations between the two bases

$$\begin{bmatrix} w_1 \\ w_2 \end{bmatrix} = \begin{bmatrix} 2 & 0 \\ (\tfrac{1}{2})^{\frac{1}{2}} & (\tfrac{1}{2})^{\frac{1}{2}} \end{bmatrix} \begin{bmatrix} x_1 \\ x_2 \end{bmatrix}$$

$$a_1 = \begin{bmatrix} 1 & 0 \end{bmatrix} \begin{bmatrix} w_1 \\ w_2 \end{bmatrix}$$

$$\begin{bmatrix} 1 \\ 0 \end{bmatrix} = \begin{bmatrix} \tfrac{1}{2} & -\tfrac{1}{2} \\ 0 & 2^{\frac{1}{2}} \end{bmatrix} \begin{bmatrix} 2 \\ 0 \end{bmatrix}$$

$$b_1 = \begin{bmatrix} -1 & 2^{\frac{1}{2}} \end{bmatrix} \begin{bmatrix} w_1 \\ w_2 \end{bmatrix}$$

$$\begin{bmatrix} -1 \\ 2^{\frac{1}{2}} \end{bmatrix} = \begin{bmatrix} \tfrac{1}{2} & -\tfrac{1}{2} \\ 0 & 2^{\frac{1}{2}} \end{bmatrix} \begin{bmatrix} -1 \\ 1 \end{bmatrix}$$

$$\begin{bmatrix} -1 \\ 2^{\frac{1}{2}} \end{bmatrix} = \begin{bmatrix} -1 & -\tfrac{2^{\frac{1}{2}}}{4} \\ 2^{\frac{1}{2}} & 0 \end{bmatrix} \begin{bmatrix} 1 \\ 0 \end{bmatrix} \quad \begin{bmatrix} -1 & -\tfrac{2^{\frac{1}{2}}}{4} \\ 2^{\frac{1}{2}} & 0 \end{bmatrix} = \begin{bmatrix} \tfrac{1}{2} & -\tfrac{1}{2} \\ 0 & 2^{\frac{1}{2}} \end{bmatrix} \begin{bmatrix} -\tfrac{1}{2} & -\tfrac{1}{2} \\ \tfrac{1}{2} & -\tfrac{1}{2} \end{bmatrix} \begin{bmatrix} 2 & (\tfrac{1}{2})^{\frac{1}{2}} \\ 0 & (\tfrac{1}{2})^{\frac{1}{2}} \end{bmatrix}$$

Relations on the x_i basis

$$a_1 = \begin{bmatrix} 2 & 0 \end{bmatrix} \begin{bmatrix} x_1 \\ x_2 \end{bmatrix}$$

$$b_1 = \begin{bmatrix} -1 & 1 \end{bmatrix} \begin{bmatrix} x_1 \\ x_2 \end{bmatrix}$$

$$\begin{bmatrix} -1 \\ 1 \end{bmatrix} = \begin{bmatrix} -\tfrac{1}{2} & -\tfrac{1}{2} \\ \tfrac{1}{2} & -\tfrac{1}{2} \end{bmatrix} \begin{bmatrix} 2 \\ 0 \end{bmatrix}$$

acterized by it. First of all, H must be square and must possess an inverse; i.e., it must be nonsingular. If we write H in terms of the elements in its various columns, i.e., if we let H_i be the column matrix whose elements are those in the ith column of H, then

$$H = [H_1 \mid H_2 \mid \cdots \mid H_n] \tag{2}$$

The matrix H^t can now be represented in terms of the row matrices $H_i{}^t$, whose elements are those of the ith row of H^t. Thus, we can write

$$H^t = \begin{bmatrix} H_1{}^t \\ \hline H_2{}^t \\ \hline \cdot\ \cdot\ \cdot \\ \hline H_n{}^t \end{bmatrix} \tag{3}$$

Form the matrix product H^tH; from the defined property (1), this is the same as forming the matrix product $H^{-1}H = 1$. Therefore, from (2) and (3), we see that

$$H^tH = \begin{bmatrix} H_1{}^t \\ \hline H_2{}^t \\ \hline \cdot\ \cdot\ \cdot \\ \hline H_n{}^t \end{bmatrix} [H_1 \mid H_2 \mid \cdots \mid H_n] = 1 \tag{4}$$

In terms of the partitioning indicated in (4), we may write the matrix product H^tH, indicating the separate row and column matrices $H_i{}^t$ and H_i, respectively. Thus, (4) becomes

$$\begin{bmatrix} H_1{}^tH_1 & H_1{}^tH_2 & \cdots & H_1{}^tH_n \\ H_2{}^tH_1 & H_2{}^tH_2 & \cdots & H_2{}^tH_n \\ \cdot\ \cdot\ \cdot\ \cdot\ \cdot\ \cdot\ \cdot\ \cdot\ \cdot\ \cdot\ \cdot\ \cdot\ \cdot\ \cdot \\ H_n{}^tH_1 & H_n{}^tH_2 & \cdots & H_n{}^tH_n \end{bmatrix} = \begin{bmatrix} 1 & 0 & \cdots & 0 \\ 0 & 1 & \cdots & 0 \\ \cdot\ \cdot\ \cdot\ \cdot\ \cdot\ \cdot\ \cdot\ \cdot \\ 0 & 0 & \cdots & 1 \end{bmatrix} \tag{5}$$

From the above we see that the products of the row and column matrices on the main diagonal equal 1, while the off-diagonal products of the row and column matrices equal zero. We may write

$$H_i{}^tH_j = \delta_{ij} \tag{6}$$

This is exactly the relation for a set of orthonormal basis vectors as given by (10) in Sec. 5.3. Thus we see that an orthogonal matrix has the property that its columns may be thought of as defining the measure numbers of a set of orthonormal vectors. The same statement may be made with respect to the rows of an orthogonal matrix. It should be noted here that if the row and column matrices of (6) are considered to consist of measure numbers, it is necessary that these measure numbers be defined with respect to an orthonormal basis, since it is only for an orthonormal basis that the matrix product of (6) represents the scalar product, and it is by means of the scalar product that orthonormal vectors are defined. The property described above actually forms the necessary and sufficient condition that a matrix be orthogonal. Thus, we may say that, for a given square matrix composed of real elements to be orthogonal, it is necessary and sufficient that the elements of the rows (or of the columns) be the measure numbers of a set of orthonormal vectors.

In Prob. 2.5, it was pointed out that the determinant of the product of two matrices is equal to the product of the determinants of the individual matrices. In Prob. 2.3, it was shown that the determinant of a transposed matrix is equal to the determinant of the matrix itself. Since, if H is an orthogonal transformation, $H^t H = 1$, we conclude that

$$(\det H)(\det H^t) = (\det H)(\det H) = \det 1 = 1$$

Since $\det H$ must be real, there are only two possible choices for it, namely, $+1$ or -1. If H is orthogonal, and if $\det H = +1$, H is called a proper orthogonal transformation (H is sometimes spoken of as being unimodular). Similarly, if $\det H = -1$, H is referred to as an improper orthogonal transformation.

An important property of orthogonal transformations concerns the scalar product. Suppose two vectors a_1 and b_1 are defined on an orthonormal basis so that a_1 is defined by its measure numbers $\alpha_i^{(1)}$, and b_1 is defined by its measure numbers $\beta_i^{(1)}$. The scalar product $a_1 \cdot b_1$ is defined as

$$a_1 \cdot b_1 = (\alpha^{(1)})^t \beta^{(1)} = k$$

If each of the vectors a_1 and b_1 is now subjected to an orthogonal transformation H, then we may define

$$\begin{aligned} \alpha^{(2)} &= H\alpha^{(1)} \\ \beta^{(2)} &= H\beta^{(1)} \end{aligned} \tag{7}$$

The $\alpha_i^{(2)}$ and the $\beta_i^{(2)}$ are the measure numbers of the transformed vectors a_2 and b_2, respectively. These measure numbers are still defined on the original orthonormal basis. Since, from (7),

$$(\alpha^{(2)})^t = (\alpha^{(1)})^t H^t$$

it is easy to see that we may write

$$(\alpha^{(2)})^t \beta^{(2)} = (\alpha^{(1)})^t H^t H \beta^{(1)} = (\alpha^{(1)})^t \beta^{(1)} = k \tag{8}$$

Thus we see that the scalar product of two vectors is invariant under an orthogonal transformation. As a special case of this, we may take $b_1 = a_1$. Then the scalar product simply gives the square of the length of the vector a_1. Thus we see that the length of a vector is invariant under an orthogonal transformation. Another special case is of interest: If a_1 and b_1 are two orthonormal vectors, then their scalar product is zero, and they are of unit length. Clearly, by the above properties, the vectors a_2 and b_2 which result from an orthogonal transformation are also orthonormal. Thus we may say that an orthogonal transformation transforms a set of orthonormal vectors into another set of orthonormal vectors.

As an example of an orthogonal transformation, consider the matrix

$$H = \begin{bmatrix} \cos \varphi & -\sin \varphi \\ \sin \varphi & \cos \varphi \end{bmatrix} \tag{9}$$

If the first column is defined on the orthonormal basis x_i in Fig. 5.11, these measure numbers define the vector h_1 as indicated. Similarly, the measure numbers of the second column define the vector h_2. Clearly, these vectors are orthonormal. This is a proper orthogonal transformation, since det $H = 1$. It is easily established that the length of any vector remains invariant under the transformation and that the scalar product of any two vectors is unchanged.

The above example illustrates a geometrical significance which can be connected with an orthogonal transformation. It indicates that this type of transformation is simply the rotation of a vector around the origin of the coordinate system by an angle φ. This is indicated more clearly in the

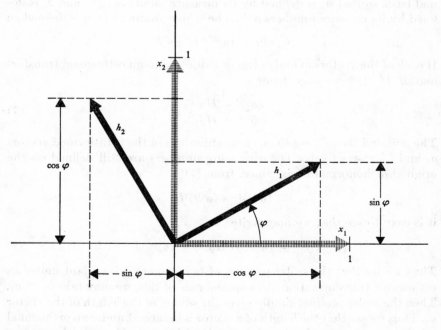

Figure 5.11   An example of an orthogonal transformation.

example of Sec. 5.4, shown in Fig. 5.10, where the vector a_1 is transformed into the vector b_1 by a rotation through an angle φ. A similar geometrical interpretation is possible in three dimensions, and the same concept minus the geometrical interpretation applies to the n-dimensional case. In the next section we shall discuss a more pertinent application of the orthogonal transformation.

In preceding paragraphs, the properties of an orthogonal transformation have been discussed. It was pointed out that such a transformation is represented by a matrix with real elements and that, if H is this matrix, then $H^t H = 1$. In some applications it is desirable not to restrict the matrix to real elements, but to include the case in which the elements may be complex quantities. We may now define a matrix M with the property that

$$M(M^*)^t = (M^*)^t M = MM^{-1} = M^{-1}M = 1$$

In other words, this matrix has the property that

$$(M^*)^t = M^{-1} \tag{10}$$

Such a matrix is described as a *unitary matrix*, and a transformation involving such a matrix is referred to as a *unitary transformation*. It is easily shown, following the general procedure used for the orthogonal transformation, that the necessary and sufficient condition for a matrix to be unitary is that its columns (or its rows) form a set of orthonormal vectors. The test for orthonormality is, of course, defined in terms of the scalar product. The definition given for the scalar product of two vectors defined with real measure numbers must be extended to include the case in which the elements of the pertinent matrices are complex numbers. For two vectors a_1 and b_1, where a_1 is defined in terms of some complex measure numbers α_i, and b_1 is defined in terms of some complex measure numbers β_i, both specified with respect to an orthonormal basis, we define

$$a_1 \cdot b_1 = (\alpha^*)^t \beta \tag{11}$$

It should be noted that, in general, for complex measure numbers, $a_1 \cdot b_1 \neq b_1 \cdot a_1$. The properties discussed above for the orthogonal transformation can be easily modified for the unitary case. First, we may show that the magnitude of det M is unity; that is,

$$|\det M| = 1 \tag{12}$$

Second, it may be shown that the scalar product of two vectors is invariant under a unitary transformation. Third, any vectors which are orthonormal before a unitary transformation is applied will be orthonormal after they have been transformed. For convenience, a comparison between orthogonal and unitary transformations is given in Table 5.4.

Table 5.4   *Orthogonal and unitary transformations*

Orthogonal	Unitary

If H is an *orthogonal matrix* and is written in the form
$$H = [H_1 \mid \cdots \mid H_n]$$
where the H_i are column matrices, then the following are true:

1. The elements h_{ij} of H are real.
2. H is a square matrix.
3. H is nonsingular.
4. $H^t = H^{-1}$
5. $\det H = \pm 1$
6. The elements of the H_i are the measure numbers of a set of orthonormal vectors h_i.
7. A transformation involving H is an orthogonal transformation.
8. The scalar product of two vectors (with real measure numbers) $\alpha^t \beta = k$ is invariant under the transformation.
9. A set of linearly independent vectors is transformed into another set of linearly independent vectors by the transformation.
10. A set of orthonormal vectors is transformed into a set of orthonormal vectors by the transformation.

If M is a *unitary matrix* and is written in the form
$$M = [M_1 \mid \cdots \mid M_n]$$
where the M_i are column matrices, then the following are true:

1. The elements m_{ij} of M are complex.
2. M is a square matrix.
3. M is nonsingular.
4. $(M^*)^t = M^{-1}$
5. $|\det M| = 1$
6. The elements of the M_i are the measure numbers of a set of orthonormal vectors m_i.
7. A transformation involving M is a unitary transformation.
8. The scalar product of two vectors (with complex measure numbers) $(\alpha^*)^t \beta = k$ is invariant under the transformation.
9. A set of linearly independent vectors is transformed into another set of linearly independent vectors by the transformation.
10. A set of orthonormal vectors is transformed into a set of orthonormal vectors by the transformation.

5.6   *Eigenvalues and eigenvectors*

The preceding sections introduced the concept of linear transformations. We saw how an $n \times n$ nonsingular matrix can be considered as a transformation which will transform any vector in an n-dimensional space into another vector in that space. We also discussed the effect of changing the basis on which the vectors are defined, and we saw that changing the basis changes the values of the elements in the matrix, even though the transformation of the vectors themselves is unchanged. The idea of being able to change the matrix elements while still preserving the exact nature of the transformation is a challenging one. For example, it would be very useful to be able to choose a basis in such a way that as many elements of the transformation matrix as possible become zero. This would yield considerable simplification to the transformation and to the steps actually required in the process of transforming.

In this section we shall consider a preliminary step in this search for simplification. Let F be an $n \times n$ matrix. Let us define a set of basis vectors x_i. Any vector defined on this basis will be transformed by F into some other vector. Let us see if we can find a very special vector for F to transform. Specifically, let us see if we can find a vector of such a nature that, after transformation by F, it becomes a vector whose orientation is the same, but whose magnitude may be different. In other words, we desire to find a vector that is transformed into itself, or at least into a scalar multiple of itself, under the transformation F. This may be expressed by an equation. Let a_1 be the desired vector. Its measure numbers, defined on a set of basis vectors x_i, will be considered as the quantities a_{i1}. We shall define A_1 as the column matrix whose elements are the a_{i1}. Thus, we may write

$$a_1 = A_1{}^t x \tag{1}$$

If λ is the scalar multiple mentioned above, the desired criterion is

$$F A_1 = \lambda A_1 \tag{2}$$

This may be written in the form

$$(F - \lambda I) A_1 = 0 \tag{3}$$

The matrix equation (3) represents a set of homogeneous equations. This situation was discussed in Sec. 2.6, where it was pointed out that a solution will exist only under the conditions

$$\det (F - \lambda I) = 0 \tag{4}$$

This may be written in terms of the elements of F as

$$\begin{vmatrix} f_{11} - \lambda & f_{12} & \cdots & f_{1n} \\ f_{21} & f_{22} - \lambda & \cdots & f_{2n} \\ \cdots\cdots\cdots\cdots\cdots\cdots\cdots\cdots \\ f_{n1} & f_{n2} & \cdots & f_{nn} - \lambda \end{vmatrix} = 0 \tag{5}$$

The equation in λ represented by (5) is termed the *characteristic equation* of F. If we designate the roots of the characteristic equation by λ_i, then we may also write (5) as

$$(-1)^n \prod_{i=1}^{n} (\lambda - \lambda_i) = 0 \tag{6}$$

As an example of finding the characteristic equation, consider the case in which F is a 2×2 matrix. The characteristic equation is

$$(f_{11} - \lambda)(f_{22} - \lambda) - f_{12}f_{21} = \lambda^2 - \lambda(f_{11} + f_{22}) + (f_{11}f_{22} - f_{12}f_{21}) = 0 \tag{7}$$

If F is a higher-order matrix, similar results are easily obtained. We may conclude that, in general, if F is an $n \times n$ matrix, equation (4) produces a polynomial in λ; the degree of this polynomial is n. Thus we may expect that there are n roots of the polynomial, and thus n values of λ which satisfy (4). For the present we shall assume that all these values of λ are distinct, i.e., that there are no repeated roots in the characteristic equation. The values of λ which satisfy (4) are termed the *eigenvalues* of F.[1]

As an example of finding the eigenvalues, consider

$$F = \begin{bmatrix} 2 & 1 \\ 1 & 2 \end{bmatrix} \tag{8}$$

Then $\det (F - \lambda I) = (2 - \lambda)(2 - \lambda) - 1 = \lambda^2 - 4\lambda + 3 = 0$

Thus we have the eigenvalues $\lambda = 1$ and $\lambda = 3$.

When the eigenvalues have been determined, it is easy to find a vector a_1 which satisfies (2). To do this, we need only substitute any of the eigenvalues in (3) and solve for the components of a_1. In general, there will be a different solution for each different eigenvalue. Thus, if we characterize F as an $n \times n$ matrix and assume that there are n distinct eigenvalues λ_i, there will be n vectors a_i which may be found by inserting the various values of λ_i into (3). The vectors a_i are called the *eigenvectors* of F.[2] In general, the process described above will yield the orientations, but not the magnitudes, of the a_i. Thus, once the vectors have been found, we are free to normalize them to any convenient lengths. It is usually convenient to normalize the vectors to unit length.

As an example, consider the transformation of (8). Let $\lambda_1 = 1$, and let the components of a_1 be a_{11} and a_{21}. From (3),

$$\left\{ \begin{bmatrix} 2 & 1 \\ 1 & 2 \end{bmatrix} - \begin{bmatrix} 1 & 0 \\ 0 & 1 \end{bmatrix} \right\} \begin{bmatrix} a_{11} \\ a_{21} \end{bmatrix} = \begin{bmatrix} 0 \\ 0 \end{bmatrix}$$

This matrix equation may be written as the two identical equations

$$a_{11} + a_{21} = 0$$
$$a_{11} + a_{21} = 0$$

Clearly, there are an infinite number of solutions to this equation. For example, we might choose $a_{11} = 1$, $a_{21} = -1$ as the components of the eigenvector a_1 corresponding with the eigenvalue $\lambda_1 = 1$. Similarly, for

---

[1] The terms *characteristic values* and *characteristic roots* are also used.

[2] The term *characteristic vector* is also used.

$\lambda_2 = 3$, if we let the components of a_2 be a_{12} and a_{22}, we see that

$$\left\{ \begin{bmatrix} 2 & 1 \\ 1 & 2 \end{bmatrix} - \begin{bmatrix} 3 & 0 \\ 0 & 3 \end{bmatrix} \right\} \begin{bmatrix} a_{12} \\ a_{22} \end{bmatrix} = \begin{bmatrix} 0 \\ 0 \end{bmatrix}$$

This has the solution $a_{12} = a_{22}$. Thus we might choose $a_{12} = 1$, $a_{22} = 1$ as the components of the eigenvector a_2. The above choices for a_1 and a_2 would not, of course, give us eigenvectors of unit length; however, if the a_i are defined on an orthonormal basis, the magnitude of each of the above vectors is clearly $2^{\frac{1}{2}}$, and we can easily normalize by dividing each component of the vectors by this magnitude to produce vectors of unit length.

Let us now derive some properties of the eigenvalues and their corresponding eigenvectors. For example, let us consider the conditions under which an eigenvalue might be zero. In this case, we have

$$FA_1 = \lambda A_1 = 0A_1 = 0$$

Here we see that we have a set of homogeneous equations. Thus, a matrix F can have an eigenvalue of value zero if and only if F is singular.

Let us now assume that λ is an eigenvalue of a matrix F, and that a_1 is an eigenvector with the column matrix of measure numbers represented by A_1. If we premultiply both sides of (2) by F^{-1}, we see that

$$F^{-1}FA_1 = 1A_1 = A_1 = F^{-1}\lambda A_1 = \lambda F^{-1}A_1$$

From this we see that

$$F^{-1}A_1 = \frac{1}{\lambda} A_1$$

Thus we conclude that the eigenvectors of F^{-1} are the same as the eigenvectors of F, but that the eigenvalues of F^{-1} are the reciprocals of the eigenvalues of F.

Now suppose that F is a real symmetric matrix with eigenvalues λ_i and eigenvectors a_i, the latter defined on an orthonormal basis. Let us assume further that the a_i have been normalized; i.e., they are of unit length. We may write

$$FA_i = \lambda_i A_i \tag{9}$$

Suppose, for the moment, that we permit the elements of A_i to be complex. If we premultiply both sides of the above by $(A_i{}^*)^t$, we obtain

$$(A_i{}^*)^t FA_i = (A_i{}^*)^t \lambda_i A_i = \lambda_i (A_i{}^*)^t A_i = \lambda_i \tag{10}$$

Here we have taken advantage of the fact that $(A_i{}^*)^t A_i = |a_i|^2 = 1$. Since F is real and symmetric, $(F^*)^t = F$. Thus, we may apply Theorem 2 of Sec. 2.9 to show that

$$\{[(A_i{}^*)^t FA_i]^*\}^t = (A_i{}^*)^t (F^*)^t A_i = (A_i{}^*)^t FA_i = \lambda_i{}^* \tag{11}$$

If we compare (10) and (11), we see that λ_i is equal to its own complex conjugate. Clearly, this can only be true if λ_i is real. We conclude that the eigenvalues of a real symmetric matrix are real. The same proof may be applied to the case in which F is a hermitian matrix. Again we conclude that the eigenvalues of a hermitian matrix are real. The proof is left as an exercise for the reader.

Let us now reconsider (9) for the case in which F is real and symmetric. Since all the λ_i are real, the equation can clearly be satisfied if the measure numbers of the a_i are restricted to real numbers. In general, when discussing the eigenvectors of a real symmetric matrix, we will restrict ourselves to the case in which this is true.

A most important property of eigenvectors of certain types of matrices is orthogonality. For example, consider a real symmetric matrix F. Let λ_1 and λ_2 be any two eigenvalues, where $\lambda_1 \neq \lambda_2$. Let a_1 and a_2 be the associated eigenvectors. In addition, let these vectors be defined on an orthonormal basis, and let A_1 and A_2 be the column matrices whose elements are the measure numbers. We may write

$$FA_1 = \lambda_1 A_1 \qquad FA_2 = \lambda_2 A_2$$

If we premultiply the left equation by $A_2{}^t$ and the right equation by $A_1{}^t$, we obtain

$$A_2{}^t F A_1 = \lambda_1 A_2{}^t A_1 \qquad A_1{}^t F A_2 = \lambda_2 A_1{}^t A_2 \tag{12}$$

If we take the transpose of the left equation, we see that

$$A_1{}^t F^t A_2 = A_1{}^t F A_2 = \lambda_1 A_1{}^t A_2 \tag{13}$$

If we compare (12) and (13), we see that

$$\lambda_2 A_1{}^t A_2 = \lambda_1 A_1{}^t A_2$$

Since the two eigenvalues λ_1 and λ_2 were specifically chosen unequal, we conclude that $A_1{}^t A_2 = 0$, i.e., that the eigenvectors are orthogonal. A similar proof may be used to show that the eigenvectors of a hermitian matrix are orthogonal. The proof is left to the reader as an exercise.

One other case that will be of interest in future work concerns the eigenvalues and eigenvectors of a nonsymmetric matrix, all of whose elements are real. If F is such a matrix, the characteristic equation $\det (F - \lambda I) = 0$ is an equation involving various powers of λ and real coefficients. As a result of the real property of these coefficients, we know that the values of λ which are the solutions to this equation will occur in complex-conjugate pairs or will be real. Let us consider two complex-conjugate eigenvalues λ_1 and λ_2, where $\lambda_2 = \lambda_1{}^*$. We may now define two eigenvectors a_1 and a_2 whose measure numbers are the elements of the column matrices A_1 and A_2, respectively. These must satisfy the equations

$$FA_1 = \lambda_1 A_1 \qquad FA_2 = \lambda_2 A_2 = (\lambda_1{}^*)A_2$$

If we premultiply the equation on the left above by $(A_2{}^*)^t$, and the equation on the right by $(A_1{}^*)^t$, we obtain

$$(A_2{}^*)^tFA_1 = \lambda_1(A_2{}^*)^tA_1 \qquad (A_1{}^*)^tFA_2 = (\lambda_1{}^*)(A_1{}^*)^tA_2 \qquad (14)$$

The terms on the right in each of the above equations include the complex scalar product of the vectors a_1 and a_2. It is easily seen that

$$(A_2{}^*)^tA_1 = [(A_1{}^*)^tA_2]^*$$

We may now take the complex conjugates of both sides of the equation on the right in (14). We obtain

$$[(A_1{}^*)^tFA_2]^* = A_1{}^tFA_2{}^* = [\lambda_1{}^*(A_1{}^*)^tA_2]^* = \lambda_1 A_1{}^tA_2{}^* = \lambda_1(A_2{}^*)^tA_1$$

Comparing this result with the left equation in (14), we see that

$$(A_2{}^*)^tFA_1 = A_1{}^tFA_2{}^*$$

This will only be true if $A_2 = A_1{}^*$. We conclude that if F is a real nonsymmetric matrix, the eigenvalues are real or occur in complex-conjugate pairs. The eigenvectors associated with complex-conjugate eigenvalues are composed of complex measure numbers which are also complex conjugates.

At the beginning of this section it was pointed out that transformations of bases might be used to simplify the form of a given linear transformation. Let us comment briefly on what is meant by the word "simplification." We would like to make as many as possible of the elements of the transformation matrix equal zero. If our original matrix was nonsingular, however, the new matrix must also remain nonsingular. Therefore the optimum that we can achieve in simplification is to have one nonzero element in each row and each column, and at the same time to have all the other elements equal to zero. It will be especially convenient if we place the nonzero elements so that they form the main diagonal of the matrix. Thus we may say that a nonsingular transformation matrix is in its simplest form when all its elements are zero except those on the main diagonal; these latter must all be nonzero. Let us see how eigenvectors may be used to provide this simplification.

In the above paragraphs we have seen that the eigenvectors of a real symmetric matrix form an orthogonal set of vectors. Thus, they can be used as a basis for the space. This basis has the property that the matrix of transformation becomes a diagonal matrix. In other words, it has just the property of simplification that we have been looking for. To see this, consider an arbitrary vector b_1 with measure numbers b_{i1} defined on an orthonormal basis x_i. If B_1 is a column matrix whose elements are the measure numbers b_{i1}, we may write

$$b_1 = B_1{}^tx = x^tB_1 \qquad (15)$$

Now consider a transformation matrix F with eigenvectors a_i. Let β_i be the measure numbers of the vector b_1 expressed on the a_i basis, and let β be a column matrix whose elements are these measure numbers. We may write

$$b_1 = \beta^t a \tag{16}$$

If the a_i are specified by their measure numbers on the original x_i basis, and if these are arranged as elements of the column matrices A_i, then

$$a_i = A_i^t x \tag{17}$$

and

$$a = A^t x \tag{18}$$

where a is a column matrix whose elements are the vectors a_i, and A is an $n \times n$ matrix whose columns are the A_i. We may now equate (15) and (16) and substitute from (18) to obtain

$$B_1^t x = \beta^t a = \beta^t A^t x \tag{19}$$

Thus, we see that

$$B_1^t = \beta^t A^t$$

If we take the transposes of both sides of the above, we obtain

$$B_1 = A\beta \tag{20}$$

This may also be written in the summation form:

$$B_1 = \sum_i \beta_i A_i \tag{21}$$

The latter equation is more easily compared with (20) if it is written in the expanded form:

$$B_1 = \begin{bmatrix} b_{11} \\ \cdot\cdot \\ b_{n1} \end{bmatrix} = \beta_1 \begin{bmatrix} a_{11} \\ \cdot\cdot \\ a_{n1} \end{bmatrix} + \cdots + \beta_n \begin{bmatrix} a_{1n} \\ \cdot\cdot \\ a_{nn} \end{bmatrix}$$

If two vectors b_1 and b_2 are related by a transformation matrix F, and if the column matrices of measure numbers for these vectors are B_1 and B_2, respectively, then we may write

$$B_2 = FB_1 = FA\beta = \sum_i \beta_i FA_i = \sum_i \beta_i \lambda_i A_i \tag{22}$$

In the last step in (22), we have taken advantage of the fact that the A_i are the measure numbers of eigenvectors; thus, applying the transformation F to them has the same effect as multiplying the measure numbers by the eigenvalues associated with the specific eigenvectors. We may use a matrix D to remove the summation in (22) by defining this matrix as a diagonal matrix whose elements are the eigenvalues. Thus,

$$D = \begin{bmatrix} \lambda_1 & 0 & \cdots & 0 \\ 0 & \lambda_2 & \cdots & 0 \\ \cdots & \cdots & \cdots & \cdots \\ 0 & 0 & \cdots & \lambda_n \end{bmatrix} \tag{23}$$

and (22) becomes

$$B_2 = FA\beta = AD\beta \tag{24}$$

The above will only be true if

$$FA = AD \tag{25}$$

Since A is an orthogonal matrix, $A^t = A^{-1}$. Thus we may premultiply both sides of (25) by A^t to obtain

$$A^t FA = D \tag{26}$$

We have now obtained in (26) an additional, very significant result from our study of eigenvectors and eigenvalues. We see that a real symmetric matrix with distinct eigenvalues (i.e., there are no repeated roots in the characteristic equation) may be diagonalized by the process indicated in (26). The diagonalizing matrix simply consists of the normalized eigenvectors. The diagonal matrix that results consists of the various eigenvalues. This is a most important result.

As an example, consider the matrix F in (8). The normalized eigenvectors a_1 and a_2 corresponding with the eigenvalues $\lambda_1 = 1$ and $\lambda_2 = 3$ are

$$A_1 = \begin{bmatrix} \dfrac{1}{2^{\frac{1}{2}}} \\ \dfrac{-1}{2^{\frac{1}{2}}} \end{bmatrix} \qquad A_2 = \begin{bmatrix} \dfrac{1}{2^{\frac{1}{2}}} \\ \dfrac{1}{2^{\frac{1}{2}}} \end{bmatrix}$$

We may form the matrix product $A^t FA$ directly from these values of A_1 and A_2. Thus,

$$\begin{bmatrix} \dfrac{1}{2^{\frac{1}{2}}} & \dfrac{-1}{2^{\frac{1}{2}}} \\ \dfrac{1}{2^{\frac{1}{2}}} & \dfrac{1}{2^{\frac{1}{2}}} \end{bmatrix} \begin{bmatrix} 2 & 1 \\ 1 & 2 \end{bmatrix} \begin{bmatrix} \dfrac{1}{2^{\frac{1}{2}}} & \dfrac{1}{2^{\frac{1}{2}}} \\ \dfrac{-1}{2^{\frac{1}{2}}} & \dfrac{1}{2^{\frac{1}{2}}} \end{bmatrix} = \begin{bmatrix} 1 & 0 \\ 0 & 3 \end{bmatrix}$$

We see that the resulting diagonal matrix is composed of the eigenvalues of the original matrix, as predicted. Note that this method can be used as a check to make certain that the eigenvalues and eigenvectors of a given real symmetric matrix have been correctly determined. Conclusions similar to the above apply to the case in which F is a hermitian matrix. In this situation, the matrix A will be unitary, rather than orthogonal (see Table 5.4).

As we conclude this section, we may note one other interesting property of matrices which involves the characteristic equation.[1] If we consider the characteristic equation for a given matrix (which, as we have seen, involves an nth-degree polynomial in λ) and replace λ by the matrix itself, thus producing a matrix equation of the type discussed in Sec. 2.11, the equation is satisfied. In other words, a matrix satisfies its own characteristic equation. This is clearly a most unusual property. As an example, consider the matrix F of (8). The characteristic equation for this matrix is $\lambda^2 - 4\lambda + 3 = 0$. It is easily verified that

$$\begin{bmatrix} 2 & 1 \\ 1 & 2 \end{bmatrix}^2 - 4 \begin{bmatrix} 2 & 1 \\ 1 & 2 \end{bmatrix} + 3 \begin{bmatrix} 1 & 0 \\ 0 & 1 \end{bmatrix} = \begin{bmatrix} 0 & 0 \\ 0 & 0 \end{bmatrix}$$

Thus we see that $F^2 - 4F + 3(1) = 0$.

5.7 *Quadratic forms*

Given a vector a_1, defined on an arbitrary basis, with measure numbers α_i, we have seen that we may consider α as a column matrix whose elements are these measure numbers. In addition, we have seen that the matrix product $\alpha^t \alpha$ yields a matrix with only a single element, which we may consider as a scalar c. Actually, in equation form, this scalar is expressed in terms of the measure numbers as

$$c = \alpha^t \alpha = \sum_{i=1}^{n} \alpha_i{}^2 \tag{1}$$

If the basis vectors are orthonormal, the scalar c of (1) gives the magnitude squared of the vector a_1. In this section, however, we shall not be concerned with the length of a vector, but with some more general properties of this type of a transformation; therefore we shall *not* restrict ourselves to the case in which the basis is orthonormal.

A relation similar to that of (1) can be written, which also involves a square matrix F. Thus we may define a scalar k by the relation

$$
\begin{aligned}
k &= \alpha^t F \alpha \\
&= \begin{bmatrix} \alpha_1 & \cdots & \alpha_n \end{bmatrix} \begin{bmatrix} f_{11} & \cdots & f_{1n} \\ \cdots \cdots \cdots \\ f_{n1} & \cdots & f_{nn} \end{bmatrix} \begin{bmatrix} \alpha_1 \\ \cdots \\ \alpha_n \end{bmatrix} \\
&= \begin{bmatrix} \alpha_1 & \cdots & \alpha_n \end{bmatrix} \begin{bmatrix} \alpha_1 f_{11} + \cdots + \alpha_n f_{1n} \\ \cdots \cdots \cdots \\ \alpha_1 f_{n1} + \cdots + \alpha_n f_{nn} \end{bmatrix} \\
k &= \alpha_1(\alpha_1 f_{11} + \cdots + \alpha_n f_{1n}) + \cdots + \alpha_n(\alpha_1 f_{n1} + \cdots + \alpha_n f_{nn})
\end{aligned}
\tag{2}
$$

[1] This property is stated in a theorem called the Cayley-Hamilton theorem.

From the above development, we see that we can also define the resulting scalar k by using summation notation. There will be n^2 terms in the summation. We may write

$$k = \sum_{i,j=1}^{n} f_{ij}\alpha_i\beta_j \tag{3}$$

where, by the double-summation subscript, we simply mean that we let i and j take on all possible combinations of values between 1 and n. The expressions (2) and (3) are called *quadratic forms*. A quadratic form is a special case of a general class of functions which produce scalars as a result of matrix multiplication. The scalar product which was discussed in Sec. 5.3 is another example of this type of function. The terms *bilinear form* and *linear functional* are also applied to operations similar to this.[1]

As an example of a quadratic form, consider the case in which F is a 2×2 matrix. Then

$$k = \alpha_1\ \alpha_2 \begin{bmatrix} f_{11} & f_{12} \\ f_{21} & f_{22} \end{bmatrix} \begin{bmatrix} \alpha_1 \\ \alpha_2 \end{bmatrix}$$
$$= \alpha_1{}^2 f_{11} + \alpha_1\alpha_2 f_{12} + \alpha_2\alpha_1 f_{21} + \alpha_2{}^2 f_{22}$$

This may be written in the form

$$k = \alpha_1{}^2 f_{11} + \alpha_1\alpha_2(f_{12} + f_{21}) + \alpha_2{}^2 f_{22}$$

Since it is only the sum of the elements f_{12} and f_{21} that appears in the formula for the quadratic form, the original matrix F, where $f_{12} \neq f_{21}$, may be replaced by a symmetric matrix F', whose elements f'_{ij} are defined as

$$f'_{11} = f_{11}$$
$$f'_{12} = f'_{21} = \frac{f_{12} + f_{21}}{2}$$
$$f'_{22} = f_{22}$$

without changing the value of the quadratic form. This will also be true for quadratic forms that involve matrices of higher order. We shall assume, therefore, in future developments, that all square matrices which define a quadratic form have been first made symmetric. From the above discus-

---

[1] Actually, the bilinear form is given as $\alpha^t F\beta$, and thus we see that it involves the measure numbers of two vectors a_1 and b_1 (with measure numbers α_i and β_i, respectively), while the quadratic form involves only a single vector. A linear functional, on the other hand, uses a specific vector b_1, defined in terms of its measure numbers β_i, to generate a scalar function of an arbitrary vector a_1. The mechanism by which this scalar function is generated is simply the scalar product; thus we may write $f(a_1) = \beta^t\alpha$, where $f(a_1)$ is a linear functional. See F. E. Hohn, "Elementary Matrix Algebra," pp. 234–238, The Macmillan Company, New York, 1960; B. Friedman, "Principles and Techniques of Applied Mathematics," pp. 19–20, John Wiley & Sons, Inc., New York, 1956.

sion it should be clear that this can always be done and that it will not change the value of the quadratic form.

Quadratic forms have considerable physical significance in circuit theory and in systems theory. For example, if we consider the matrix formulation for the network equations given in (8) of Sec. 3.8, we may define

$$P = i^t R i \tag{4a}$$
$$E_m = \tfrac{1}{2} i^t L i \tag{4b}$$
$$E_e = \tfrac{1}{2} i^t S i \tag{4c}$$

Clearly, these are quadratic forms. The one given as (4a) is the instantaneous power dissipated by a circuit with resistance matrix R and loop currents i_j (the currents are, of course, functions of time) the elements of i. The quadratic form (4b) is the instantaneous value of the energy stored in the inductors (actually, in the magnetic field associated with the inductors) of a circuit with inductance matrix L and loop currents i_j. The quadratic form (4c) is the instantaneous value of the energy stored in the capacitors (actually, in the electric field associated with the capacitors) of a circuit with elastance matrix S and loop currents i_j. Similar quadratic forms may be written for a circuit in terms of its nodal voltages and the G, C, and Γ matrices of equation (12) of Sec. 3.8.[1] The reader should note the similarity of the terms of the quadratic forms (4) with the conventional expressions for the energy stored in the fields of a single inductor or capacitor.

If we change the basis on which a quadratic form is defined, the representation for the quadratic form may be considerably simplified. For example, consider the quadratic form

$$k = \alpha^t F \alpha \tag{5}$$

The α_i may be considered as measure numbers referred to a set of basis vectors a_i. If we now consider a set of basis vectors b_i and measure numbers β_i referred to these basis vectors, then we may relate the α_i and the β_i by a nonsingular transformation M, where

$$\alpha = M\beta \tag{6}$$

Our quadratic form of (5) may now be expressed as

$$k = \beta^t M^t F M \beta \tag{7}$$

Thus we see that, with respect to the new basis, the matrix of the quadratic form is now $M^t F M$. This implies that if we choose our new basis vectors b_i correctly, and thus specify the proper matrix M, we may be able

[1] See D. F. Tuttle, Jr., "Network Synthesis," vol. I, chap. 4, John Wiley & Sons, Inc., New York, 1958.

to take a matrix of a quadratic form such as F in (5) and produce a simplified matrix of a quadratic form M^tFM. The "simplification" that we would hope to achieve would be setting as many as possible of the elements of the matrix M^tFM equal to zero. The optimum simplification that we could attain without making M^tFM singular would be to make all the elements zero except the elements on the main diagonal. Clearly, this is just the process that was described in the last section. In other words, since the matrix of a quadratic form can always be put in symmetrical form, if the eigenvalues of this matrix are distinct, the matrix M is simply one whose columns are the normalized eigenvectors, and the resulting quadratic form will have the simplified representation

$$k = \sum_i \lambda_i \beta_i{}^2 \tag{8}$$

This is frequently referred to as the *canonical form* of the quadratic form.

If the matrix of the quadratic form is real and nonsingular (we have already seen that it can always be made symmetric), there are special cases of interest. One of these is the case in which the quadratic form will always be greater than zero, regardless of the choice of the vector involved in the quadratic form. For example, we would expect that this would be the case for (4a), since this quadratic form represents the instantaneous power dissipated in the resistances of a given network. If we permit only positive-valued resistors, and if some resistance is present in each loop, then this power, and thus the quadratic form, will always be a positive quantity. This type of quadratic form is called a *positive-definite quadratic form*. The key to the qualities of the matrix of such a quadratic form is given in (8). In this expression, we see that for any positive or negative values of the measure numbers β_i of an arbitrary vector b, the quadratic form will always be positive (as long as we exclude the trivial case in which all the β_i are zero) if the eigenvalues of the matrix are all positive. Thus we conclude that a real symmetric matrix with positive distinct eigenvalues is the matrix of a positive-definite quadratic form. We frequently simply say that the *matrix is positive definite*. An example is the matrix of (8) of Sec. 5.6. Once we have established this property, since the quadratic form remains invariant under the transformation indicated in (6), it is obviously always positive, no matter what basis is used to describe the vectors.

Frequently, in practical applications, we find situations in which some of the eigenvalues are zero. In this case, the canonical representation of the quadratic form as given in (8) will be either zero or positive (assuming the remaining eigenvalues are positive) for any nontrivial vector b_1. Then we say that the quadratic form is *positive semidefinite*. Similarly, we say that the matrix of the quadratic form is positive semidefinite. Of somewhat less interest is the case in which all the eigenvalues are negative (the quadratic form is then said to be *negative definite*) and the case in which the eigenvalues are either negative or zero (the quadratic form is then said to be *negative semidefinite*).[1]

5.8 *Simultaneous diagonalization of two matrices*

In Sec. 5.6 we showed that it was possible to diagonalize a transformation matrix by the proper choice of the basis on which that transformation was defined. We showed that this could always be done for a real, symmetric matrix. In this section we shall consider the more interesting and more important problem of simultaneously diagonalizing *two* matrices, both of which are real and symmetric. In addition, we shall see that it is necessary to require that one of these matrices be positive definite.

As a means of attacking this problem, let us follow the general procedure of Sec. 5.6, where, given a matrix F, we searched for a vector a_1 and a scalar λ such that $FA_1 = \lambda A_1$ was satisfied. In this section we shall consider two matrices C and G and look for vectors u_i and scalars λ_i such that the effect of applying the transformation G to the vector u_1 is the same as applying the transformation C to the vector u_1 multiplied by the scalar λ_1. In other words, given G and C, we desire to find u_1 and λ such that

$$GU_1 = \lambda CU_1 \tag{1}$$

We may write (1) as

$$(G - \lambda C)U_1 = 0 \tag{2}$$

We now have a set of homogeneous equations, a situation which was discussed in Sec. 2.6. A solution will exist only under the conditions

$$\det (G - \lambda C) = 0 \tag{3}$$

We could, of course, compute a characteristic equation and solve directly for the eigenvalues. Instead, let us take a different approach. Let us assume that both C and G are real and symmetric, and that in addition, C is positive definite. We may now, for the moment, concentrate our attention on the diagonalization of the matrix C. Since it is real and symmetric, we know that there exists an orthogonal matrix F whose columns contain the measure numbers of the various normalized eigenvectors of C such that $F^tCF = M$, where M is a diagonal matrix whose elements are the eigenvalues of C. In addition, since C is positive definite, all these eigenvalues will be positive. Let these eigenvalues be μ_i; thus, $m_{11} = \mu_1$, $m_{22} = \mu_2$, etc.

---

[1] Some additional information on positive-definite matrices may be found in the appendix of L. Weinberg and P. Slepian, Realizability Conditions on n-port Networks, *IRE Trans. on Circuit Theory*, vol. CT-5, no. 3, pp. 220–221, September, 1958.

We may write

$$F^t C F = M = \begin{bmatrix} \mu_1 & 0 & \cdots & 0 \\ 0 & \mu_2 & \cdots & 0 \\ \cdots & \cdots & \cdots & \cdots \\ 0 & 0 & \cdots & \mu_n \end{bmatrix} \tag{4}$$

Let us now define a matrix B, a diagonal matrix with real elements defined by the relationship $b_{ii} = \mu_i^{-\frac{1}{2}}$. We may write

$$B = \begin{bmatrix} \left(\dfrac{1}{\mu_1}\right)^{\frac{1}{2}} & 0 & \cdots & 0 \\ 0 & \left(\dfrac{1}{\mu_2}\right)^{\frac{1}{2}} & \cdots & 0 \\ \cdots & \cdots & \cdots & \cdots \\ 0 & 0 & \cdots & \left(\dfrac{1}{\mu_n}\right)^{\frac{1}{2}} \end{bmatrix} \tag{5}$$

It is easy to see that $B^t = B$, and thus that $B^t M B = 1$. The reason for requiring C to be positive definite should now be apparent. If the eigenvalues of C were negative, it would be necessary for the elements of B to be imaginary. The steps in the transformation of C from a real symmetric positive-definite matrix to the identity matrix may be summarized as follows:

$$B^t F^t C F B = B^t M B = 1 \tag{6}$$

Clearly, since F is nonsingular and B is diagonal, FB will be nonsingular; therefore det FB is not equal to zero. Since the determinant of a product of matrices is equal to the product of the determinants, and since, from (3), the determinant of the matrix $(G - \lambda C)$ is zero, we may write

$$\det B^t F^t (G - \lambda C) F B = 0 \tag{7}$$

This may also be written in the form

$$\det (B^t F^t G F B - \lambda I) = 0 \tag{8}$$

Since G is real and symmetric, $B^t F^t G F B$ will also be real and symmetric. Thus the situation shown in (8) is exactly the same as that shown in (4) of Sec. 5.6. We may emphasize this by rewriting (8) as

$$\det (H - \lambda I) = 0 \tag{9}$$

where $H = B^t F^t G F B$. Since H is real and symmetric, we may find eigenvectors and eigenvalues for this equation. The eigenvalues will be real, and the normalized eigenvectors will form an orthogonal matrix. Let the normalized eigenvectors be r_i, and let the matrix R consist of the measure numbers of these eigenvectors arranged in column matrices R_i. Then,

$$R^tHR = R^tB^tF^tGFBR = D = \begin{bmatrix} \lambda_1 & 0 & \cdots & 0 \\ 0 & \lambda_2 & \cdots & 0 \\ \cdots & \cdots & \cdots & \cdots \\ 0 & 0 & \cdots & \lambda_n \end{bmatrix} \quad (10)$$

If we let $A = FBR$, we may summarize the above as

$$A^tGA = D \quad (11)$$

Now let us take stock of what we have accomplished. By applying successive transformations to the two matrices C and G in (1), both of which were real and symmetric, we have reduced one of the matrices (i.e., C, the one that was positive definite) to the identity matrix, and we have reduced the other matrix, G, to a diagonal matrix whose elements are the eigenvalues of the matrix H. Thus we see that, starting with the matrices C and G, we have found a matrix A that simultaneously diagonalizes G and reduces C to the identity matrix. The steps of the procedure are illustrated in Fig. 5.12.

As an example, consider the two real symmetric matrices

$$G = \begin{bmatrix} -1.6 & 1.2 \\ 1.2 & 4.1 \end{bmatrix} \qquad C = \begin{bmatrix} 1.6 & -1.2 \\ -1.2 & 3.4 \end{bmatrix}$$

If we first consider C, we find that its eigenvalues μ_1 and μ_2 are given by the equation $(\mu - 1.6)(\mu - 3.4) - 1.44 = \mu^2 - 5\mu + 4 = 0$. Thus $\mu_1 = 1$, and $\mu_2 = 4$. Since the eigenvalues are both positive, we see that C is positive definite. It is easy to find the normalized eigenvectors corresponding to these eigenvalues. They are, respectively, f_1 and f_2, with measure numbers which are the elements of the column matrices F_1 and F_2. Thus,

$$F_1 = \begin{bmatrix} \dfrac{2}{5^{\frac{1}{2}}} \\ \dfrac{1}{5^{\frac{1}{2}}} \end{bmatrix} \qquad F_2 = \begin{bmatrix} \dfrac{-1}{5^{\frac{1}{2}}} \\ \dfrac{2}{5^{\frac{1}{2}}} \end{bmatrix}$$

We may now follow the development of (4) by forming a matrix F using the eigenvectors as columns. Thus, (4) becomes

$$F^tCF = \frac{1}{5^{\frac{1}{2}}}\begin{bmatrix} 2 & 1 \\ -1 & 2 \end{bmatrix}\begin{bmatrix} 1.6 & -1.2 \\ -1.2 & 3.4 \end{bmatrix}\frac{1}{5^{\frac{1}{2}}}\begin{bmatrix} 2 & -1 \\ 1 & 2 \end{bmatrix} = \begin{bmatrix} 1 & 0 \\ 0 & 4 \end{bmatrix} = M$$

The matrix B of (5) is easily found from the eigenvalues μ_1 and μ_2. It is

$$B = \begin{bmatrix} 1 & 0 \\ 0 & \frac{1}{2} \end{bmatrix}$$

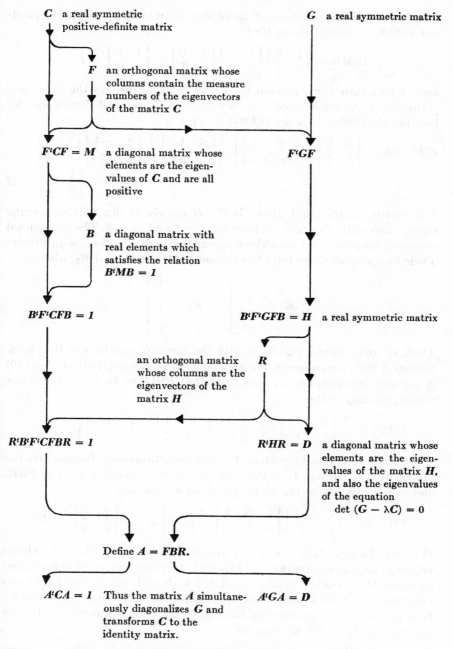

C   a real symmetric
     positive-definite matrix

G   a real symmetric matrix

F   an orthogonal matrix whose
     columns contain the measure
     numbers of the eigenvectors
     of the matrix *C*

$F^t C F = M$ a diagonal matrix whose
                 elements are the eigen-
                 values of *C* and are all
                 positive

$F^t G F$

B   a diagonal matrix with
     real elements which
     satisfies the relation
     $B^t M B = 1$

$B^t F^t C F B = 1$

$B^t F^t G F B = H$ a real symmetric matrix

R   an orthogonal matrix
     whose columns are the
     eigenvectors of the
     matrix *H*

$R^t B^t F^t C F B R = 1$

$R^t H R = D$ a diagonal matrix whose
                 elements are the eigen-
                 values of the matrix *H*,
                 and also the eigenvalues
                 of the equation
                 $\det (G - \lambda C) = 0$

Define $A = FBR$.

$A^t C A = 1$ Thus the matrix *A* simultane-
                ously diagonalizes *G* and
                transforms *C* to the
                identity matrix.

$A^t G A = D$

Figure 5.12   The simultaneous diagonalization of two matrices.

The final step in transforming C to an identity matrix is to form the product B^tMB. As in (6) we see that

$$B^tMB = \begin{bmatrix} 1 & 0 \\ 0 & \frac{1}{2} \end{bmatrix}\begin{bmatrix} 1 & 0 \\ 0 & 4 \end{bmatrix}\begin{bmatrix} 1 & 0 \\ 0 & \frac{1}{2} \end{bmatrix} = \begin{bmatrix} 1 & 0 \\ 0 & 1 \end{bmatrix} = I$$

Now let us turn our attention to the matrix G. Since all the preceding transformations are applied to it as well as to C, we must "catch up" by forming the matrix product B^tF^tGFB. This is

$$B^tF^tGFB = \begin{bmatrix} 1 & 0 \\ 0 & \frac{1}{2} \end{bmatrix}\frac{1}{5^{\frac{1}{2}}}\begin{bmatrix} 2 & 1 \\ -1 & 2 \end{bmatrix}\begin{bmatrix} -1.6 & 1.2 \\ 1.2 & 4.1 \end{bmatrix}\frac{1}{5^{\frac{1}{2}}}\begin{bmatrix} 2 & -1 \\ 1 & 2 \end{bmatrix}\begin{bmatrix} 1 & 0 \\ 0 & \frac{1}{2} \end{bmatrix}$$

$$= \begin{bmatrix} \frac{1}{2} & \frac{3}{2} \\ \frac{3}{2} & \frac{1}{2} \end{bmatrix} = H$$

The matrix on the right above is the H matrix of (9). Solving for the eigenvalues of this matrix, we have $\lambda_1 = -1$ and $\lambda_2 = 2$. The normalized eigenvectors associated with these eigenvalues are r_1 and r_2, respectively. Their measure numbers form the column matrices R_1 and R_2, where

$$R_1 = \begin{bmatrix} \frac{1}{2^{\frac{1}{2}}} \\ \frac{-1}{2^{\frac{1}{2}}} \end{bmatrix} \qquad R_2 = \begin{bmatrix} \frac{1}{2^{\frac{1}{2}}} \\ \frac{1}{2^{\frac{1}{2}}} \end{bmatrix}$$

Thus, we may form a matrix R with the measure numbers of the eigenvectors r_1 and r_2 as columns. We may now follow the step indicated as (10) in our development; i.e., we may show that $R^tHR = D$. Using the above values, we may write

$$R^tHR = \frac{1}{2^{\frac{1}{2}}}\begin{bmatrix} 1 & -1 \\ 1 & 1 \end{bmatrix}\begin{bmatrix} \frac{1}{2} & \frac{3}{2} \\ \frac{3}{2} & \frac{1}{2} \end{bmatrix}\frac{1}{2^{\frac{1}{2}}}\begin{bmatrix} 1 & 1 \\ -1 & 1 \end{bmatrix} = \begin{bmatrix} -1 & 0 \\ 0 & 2 \end{bmatrix} = D$$

We have now found a matrix A which simultaneously diagonalizes the matrix G and reduces C to the identity matrix. Specifically, $A = FBR$, and substituting from the above relations we see that

$$FBR = \frac{1}{5^{\frac{1}{2}}}\begin{bmatrix} 2 & -1 \\ 1 & 2 \end{bmatrix}\begin{bmatrix} 1 & 0 \\ 0 & \frac{1}{2} \end{bmatrix}\frac{1}{2^{\frac{1}{2}}}\begin{bmatrix} 1 & 1 \\ -1 & 1 \end{bmatrix} = \frac{1}{10^{\frac{1}{2}}}\begin{bmatrix} \frac{5}{2} & \frac{3}{2} \\ 0 & 2 \end{bmatrix} = A$$

It is easy to show that $A^tCA = I$ and that $A^tGA = D$. Since the eigenvalues λ_1 and λ_2 are known, we can find the eigenvectors of the original equation (1). In other words, associated with each eigenvalue λ_i, we can find an eigenvector u_i such that the effect of transforming the vector by G is the same as transforming the vector by C and multiplying by the constant λ_i. From (2) we may write

$$\left\{\begin{bmatrix} -1.6 & 1.2 \\ 1.2 & 4.1 \end{bmatrix} - \lambda_i\begin{bmatrix} 1.6 & -1.2 \\ -1.2 & 3.4 \end{bmatrix}\right\}\begin{bmatrix} u_{1i} \\ u_{2i} \end{bmatrix} = \begin{bmatrix} 0 \\ 0 \end{bmatrix}$$

When the eigenvalues $\lambda_1 = -1$ and $\lambda_2 = 2$ are substituted in the above expression, we find that the two eigenvectors u_1 and u_2 may be expressed by the column matrices U_1 and U_2, where

$$U_1 = \begin{bmatrix} u_{11} \\ u_{21} \end{bmatrix} = \begin{bmatrix} c \\ 0 \end{bmatrix} \qquad U_2 = \begin{bmatrix} u_{12} \\ u_{22} \end{bmatrix} = \begin{bmatrix} \dfrac{3k}{4} \\ k \end{bmatrix} \qquad (12)$$

where c and k are real numbers. It should be noted here that we could have developed the same knowledge of the eigenvalues and eigenvectors by using (3) to generate an expression in λ. Thus, for the matrices C and G used in this example, we might have evaluated

$$\det \left\{ \begin{bmatrix} -1.6 & 1.2 \\ 1.2 & 4.1 \end{bmatrix} - \lambda \begin{bmatrix} 1.6 & -1.2 \\ -1.2 & 3.4 \end{bmatrix} \right\} = 0$$

The characteristic equation is

$$4\lambda^2 - 4\lambda - 8 = 0$$

Thus we see that the eigenvalues are the same as those previously determined; we may also find the eigenvectors by this method.

It is important to note that there are both differences and similarities in the results as found by these two procedures. When we go through the steps which determine the matrix A, where A can simultaneously be used to diagonalize one matrix (i.e., the real symmetric matrix G) and transform another into an identity matrix (i.e., the real symmetric positive-definite matrix C), we have in effect defined a new basis for our n-dimensional space. In terms of this basis, the transformations C and G become exceedingly simple, and thus any vectors defined in terms of this basis will have extremely simple relationships existing among their measure numbers. The matrix A can also be viewed as determining a set of quite special eigenvectors which have been normalized, *not* to unit length, but to another quite different normalization. Specifically, if we consider the elements of the columns of A as being the measure numbers (referred, as usual, to an orthonormal basis), of a set of eigenvectors a_i, then, since $A^tCA = 1$, we see that we have set up orthogonality conditions which require

$$A_i{}^t C A_j = \delta_{ij} \qquad (13)$$

where the A_i are the column matrices of the matrix A. It is only in the sense indicated by the above equation that the eigenvectors are orthonormal, since they do not satisfy the formal condition of orthonormality, i.e.,

$$A_i{}^t A_j \neq \delta_{ij}$$

It is precisely the information on this normalization that is not provided when we solve directly for the eigenvalues and eigenvectors. This is readily apparent from a consideration of the two eigenvectors u_1 and u_2 of (12). If we specify the magnitudes of these vectors by letting $c = 5/40^{\frac{1}{2}}$ and $k = 2/10^{\frac{1}{2}}$, then these eigenvectors are identical with the a_i vectors referred to above. In other words, they satisfy the normalization requirements of (13). Naturally, any other values of c and k will also satisfy (1). This procedure actually provides an easy way to find the matrix A or to check a result found by the other method.

In conclusion, in this section we have seen that it is possible simultaneously to reduce any two real symmetric matrices, one of which is positive definite. The positive-definite matrix is reduced to the identity matrix, and the other matrix is reduced to a diagonal matrix whose elements are the eigenvalues of the matrix equation (1).

5.9 *Reciprocal bases*

In preceding sections we have introduced some of the more fundamental concepts of linear vector spaces. Among these, the concept of a basis is quite important, as the basis provides the directional signposts by means of which we can orient ourselves in an otherwise meaningless n-dimensional world. Since any set of linearly independent vectors will form a basis (assuming that we have a sufficient number of them to span the dimensions of the space), there can be several different types of bases. For example, we have discussed an orthonormal basis, i.e., one characterized by the relationship

$$x_i \cdot x_j = \delta_{ij} \tag{1}$$

where the x_i are the basis vectors. We have seen that there are operations, such as the scalar product, which are considerably simplified by the use of an orthonormal basis. As another example of a basis, in Sec. 5.6 it was shown that the eigenvectors of a specific transformation matrix may be used as a basis for the space. These eigenvectors may or may not be orthogonal, depending on the nature of the transformation from which they were derived. They will, however, be linearly independent (if the eigenvalues are distinct), and thus they may be used as a basis. In this section we shall present another type of basis, the *reciprocal basis*.

To introduce the concept of a reciprocal basis, let us assume that we already have a set of basis vectors for our space. We shall *not* require that these be orthogonal. Let us, however, assume that the vectors have been normalized to unit length. If we call these vectors a_i, then our normalization requirement is realized by the relation

$$a_i \cdot a_i = 1 \tag{2}$$

We may now define a new set of vectors, which we shall call b_i, by the relationship

$$a_i \cdot b_j = \delta_{ij} \tag{3}$$

This definition requires that each of the vectors b_i will be orthogonal to $n - 1$ of the a_i vectors. For example, b_1 is defined by the relationships

$$
\begin{aligned}
a_1 \cdot b_1 &= 1 \\
a_2 \cdot b_1 &= 0 \\
&\cdots\cdots \\
a_n \cdot b_1 &= 0
\end{aligned} \tag{4}
$$

Thus, b_1 is orthogonal to the vectors $a_2, a_3, \ldots, a_n$, and its scalar product with the vector a_1 is unity. We can think of the vectors $a_2, a_3, \ldots, a_n$ as forming a hyperplane. The vector b_1 will thus be "perpendicular" to this hyperplane. Note that b_1 need not be collinear with a_1. Thus, in general, we may expect to find that the vector b_1 will not be of unit length, in order that its scalar product with a_1 will be unity.

The relationships given by (4) not only serve to define b_1, but they also provide a means of determining this vector. Let the measure numbers of the vector a_i be a_{ki} $(k = 1, 2, \ldots, n)$. Thus the measure numbers of the vector a_1 will be $a_{11}, \ldots, a_{n1}$; the measure numbers of the vector a_2 will be $a_{12}, \ldots, a_{n2}$, etc. If these measure numbers are referred to an orthonormal basis, then the relations of (4) may be written

$$
\begin{aligned}
a_{11}b_{11} + a_{21}b_{21} + \cdots + a_{n1}b_{n1} &= 1 \\
a_{12}b_{11} + a_{22}b_{21} + \cdots + a_{n2}b_{n1} &= 0 \\
&\cdots\cdots\cdots\cdots\cdots\cdots \\
a_{1n}b_{11} + a_{2n}b_{21} + \cdots + a_{nn}b_{n1} &= 0
\end{aligned} \tag{5}
$$

where the measure numbers of b_1 have been taken as $b_{11}, b_{21}, \ldots, b_{n1}$. The above relationships may be written in matrix form as

$$
\begin{bmatrix}
a_{11} & a_{21} & \cdots & a_{n1} \\
a_{12} & a_{22} & \cdots & a_{n2} \\
\cdots & \cdots & \cdots & \cdots \\
a_{1n} & a_{2n} & \cdots & a_{nn}
\end{bmatrix}
\begin{bmatrix}
b_{11} \\
b_{21} \\
\cdots \\
b_{n1}
\end{bmatrix}
=
\begin{bmatrix}
1 \\
0 \\
\cdots \\
0
\end{bmatrix}
\tag{6}
$$

Thus we see that we have a set of simultaneous equations which may be solved for the coefficients b_{i1}. The square matrix of (6) must be nonsingular, since it is formed of the measure numbers of a set of linearly independent vectors (see Prob. 5.14). Therefore we know that a solution does exist, and thus that the vector b_1 can always be found. The coefficients of the square matrix in (6) are arranged so that this matrix may be referred to as A^t; similarly, the column matrix with elements b_{i1} may be designated B_1.

Thus we may write this equation as

$$A^t B_1 = \begin{bmatrix} 1 \\ 0 \\ 0 \\ \cdots \\ 0 \end{bmatrix} \qquad (7)$$

In the same manner, we may solve for the measure numbers of all the other vectors b_i in terms of their measure numbers b_{ki} $(k = 1, 2, \ldots, n)$ and column matrices B_i. For example, for b_2 we need only solve the matrix equation

$$A^t B_2 = \begin{bmatrix} 0 \\ 1 \\ 0 \\ \cdots \\ 0 \end{bmatrix} \qquad (8)$$

The measure numbers of all the vectors b_i as defined above will form a matrix B. Thus we see that all the information on the relations between the vectors a_i and b_i may be summarized by the matrix equation

$$A^t B = 1 \qquad (9)$$

Thus the elements of the B matrix are seen to be the elements of $(A^t)^{-1}$, and all the measure numbers of the b_i vectors may be found by computing $(A^t)^{-1}$.

The vectors b_i form a set of linearly independent vectors, since the matrix of their measure numbers is nonsingular. Thus, they may be used as a basis for the space. They are referred to as the *reciprocal basis*. Note that a basis can only be reciprocal with respect to some other basis which is already defined. In other words, first we must have a basis, then we can find another basis reciprocal to it.

As an example, consider the basis consisting of the vectors a_1 and a_2 shown in Fig. 5.13. The measure numbers of these vectors (referred to the orthonormal basis vectors x_i) form the columns of the matrix A. Thus,

$$A = \begin{bmatrix} 1 & 0 \\ 1 & 2 \end{bmatrix}$$

From (9) we may find the matrix B. The columns of this matrix are the measure numbers of the reciprocal basis vectors b_i. We see that

$$B = (A^t)^{-1} = \begin{bmatrix} 1 & 1 \\ 0 & 2 \end{bmatrix}^{-1} = \begin{bmatrix} 1 & -\frac{1}{2} \\ 0 & \frac{1}{2} \end{bmatrix}$$

The vectors b_i are shown in Fig. 5.14. It is easily seen that b_1 is orthogonal to a_2, and that $a_1 \cdot b_1 = 1$. Similarly, b_2 is orthogonal to a_1, and $a_2 \cdot b_2 = 1$.

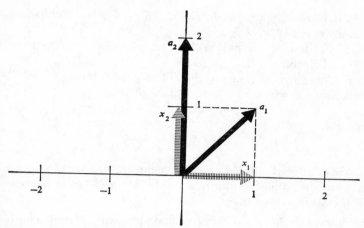

Figure 5.13   A set of basis vectors a_i.

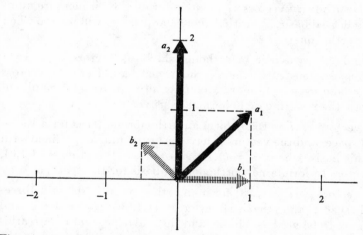

Figure 5.14   The reciprocal basis vectors b_i.

Thus the relations (3) are satisfied, and the vectors b_i form a reciprocal basis. We shall use the reciprocal basis in one of our studies of networks in the next chapter.

5.10 *Further reading*

Most of the texts listed in Sec. 2.12 have sections on linear vector spaces. The following list gives some additional references on this subject:

Birkhoff, G., and S. MacLane: "A Survey of Modern Algebra," The Macmillan Company, New York, 1953.

Gantmacher, F. R.: "The Theory of Matrices," vol. 1, Chelsea Publishing Company, New York, 1959.

Halmos, P. R.: "Finite-dimensional Vector Spaces," D. Van Nostrand Company, Inc., Princeton, N.J., 1958.

Shilov, G. E.: "An Introduction to the Theory of Linear Spaces," Prentice-Hall, Inc., Englewood Cliffs, N.J., 1961.

PROBLEMS

5.1 Does the set of all real numbers form a linear vector space? The set of all complex numbers? What definitions of addition and multiplication are possible if these are vector spaces?

5.2 If the basis vectors for a two-dimensional space are of unit length but at an angle φ to each other (where $\varphi \neq 90$ degrees), find the scalar product of two arbitrary vectors a_1 and b_1 in terms of their measure numbers on the indicated basis. Show that the scalar product will be zero when a_1 and b_1 are orthogonal.

5.3 If x_1 and x_2 are a pair of orthonormal basis vectors for a two-dimensional space, construct a new orthonormal basis from the vectors $a_1 = 2x_1 + x_2$ and $a_2 = -x_1 - x_2$. Compute all steps by the formulas of Sec. 5.3. Draw the resulting orthonormal basis vectors.

5.4 If the vectors x_i ($i = 1,2,3$) form an orthonormal basis for a three-dimensional space, and the vectors a_i have measure numbers defined with respect to this basis, where $a_1 = (1,1,1)$, $a_2 = (1,0,1)$, and $a_3 = (1,1,0)$, use these vectors to form a new orthonormal basis for the space.

5.5 If the vectors x_i ($i = 1,2,3$) form an orthonormal basis for a three-dimensional space, and the vectors $a_1 = (1,1,0)$, $a_2 = (1,0,0)$, and $a_3 = (0,0,1)$ are to be used as a basis, find the scalar product of two arbitrary vectors b_1 and c_1 in terms of their measure numbers defined on the a_i basis.

5.6 If the vectors x_i ($i = 1,2,3$) form an orthonormal basis for a three-dimensional space, find a transformation which will rotate any vector in the plane formed by vectors x_1 and x_2 by φ degrees, but will leave a vector collinear with x_3 invariant.

5.7 If the vectors a_i of Prob. 5.5 are used as a basis for a three-dimensional space, find a transformation which will rotate any vector in the plane formed by a_1 and a_2 by 45 degrees, but will leave a vector at right angles to this plane invariant.

5.8 A transformation defined on the x_i basis of Prob. 5.5 is given below. Find the same transformation defined on the a_i basis as given in that problem.

$$\begin{bmatrix} 1 & 2 & 1 \\ -1 & 1 & 0 \\ 1 & 3 & 1 \end{bmatrix}$$

5.9 Show by example that the transformation given below is not unique; i.e., there exists more than one vector a_1 which may be transformed into some specific vector b_1. The α_i are the measure numbers of a_1, and the β_i are the measure numbers of b_1.

$$\begin{bmatrix} \beta_1 \\ \beta_2 \\ \beta_3 \end{bmatrix} = \begin{bmatrix} 1 & 0 & 1 \\ 3 & 2 & -1 \\ 1 & 2 & -3 \end{bmatrix} \begin{bmatrix} \alpha_1 \\ \alpha_2 \\ \alpha_3 \end{bmatrix}$$

5.10 Find the transformation in the two-dimensional space which will rotate a given vector by a clockwise angle of φ degrees. Is this an orthogonal transformation? If so, is it a proper or an improper one?

5.11 If the vectors a_1 and b_1 are defined on an orthonormal basis such that $a_1 = (1,2,3)$ and $b_1 = (0,1,1)$, find the scalar product $a_1 \cdot b_1$. If the measure numbers of each of the vectors are subjected to the following transformation, find the scalar product of the transformed vectors:

$$\begin{bmatrix} 1 & 0 & 1 \\ 0 & 1 & 1 \\ -1 & 1 & 1 \end{bmatrix}$$

5.12 If the vectors a_1, b_1, c_1, and d_1 are defined in terms of their measure numbers on an orthonormal basis as

$$a_1 = (1,0,0)$$
$$b_1 = (1,1,0)$$
$$c_1 = (1,0,1)$$
$$d_1 = (1,1,1)$$

prove that any three of these vectors are linearly independent, but that the set of all four of them is linearly dependent.

5.13 The vectors a_1, b_1, and c_1 are defined in terms of their measure numbers referred to an orthonormal basis as

$$a_1 = (1,k,0)$$
$$b_1 = (1,0,k)$$
$$c_1 = (k-1,0,1)$$

For what values of the scalar k will these vectors form a basis for the three-dimensional space?

5.14 Show that a set of n vectors in an n-dimensional space may be tested for linear dependence by considering the determinant of the matrix formed by their measure numbers. Specifically, show that the vectors are linearly dependent if and only if the determinant is zero.

5.15 Find the eigenvalues and eigenvectors of the following transformation and show that the eigenvectors are orthogonal:

$$\begin{bmatrix} 1 & -1 & 1 \\ -1 & 2 & 0 \\ 1 & 0 & 1 \end{bmatrix}$$

5.16 Find the eigenvalues and eigenvectors of the following transformation and show that the eigenvectors are orthogonal:

$$\begin{bmatrix} 1 & -1 \\ 1 & 1 \end{bmatrix}$$

5.17 Find the inverse of the transformation given in Prob. 5.15 and show that the eigenvectors of the inverse matrix are the same as those of the original matrix.

5.18 Find the inverse of the transformation given in Prob. 5.16 and show that the eigenvectors of the inverse matrix are the same as those of the original matrix.

5.19 Find a transformation S such that $S^t G S$ is a diagonal matrix, where

$$G = \begin{bmatrix} 1 & -1 & 2 \\ -1 & 3 & 1 \\ 2 & 1 & 2 \end{bmatrix}$$

5.20 Show that the matrix of Prob. 5.15 satisfies its own characteristic equation.

5.21 Show that the matrix of Prob. 5.16 satisfies its own characteristic equation.

5.22 Find the quadratic form for the instantaneous power dissipated in the resistive network shown in Fig. P5.22.

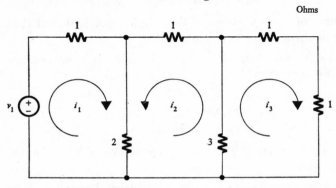

Figure P5.22

5.23 Prove that the quadratic form of Prob. 5.22 is positive definite.

5.24 Determine whether the following matrices are positive definite, positive semidefinite, negative definite, etc.:

$$(a) \begin{bmatrix} 2 & 1 \\ 1 & 2 \end{bmatrix} \qquad (b) \begin{bmatrix} 3 & 1 & 0 \\ 1 & 2 & -1 \\ 0 & -1 & 1 \end{bmatrix} \qquad (c) \begin{bmatrix} 1 & 2 & 1 \\ 1 & 3 & 1 \\ 1 & 2 & 2 \end{bmatrix}$$

5.25 Find a 3×3 nonsymmetric negative-definite matrix.

5.26 Prove that any nonsingular transformation will transform a set of linearly independent vectors into another set of vectors which will also be linearly independent.

5.27 Find the transformation in a two-dimensional space that transforms the vector $a_1 = (1,2)$ into the vector $b_1 = (3,1)$ and also transforms the vector $a_2 = (1,-1)$ into the vector $b_2 = (\frac{3}{2},4)$.

5.28 Find a transformation which will transform the vector $a_1 = (1,1,1)$ into the vector $b_1 = (0,1,0)$ and the vector $a_2 = (2,-1,0)$ into the vector $b_2 = (0,0,1)$ in a three-dimensional space.

5.29 Is it possible to find a nonsingular transformation that will transform the vectors $a_1 = (1,0,0)$, $a_2 = (0,1,0)$, and $a_3 = (0,0,1)$ into the vectors $b_1 = (1,2,1)$, $b_2 = (0,1,3)$, and $b_3 = (2,5,5)$? If so, find it. If not, why not?

5.30 In a three-dimensional space, the vectors $a_1 = (j,1,0)$ and $a_2 = (0,1,j)$ are defined on an orthonormal basis and are both orthogonal to a third vector. Find the third vector.

5.31 Prove that the coefficient of λ^{n-1} in (6) of Sec. 5.6 is equal to the sum of the diagonal elements of the matrix F in (4) of the same section. This sum is called the *trace* of the matrix.

5.32 Show that, if A is real and nonsingular, the quadratic form $X^t(A^tA)X$ is positive definite, where X is a column matrix.

5.33 Find a transformation that will transform one of the following matrices to the identity matrix and the other to a diagonal matrix:

$$A = \begin{bmatrix} 1 & 2 \\ 2 & 1 \end{bmatrix} \qquad B = \begin{bmatrix} 3 & -1 \\ -1 & 3 \end{bmatrix}$$

5.34 Find a transformation that will transform one of the following matrices to the identity matrix and the other to a diagonal matrix:

$$A = \begin{bmatrix} 3 & -2 & -1 \\ -2 & 4 & -1 \\ -1 & -1 & 2 \end{bmatrix} \qquad B = \begin{bmatrix} 1 & 0 & 0 \\ 0 & 2 & 1 \\ 0 & 1 & 2 \end{bmatrix}$$

5.35 Find a basis which is reciprocal to the basis vectors $a_1 = 2x_1 + 3x_2$ and $a_2 = x_1 - x_2$, where x_1 and x_2 are orthonormal basis vectors.

5.36 Find a basis which is reciprocal to the basis vectors a_i, where these latter are defined on an orthonormal basis in a three-dimensional space and $a_1 = (1,1,1)$, $a_2 = (1,0,1)$, and $a_3 = (1,1,0)$.

Chapter 6   Circuit-theory applications of linear vector spaces

6.1   Introduction

In the last chapter, the concept of linear vector spaces was introduced, and a number of the properties of these spaces were developed. Let us consider once more the example which was given in Sec. 5.1. It was pointed out there that we could use the values of a set of variables associated with a given network to determine a point in a linear vector space. In the example network shown in Fig. 5.1, there were two such variables, the two nodal voltages. Thus, a two-dimensional space was necessary for the representation of these variables. If we had selected an example network with n nodal voltages, then an n-dimensional space would have been necessary for the representation. Note that the variables of the network are, in general, functions of time. The exact time dependence, of course, will depend on the network components as well as on the values of the currents which might be fed into the nodes from external current generators. The space formed by the set of n such time-varying quantities is sometimes referred to as a *configuration space*. The concept of such a space is well known in many fields, for example, in the field of classical mechanics.[1]

The network of Fig. 5.1 might have been made more complicated. For example, it might have included capacitors as well as resistors. In this case, specifying only the nodal voltages would not completely formulate the conditions existing in the network at a given instant of time. It would be necessary to specify not only the voltage variables, but, in addition, their first derivatives. Thus, if we were considering a network with n nodes, it would be necessary to specify n voltages and n derivatives of

---

[1] The parallelism between the electrical situation and its mechanical counterpart, especially with respect to the eigenvectors, was pointed out in an early paper, E. A. Guillemin, Making Normal Coordinates Coincide with the Meshes of an Electrical Network, *Proc. IRE*, vol. 15, pp. 935–945, November, 1927.

these voltages. Then the representation of the given network would require a space whose dimensionality was twice as great, namely, $2n$. Such a space, i.e., one formed by a set of n time-varying quantities and the n first derivatives of these quantities, is sometimes referred to as a *phase space*.

At this point it would seem that a further extension of our network could be made so that we might be concerned not only with the variables and their first derivatives, but also with the integrals of the variables. This would be the case if we were dealing with a network composed of resistors, capacitors, *and* inductors. If we differentiated all the variables to eliminate the integrals, then it would appear as if we might have to consider a third type of space, namely, one involving variables, their first derivatives, *and* their second derivatives. Actually, we shall see in a later part of this chapter that such a situation can be avoided by an appropriate redefinition of the variables, and thus we shall only concern ourselves with spaces which involve variables and their first derivatives, namely, phase spaces.

In this chapter we shall discuss the representation of various types of networks in linear vector spaces. To emphasize the concepts, we shall first restrict our attention to networks consisting of only two types of elements. Thus we shall study separately the RC network, the RL network, and the LC network. Finally, we shall discuss the more difficult concept of a network which contains all three types of elements.

6.2 *RC-network analysis*

As a simple example of the application of the concepts of linear vector spaces to network theory, let us consider a network composed only of resistors and capacitors. We shall restrict ourselves to the case in which all the elements are passive, i.e., positive-valued. We may assume that the network is of arbitrary complexity, i.e., that it has n nodes. The nodal equations may be written as[1]

$$c_{11}v_1' + \cdots + c_{1n}v_n' + g_{11}v_1 + \cdots + g_{1n}v_n = 0$$
$$\cdots \cdots \cdots \cdots \cdots \cdots \cdots \cdots \cdots \cdots \cdots \cdots \cdots$$
$$c_{n1}v_1' + \cdots + c_{nn}v_n' + g_{n1}v_1 + \cdots + g_{nn}v_n = 0 \tag{1}$$

In these equations g_{ij} for $i = j$ is the total conductance connected to the ith node, and g_{ij} for $i \neq j$ is the mutual conductance between nodes i and j with an appropriate positive or negative sign. Similar statements hold

---

[1] Throughout this chapter the prime symbol will be used to indicate differentiation with respect to time. Thus, $v' = dv/dt$.

for the c_{ij} elements. These elements are all real constants. The $v_i\,(t)$ are the voltage variables, and the $v_i'\,(t)$ are the derivatives of these voltage variables. We have assumed that all the driving sources are zero, as is evidenced by the zeros on the right sides of the equations. This set of equations may also, of course, be written in matrix form as

$$Cv' + Gv = 0 \tag{2}$$

If we now define the initial conditions of the voltage variables, i.e., if we define the $v_i(0)$, all conditions on the network are specified, and we should be able to find the behavior of the $v_i(t)$. Since the excitation to the network has been assumed zero, the behavior of the $v_i(t)$ in this case is frequently referred to as the free oscillation or the natural behavior of the circuit. We assume, of course, that not all the $v_i(0)$ are zero. It is also appropriate to consider the resulting $v_i(t)$ as the transient response of the network, since the establishment of the initial conditions at $t = 0$ may be considered as the excitation of the network by means of impulses of current at the various nodes.

Let us now investigate (2) from the viewpoint of linear vector spaces. We shall begin by defining an orthonormal set of basis vectors x_i. With respect to each of these basis vectors, we shall assign a measure number v_i. Note that here we diverge slightly from our convention of using lowercase roman letters with a single subscript as vectors. For the remainder of this section, the v_i will be considered as scalars. These measure numbers are the values of the voltages at the various nodes of the network. Since these voltages are functions of time, we may more appropriately describe the measure numbers as $v_i(t)$. For simplicity of representation, however, we shall not always include the functional notation, i.e., the "(t)" in our discussion.

In the n-dimensional space, we may now consider an n-dimensional vector $\bar{V}$ which represents the totality of information concerning the n nodal voltages at any given instant of time. Obviously, $\bar{V}$ is also a function of time, i.e., we may refer to it as $\bar{V}(t)$. If we define

$$x = \begin{bmatrix} x_1 \\ \cdots \\ x_n \end{bmatrix} \qquad v = \begin{bmatrix} v_1 \\ \cdots \\ v_n \end{bmatrix} \tag{3}$$

and repeat for emphasis that the x_i are vectors and the $v_i(t)$ are the scalar nodal voltages which are functions of time, then we may write

$$\bar{V} = v^t x \tag{4}$$

If we follow the development of Sec. 5.8, we know that there exists a matrix, which we shall designate as A, such that

$$A^t C A = 1$$

$$A^t G A = D = \begin{bmatrix} \lambda_1 & \cdots & 0 \\ \cdot & \cdots & \cdot \\ 0 & \cdots & \lambda_n \end{bmatrix} \tag{5}$$

In addition, we know that the measure numbers of the columns of A, referred to the basis vectors x_i on which the matrices C and G are defined, determine the eigenvectors of (2). To clarify the future development, it is very important to note here that there are two ways in which we may refer to these eigenvectors. We may consider that the matrix A is composed of individual column matrices which we shall refer to as the A_i. Thus,

$$A_1 = \begin{bmatrix} a_{11} \\ \cdots \\ a_{n1} \end{bmatrix} \quad A_2 = \begin{bmatrix} a_{12} \\ \cdots \\ a_{n2} \end{bmatrix} \quad A_n = \begin{bmatrix} a_{1n} \\ \cdots \\ a_{nn} \end{bmatrix} \tag{6}$$

and

$$A = [A_1 \mid A_2 \mid \cdots \mid A_n] \tag{7}$$

In other words, the A_i contain the measure numbers, referred to the x_i basis, that determine the ith eigenvector. Thus, the A_i serve to locate the eigenvectors once we know the details of the x_i basis. A different viewpoint will also be useful, i.e., referring to the eigenvectors by a literal symbol, rather than by a group of measure numbers. For this we shall use lowercase letters with a single subscript such as a_i. The relation between the a_i and the A_i is given by the equations

$$a_i = A_i^t x$$

Thus we may write

$$a = \begin{bmatrix} a_1 \\ \cdots \\ a_n \end{bmatrix} = \begin{bmatrix} A_1^t \\ \cdots \\ A_n^t \end{bmatrix} \begin{bmatrix} x_1 \\ \cdots \\ x_n \end{bmatrix} = A^t x \tag{8}$$

We may now express our vector in terms of the new basis vectors a_i by using a new set of measure numbers θ_i. Since the vector $\bar{V}$ may change with time, these real numbers are functions of time, just as the scalars v_i are functions of time. The vector $\bar{V}$ may be written

$$\bar{V} = \theta^t a \tag{9}$$

where

$$\theta = \begin{bmatrix} \theta_1 \\ \cdots \\ \theta_n \end{bmatrix} \tag{10}$$

If we substitute (8) in (9), we obtain

$$\bar{V} = \theta^t A^t x \tag{11}$$

When this equation is compared with (4), we see that

$$v^t = \theta^t A^t \tag{12}$$

This may also be written

$$v = A\theta \tag{13}$$

Since the elements v_i and θ_i are functions of time, while the measure numbers of A are constants, we may differentiate both sides of the above equation to obtain

$$v' = A\theta' \tag{14}$$

Now let us substitute (13) and (14) in (2). We obtain

$$CA\theta' + GA\theta = 0 \tag{15}$$

If we premultiply both sides of the above by A^t, we obtain

$$A^t C A\theta' + A^t G A\theta = 0 \tag{16}$$

This may be simplified, by the relations (5), to

$$1\theta' + D\theta = 0 \tag{17}$$

Thus we see that, in terms of the θ_i measure numbers, i.e., those that relate to the eigenvector basis, our *system* of differential equations given in (1) becomes a collection of quite straightforward differential equations which may be written individually as

$$\theta_1'(t) + \lambda_1 \theta_1(t) = 0$$
$$\cdots \cdots \cdots \cdots \tag{18}$$
$$\theta_n'(t) + \lambda_n \theta_n(t) = 0$$

We need now only find the initial conditions associated with the various variables $\theta_i(t)$, i.e., we need only find the values of the various $\theta_i(0)$. We may solve for these in the form of a column matrix, assuming that the initial values of the various nodal voltages, i.e., the $v_i(0)$, are known. From (13) we have

$$v(0) = A\theta(0) \tag{19}$$

Since we have assumed that $v(0)$ is known, we would like to solve (19) for $\theta(0)$. This can be done very simply by first premultiplying both sides by C. This yields

$$Cv(0) = CA\theta(0)$$

Now premultiply both sides of the above equation by A^t. Since $A^t CA = 1$, we obtain

$$A^t Cv(0) = A^t CA\theta(0) = \theta(0) \tag{20}$$

This points out the interesting fact that

$$A^{-1} = A^t C \tag{21}$$

This is a clear reminder of the fact that A is not orthogonal, as was pointed out in Sec. 5.8.

The final step in our development in this section will make use of a result from Sec. 2.11. We showed there that we can solve a matrix differential equation of the type

$$y' = Ay$$

by defining an exponential to a matrix power. Thus, in terms of the initial conditions $y(0)$, our solution was

$$y = e^{tA}y(0)$$

This is precisely the situation that applies to the development of this section. From (17) we have

$$\theta' = -D\theta$$

In terms of the initial conditions $\theta(0)$, our solution is

$$\theta = e^{-tD}\theta(0) \tag{22}$$

Since D is a diagonal matrix, the matrix equation above simply represents a collection of individual equations, i.e., we may also write (22) as

$$\theta_1(t) = \theta_1(0)e^{-\lambda_1 t}$$
$$\cdots \cdots \cdots \tag{23}$$
$$\theta_n(t) = \theta_n(0)e^{-\lambda_n t}$$

Thus, in terms of the measure numbers of our eigenvectors, we have found the solution for the time behavior of an n-node passive RC network. We would, of course, like this answer to be expressed in terms of the nodal voltages and their time variation. To do this, we need only convert the $\theta_i(t)$ of (23) back to the measure numbers $v_i(t)$ by means of (13).

It seems almost impossible to overemphasize the fundamental importance of the ideas and concepts of this section. The most significant conclusion lies in the equations (23). Since each of the time functions $\theta_i(t)$ is a measure of the significance of a specific eigenvector a_i in determining all the nodal voltages in the network (and thus determining the vector $\bar{V}$), and since each $\theta_i(t)$ has a specific exponential behavior determined by the eigenvalue λ_i associated with that eigenvector, we see that *the eigenvalues are the natural frequencies* of the network; i.e., they have the dimensions of reciprocal time. Any oscillation of a given RC network as it responds to an arbitrary set of initial conditions can consist only of these natural frequencies and no others. Many powerful concepts and much fruitful interpretation of network behavior is based explicitly on this fundamental concept. In the next section, we shall present a simple example to illustrate the ideas and techniques developed in this section.

6.3 *An example of RC-network analysis*

In this section we shall go through the procedure explained in the last section for a simple *RC* network. The reader is encouraged (and exhorted) to try the example himself, without additional reference to the material in this section, by following the steps in the last section. In this way, he may check his progress by comparing his results at each step with those in the text. The experience and confidence built up by this type of study are invaluable, and the techniques we are covering here are easily of enough importance to merit the additional labor.

The network we shall analyze is shown in Fig. 6.1. The nodal voltages v_1 and v_2 of the figure are measured as positive with respect to the indicated ground, and the values of the elements are given in mhos and farads. The nodal equations in the time domain are

$$0.5v_1' + 2v_1 - v_2 = 0$$
$$1v_2' - 1v_1 + 3v_2 = 0 \qquad (1)$$

These may be written in matrix form as

$$Cv' + Gv = \begin{bmatrix} \frac{1}{2} & 0 \\ 0 & 1 \end{bmatrix} \begin{bmatrix} v_1' \\ v_2' \end{bmatrix} + \begin{bmatrix} 2 & -1 \\ -1 & 3 \end{bmatrix} \begin{bmatrix} v_1 \\ v_2 \end{bmatrix} = \begin{bmatrix} 0 \\ 0 \end{bmatrix} \qquad (2)$$

Since the network of Fig. 6.1 has two nodal voltages, we may represent it in a two-dimensional space such as that shown in Fig. 6.2. The choice of an example with such a small number of nodes will permit us to follow closely the geometrical significance of the various steps of the development. This is quite essential for a physical understanding of the process we are following. Once the student has developed familiarity and confidence with these techniques, he will find that their extension to higher dimensions follows quite easily.

In Fig. 6.2 we have indicated an orthonormal basis with vectors x_1 and x_2. The measure numbers $v_1(t)$ and $v_2(t)$ referred to these basis vectors

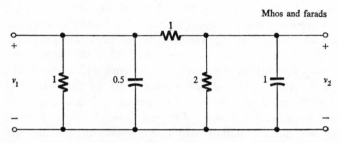

Figure 6.1   An RC network with two voltage variables.

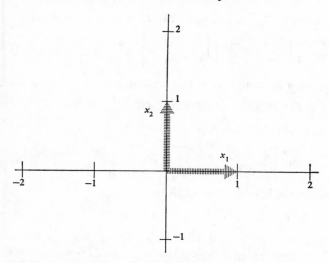

Figure 6.2   The orthonormal basis vectors x_i.

thus define a point in the plane. For example, if we have a network condition at $t = 0$ such that $v_1(0) = 2$ and $v_2(0) = 1$, then, in accordance with the notation of the previous section, we have defined a voltage vector $\bar{V}(0)$, where

$$\bar{V}(0) = 2x_1 + 1x_2$$

The vector $\bar{V}(0)$ is shown in Fig. 6.3.

Now let us return to a consideration of the matrices of (2). The C matrix is already in diagonal form. It may be reduced to the identity matrix by the transformation

$$B^tCB = \begin{bmatrix} 2^{\frac{1}{2}} & 0 \\ 0 & 1 \end{bmatrix} \begin{bmatrix} \frac{1}{2} & 0 \\ 0 & 1 \end{bmatrix} \begin{bmatrix} 2^{\frac{1}{2}} & 0 \\ 0 & 1 \end{bmatrix} = \begin{bmatrix} 1 & 0 \\ 0 & 1 \end{bmatrix} = 1 \tag{3}$$

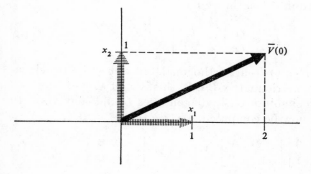

Figure 6.3   The voltage vector representing the initial conditions of the network in Fig. 6.1.

The same transformation may be applied to the G matrix to produce

$$B^tGB = \begin{bmatrix} 2^{\frac{1}{2}} & 0 \\ 0 & 1 \end{bmatrix}\begin{bmatrix} 2 & -1 \\ -1 & 3 \end{bmatrix}\begin{bmatrix} 2^{\frac{1}{2}} & 0 \\ 0 & 1 \end{bmatrix} = \begin{bmatrix} 4 & -2^{\frac{1}{2}} \\ -2^{\frac{1}{2}} & 3 \end{bmatrix} \tag{4}$$

The eigenvalues may now be found from the equation

$$\det (G - \lambda C) = \det B^t(G - \lambda C)B = \det (B^tGB - \lambda I) = 0$$

If we substitute from (4) in the above, we obtain

$$\det \begin{bmatrix} 4 - \lambda & -2^{\frac{1}{2}} \\ -2^{\frac{1}{2}} & 3 - \lambda \end{bmatrix} = 0 \tag{5}$$

The characteristic equation is easily found to be

$$(\lambda - 4)(\lambda - 3) - 2 = \lambda^2 - 7\lambda + 10 = (\lambda - 5)(\lambda - 2) = 0 \tag{6}$$

Thus we may define $\lambda_1 = 5$ and $\lambda_2 = 2$. Let us also define R_i as a column matrix composed of the measure numbers which represent an eigenvector of the matrix B^tGB. For $\lambda_1 = 5$, we have

$$\begin{bmatrix} 4 - 5 & -2^{\frac{1}{2}} \\ -2^{\frac{1}{2}} & 3 - 5 \end{bmatrix}\begin{bmatrix} r_{11} \\ r_{21} \end{bmatrix} = \begin{bmatrix} 0 \\ 0 \end{bmatrix} \tag{7}$$

Thus R_1 must have its elements satisfy the relation $r_{11} = -2^{\frac{1}{2}}r_{21}$. If we normalize this vector to unit length, we have

$$R_1 = \begin{bmatrix} r_{11} \\ r_{21} \end{bmatrix} = \begin{bmatrix} -(\frac{2}{3})^{\frac{1}{2}} \\ \frac{1}{3^{\frac{1}{2}}} \end{bmatrix} \tag{8}$$

Similarly, for the eigenvector $\lambda_2 = 2$ we have

$$\begin{bmatrix} 4 - 2 & -2^{\frac{1}{2}} \\ -2^{\frac{1}{2}} & 3 - 2 \end{bmatrix}\begin{bmatrix} r_{12} \\ r_{22} \end{bmatrix} = \begin{bmatrix} 0 \\ 0 \end{bmatrix} \tag{9}$$

Thus R_2 must have its elements satisfy the relation $r_{12} = (\frac{1}{2})^{\frac{1}{2}}r_{22}$. If we normalize this vector to unit length, we have

$$R_2 = \begin{bmatrix} r_{12} \\ r_{22} \end{bmatrix} = \begin{bmatrix} (\frac{1}{3})^{\frac{1}{2}} \\ (\frac{2}{3})^{\frac{1}{2}} \end{bmatrix} \tag{10}$$

Note that the vectors R_1 and R_2 are orthogonal. Since they are the eigenvectors of the real symmetric matrix B^tGB, this is as it should be.

The matrix A which simultaneously diagonalizes G and converts C to the unity matrix may now be computed. We see that $A = BR$.

$$A = \begin{bmatrix} 2^{\frac{1}{2}} & 0 \\ 0 & 1 \end{bmatrix}\begin{bmatrix} -2^{\frac{1}{2}} & 1 \\ 1 & 2^{\frac{1}{2}} \end{bmatrix}(\frac{1}{3})^{\frac{1}{2}} = (\frac{1}{3})^{\frac{1}{2}}\begin{bmatrix} -2 & 2^{\frac{1}{2}} \\ 1 & 2^{\frac{1}{2}} \end{bmatrix} \tag{11}$$

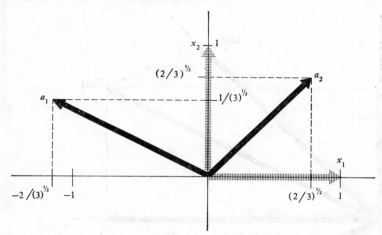

Figure 6.4   The eigenvector basis a_i for the network in Fig. 6.1.

Thus we have found two eigenvectors defined by column matrices of measure numbers A_1 and A_2, defined in terms of their measure numbers on the x_i basis, where

$$A_1 = \begin{bmatrix} a_{11} \\ a_{21} \end{bmatrix} = \begin{bmatrix} \frac{-2}{3^{\frac{1}{2}}} \\ (\frac{1}{3})^{\frac{1}{2}} \end{bmatrix} \qquad A_2 = \begin{bmatrix} a_{12} \\ a_{22} \end{bmatrix} = \begin{bmatrix} (\frac{2}{3})^{\frac{1}{2}} \\ (\frac{2}{3})^{\frac{1}{2}} \end{bmatrix} \tag{12}$$

These eigenvectors will be referred to as a_1 and a_2, following the discussion of the previous section. It should be noted that they are neither of unit length nor orthogonal. However, they are linearly independent, and thus they do provide a basis for our two-dimensional space. They are shown in Fig. 6.4.

Since the a_i provide a basis for the space, any arbitrary vector such as $\vec{V}$ may be written in terms of them. Thus we may express the nodal voltages in terms of the vectors a_i, using measure numbers θ_i for this purpose. These measure numbers are functions of time and have the solution given in (23) of Sec. 6.2. Suppose, for example, our initial conditions on the network are $v_1(0) = 2$, $v_2(0) = 1$, as shown in Fig. 6.3. Thus we define a column matrix $v(0)$, where

$$v(0) = \begin{bmatrix} 2 \\ 1 \end{bmatrix} \tag{13}$$

The $\theta_i(0)$ are easily found from (20) of Sec. 6.2, i.e., $\theta(0) = A^t C v(0)$.

$$\theta(0) = (\tfrac{1}{3})^{\frac{1}{2}} \begin{bmatrix} -2 & 1 \\ 2^{\frac{1}{2}} & 2^{\frac{1}{2}} \end{bmatrix} \begin{bmatrix} \frac{1}{2} & 0 \\ 0 & 1 \end{bmatrix} \begin{bmatrix} 2 \\ 1 \end{bmatrix} = \begin{bmatrix} \frac{-1}{3^{\frac{1}{2}}} \\ 2(\frac{2}{3})^{\frac{1}{2}} \end{bmatrix} = \begin{bmatrix} -0.578 \\ 1.632 \end{bmatrix} \tag{14}$$

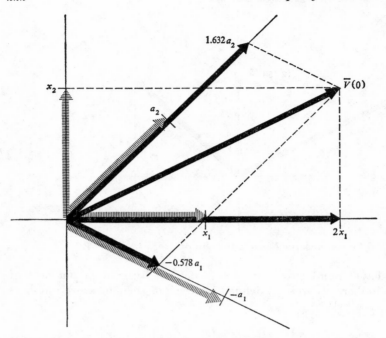

Figure 6.5   The initial condition voltage vector represented on the eigenvector basis.

In Fig. 6.5 we have indicated how -0.578 units of vector a_1 and 1.632 units of vector a_2 add to give the vector $\bar{V}(0)$. This latter vector may also be expressed as 2 units of x_1 and 1 unit of x_2. Thus we are able to express our initial conditions for the network in terms of either basis. Now let us see what happens to those initial conditions as time progresses.

At this point we illustrate the most important concept of our whole example. $\theta_1(t)$ is a measure number referred to eigenvector a_1. Therefore, since λ_1 is the eigenvalue for the eigenvector a_1, the time behavior of $\theta_1(t)$ is determined only by this eigenvalue [and, of course, by the value of $\theta_1(0)$], and by no other factor. Similar statements apply to $\theta_2(t)$ with reference to λ_2. Thus, for this example, the relations (23) of Sec. 6.2 become

$$\theta_1 = \frac{-1}{3^{\frac{1}{2}}}\, e^{-5t}$$
$$\theta_2 = 2(\tfrac{2}{3})^{\frac{1}{2}} e^{-2t} \tag{15}$$

In Fig. 6.6, we have plotted various values of $\theta_1(t)$ and $\theta_2(t)$ along the coordinate system formed by vectors a_1 and a_2. In addition, we have combined the information from these two time functions to indicate the posi-

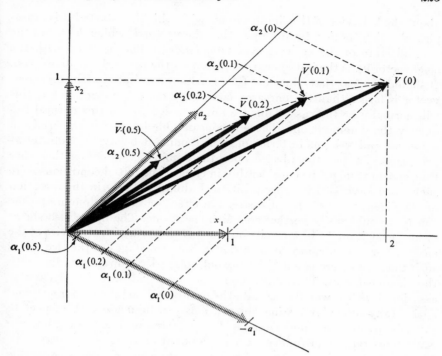

Figure 6.6   The voltage vector as a function of time.

tion of $\bar{V}(t)$ for these same values of time. The values of $v_1(t)$ and $v_2(t)$ may easily be visualized from the projections of $\bar{V}(t)$ on x_1 and x_2. They may also be computed directly from (13) of Sec. 6.2, which tells us that $v = A\theta$. Thus we see that

$$v(t) = (\tfrac{1}{3})^{\frac{1}{2}} \begin{bmatrix} -2 & 2^{\frac{1}{2}} \\ 1 & 2^{\frac{1}{2}} \end{bmatrix} \begin{bmatrix} \dfrac{-1}{3^{\frac{1}{2}}} e^{-5t} \\ 2(\tfrac{2}{3})^{\frac{1}{2}} e^{-2t} \end{bmatrix} \tag{16}$$

After multiplication, we obtain

$$v(t) = \begin{bmatrix} v_1(t) \\ v_2(t) \end{bmatrix} = \begin{bmatrix} \tfrac{2}{3}e^{-5t} + \tfrac{4}{3}e^{-2t} \\ -\tfrac{1}{3}e^{-5t} + \tfrac{4}{3}e^{-2t} \end{bmatrix} \tag{17}$$

An examination of the equations (16) and (17) further illustrates how a consideration of the eigenvectors separates the natural frequencies of a network and allows us to associate a specific vector with a specific natural frequency.

From a consideration of Fig. 6.6, we can gain considerable knowledge about the behavior of the simple circuit with which we started this example. We might notice, for example, that the vector $\bar{V}$ which describes the over-all state of the network has a tendency to line itself up with the eigenvector a_2 as the initial charges placed on the network are dissipated. It should be clear that, since the time constant associated with this eigenvector is larger than the one associated with the other eigenvector, this will normally be the case. Thus we might be led to call this natural frequency the dominant one. There is considerable interest in the study of networks and systems in terms of their dominant behavior. Note, however, that considerations based upon the dominance of one or the other time constant might be considerably in error if the initial conditions were such as to have $\bar{V}(t)$ initially positioned almost entirely in the direction of the eigenvector a_1. In this case, the effect of the nondominant time constant could easily be the most significant one. The figure also shows us how easy it might be to excite only one of the natural frequencies of the circuit. For example, any distribution of initial voltages at the two nodes such that $v_1(0)$ were equal to $v_2(0)$ would place $\bar{V}(0)$ directly in line with the eigenvector a_2. Thus $\theta_1(0)$ would be zero, and only the eigenvalue associated with a_2 would enter into the resulting time solution for $v_1(t)$ and $v_2(t)$. Many other interesting observations can be made with respect to this circuit. For example, we might be interested in determining how we could most rapidly introduce a certain amount of charge into the circuit. The conclusion, of course, would be to apportion this charge between the two nodes in such a manner that only the eigenvector whose eigenvalue had the shortest time constant was excited. The ratio of voltages that must be maintained at the two nodes in order to do this is readily apparent from the figure.

The purpose of this section has been to illustrate to the student the tremendous amount of physical introspection that can be gained concerning a network through the use of the concepts of linear vector spaces. A very simple example has been worked through at a somewhat leisurely pace to ensure that the reader has the opportunity to fix the steps and their implications firmly in his mind. At this time, further study of Sec. 6.2 is heartily suggested. A repetition of the general treatment given there, now that a numerical example has been seen, will greatly aid the student in assimilating the concepts that have been presented. Needless to say, this will smooth his way through the sections that follow.

6.4 *LC-network analysis*

This section will follow a procedure quite similar to that of Sec. 6.2. The network we shall explore here, however, will be the lossless network composed only of ideal inductors and capacitors. Actually, we might also have devoted a section to a discussion of the RL network. The development for that type of network, however (if we use loop equations), follows identically the procedure used for the RC case, the only exception being that the variables are the loop currents rather than the nodal voltages of Sec. 6.2.

In treating the LC network, it is convenient to pick a variable that enters into the equation only in the form of derivatives. Obviously, this is not possible if we choose our variable with the dimensions of either voltage or current, since the LC elements will require the integrals of one of these variables, as well as the derivatives. To avoid this, we shall choose charge as our variable and write our equations on a loop basis. Thus, the typical loop, rather than involving terms such as $li' + s\int i\,dt$ (where s is the elastance or reciprocal capacitance), will involve terms such as $lq'' + sq$. For an n-loop network without driving sources, we will have a series of equations

$$l_{11}q_1'' + \cdots + l_{1n}q_n'' + s_{11}q_1 + \cdots + s_{1n}q_n = 0$$
$$\cdots\cdots\cdots\cdots\cdots\cdots\cdots\cdots\cdots\cdots\cdots\cdots\cdots \tag{1}$$
$$l_{n1}q_1'' + \cdots + l_{nn}q_n'' + s_{n1}q_1 + \cdots + s_{nn}q_n = 0$$

The l_{ij} represent the various total- and mutual-inductance values, and the s_{ij} represent the various total- and mutual-elastance values. The $q_i(t)$ are the integrals of current in the various loops, and the $q_i''(t)$ are the second derivatives of the q_i with respect to time. In matrix form we may write

$$Lq'' + Sq = 0 \tag{2}$$

Just as in Sec. 6.2, we may consider the q_i as measure numbers referred to an orthonormal set of basis vectors x_i. If we define $\bar{Q}(t)$ as a vector representing the values of all the charges at a given instant of time, then

$$\bar{Q}(t) = q^t x \tag{3}$$

From Sec. 5.8, we know that it is possible to find a matrix A such that

$$A^t L A = 1$$
$$A^t S A = D = \begin{bmatrix} \lambda_1 & \cdots & 0 \\ \cdot & \cdots & \cdot \\ 0 & \cdots & \lambda_n \end{bmatrix} \tag{4}$$

If we partition A into column matrices, we may call these submatrices A_i. Each of these column matrices then contains the measure numbers of an eigenvector a_i, and we may express the relationships between the a_i and the x_i by the matrix equation

$$a = A^t x \tag{5}$$

Since our vector $\bar{Q}$ may now be expressed in terms of the eigenvectors a_i

using measure numbers $\theta_i(t)$, we may write

$$\overline{Q}(t) = \theta^t a \tag{6}$$

From the above equations it is easy to see that

$$q = A\theta \tag{7}$$

The elements of the matrix A are real and constant; therefore

$$q'' = A\theta'' \tag{8}$$

We may substitute (7) and (8) into our original matrix equation (2) to obtain

$$LA\theta'' + SA\theta = 0 \tag{9}$$

If we premultiply both sides of (9) by A^t, we obtain

$$A^tLA\theta'' + A^tSA\theta = 0 \tag{10}$$

The relations (4) allow us to simplify this to

$$1\theta'' + D\theta = 0 \tag{11}$$

Thus we see that, in terms of the θ_i measure numbers, i.e., the ones that relate to the eigenvector basis, our original *system* of differential equations becomes a quite straightforward collection of second-order differential equations. These may be written

$$\begin{aligned}
\theta_1'' + \lambda_1\theta_1 &= 0 \\
\cdots\cdots\cdots\cdots \\
\theta_n'' + \lambda_n\theta_n &= 0
\end{aligned} \tag{12}$$

Two sets of initial conditions are required for the solution of these, namely, the conditions $\theta_i(0)$ and the conditions $\theta_i'(0)$. We shall assume that the $q_i(0)$ and the $q_i'(0)$ are known. Then it is easy to see from (4) and (7) that

$$\begin{aligned}
\theta(0) &= A^tLq(0) \\
\theta'(0) &= A^tLq'(0)
\end{aligned} \tag{13}$$

Since the matrices L and S are positive definite, real, and symmetric, the eigenvalues λ_i will be real and positive. If we define

$$\lambda_i = \omega_i{}^2 \tag{14}$$

then the ω_i are real, and the solutions of equations (12) are easily found to be

$$\begin{aligned}
\theta_1 &= \theta_1(0) \cos \omega_1 t + \frac{\theta_1'(0)}{\omega_1} \sin \omega_1 t \\
&\cdots\cdots\cdots\cdots\cdots\cdots\cdots \\
\theta_n &= \theta_n(0) \cos \omega_n t + \frac{\theta_n'(0)}{\omega_n} \sin \omega_n t
\end{aligned} \tag{15}$$

From the above, we see that with each eigenvector a_i we have associated a certain sinusoidal behavior of the related measure number θ_i. This measure number has one and only one frequency component associated with it. In addition to the frequency, there is, of course, a phase angle determined by the relative magnitudes of $\theta_i(0)$ and $\theta_i'(0)/\omega_i$. By way of contrast, the measure numbers q_i and the mesh currents that are related to them will have, in general, all the frequencies simultaneously present in their time behavior.

As an example, consider the two-loop network shown in Fig. 6.7. The loop currents i_1 and i_2 have been chosen in such a direction that the off-diagonal elements in the L and S matrices are positive. No voltage sources are shown, since these have been assumed equal to zero. Thus all the excitation of the network comes from the initial conditions of charge on the capacitors and the derivative of charge, i.e., current, flowing in the inductors. In terms of the q_i variables, we may write the matrix equation $Lq'' + Sq = 0$ for this circuit as

$$\begin{bmatrix} 2 & 1 \\ 1 & 2 \end{bmatrix} \begin{bmatrix} q_1'' \\ q_2'' \end{bmatrix} + \begin{bmatrix} 1 & 1 \\ 1 & 2 \end{bmatrix} \begin{bmatrix} q_1 \\ q_2 \end{bmatrix} = \begin{bmatrix} 0 \\ 0 \end{bmatrix} \tag{16}$$

We may use the techniques of Sec. 5.8 to find a matrix A such that the relations of (4) are satisfied. We see that

$$A = \begin{bmatrix} (\tfrac{2}{3})^{\frac{1}{2}} & 0 \\ -(\tfrac{1}{6})^{\frac{1}{2}} & (\tfrac{1}{2})^{\frac{1}{2}} \end{bmatrix} \tag{17}$$

The eigenvalues are found from $A^t S A = D$. We see that

$$\begin{bmatrix} (\tfrac{2}{3})^{\frac{1}{2}} & -(\tfrac{1}{6})^{\frac{1}{2}} \\ 0 & (\tfrac{1}{2})^{\frac{1}{2}} \end{bmatrix} \begin{bmatrix} 1 & 1 \\ 1 & 2 \end{bmatrix} \begin{bmatrix} (\tfrac{2}{3})^{\frac{1}{2}} & 0 \\ -(\tfrac{1}{6})^{\frac{1}{2}} & (\tfrac{1}{2})^{\frac{1}{2}} \end{bmatrix} = \begin{bmatrix} \tfrac{1}{3} & 0 \\ 0 & 1 \end{bmatrix}$$

Thus our eigenvalues are $\lambda_1 = \tfrac{1}{3}$, and $\lambda_2 = 1$. The sinusoidal solutions for the measure number θ_1 will thus have only a sinusoidal component with a frequency of $(\tfrac{1}{3})^{\frac{1}{2}}$ radians per second, and the measure number θ_2 will have

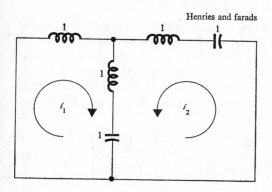

Henries and farads

Figure 6.7 A two-loop LC network.

only a sinusoidal component with a frequency of 1 radian per second; i.e., we may write

$$\theta_1 = \theta_1(0) \cos \left(\tfrac{1}{3}\right)^{\frac{1}{2}}t + \theta_1'(0)3^{\frac{1}{2}} \sin \left(\tfrac{1}{3}\right)^{\frac{1}{2}}t$$
$$\theta_2 = \theta_2(0) \cos t + \theta_2'(0) \sin t \tag{18}$$

The initial conditions of the θ_i may be found from (13). Suppose, for example, that there was an initial charge of 1 coulomb in each loop, i.e., 1 amp had flowed for 1 second in each loop. The column matrix $q(0)$ would then be

$$q(0) = \left.\begin{matrix} 1 \\ 1 \end{matrix}\right] \tag{19}$$

If we assume that the $q_i'(0)$ are zero, i.e., that there is no initial current flowing in the inductors, then $\theta(0)$ is

$$\theta(0) = A^t L q(0) = \begin{bmatrix} \left(\tfrac{2}{3}\right)^{\frac{1}{2}} & \dfrac{-1}{6^{\frac{1}{2}}} \\ 0 & \left(\tfrac{1}{2}\right)^{\frac{1}{2}} \end{bmatrix} \begin{bmatrix} 2 & 1 \\ 1 & 2 \end{bmatrix} \begin{bmatrix} 1 \\ 1 \end{bmatrix} = \begin{bmatrix} \left(\tfrac{3}{2}\right)^{\frac{1}{2}} \\ \dfrac{3}{2^{\frac{1}{2}}} \end{bmatrix} \tag{20}$$

and $\theta'(0)$ is zero. The values of $\theta_i(t)$ may be found from (18).

$$\theta_1 = \left(\tfrac{3}{2}\right)^{\frac{1}{2}} \cos \left(\tfrac{1}{3}\right)^{\frac{1}{2}}t$$
$$\theta_2 = \frac{3}{2^{\frac{1}{2}}} \cos t \tag{21}$$

As a final step, we may apply (7) to find our original variables, the q_i. We see that

$$q = A\theta = \begin{bmatrix} \left(\tfrac{2}{3}\right)^{\frac{1}{2}} & 0 \\ \dfrac{-1}{6^{\frac{1}{2}}} & \left(\tfrac{1}{2}\right)^{\frac{1}{2}} \end{bmatrix} \begin{bmatrix} \left(\tfrac{3}{2}\right)^{\frac{1}{2}} \cos \left(\tfrac{1}{3}\right)^{\frac{1}{2}}t \\ \dfrac{3}{2^{\frac{1}{2}}} \cos t \end{bmatrix} \tag{22}$$

Therefore our solution to the circuit of Fig. 6.7 with the stated initial conditions is

$$q_1 = \cos \left(\tfrac{1}{3}\right)^{\frac{1}{2}}t$$
$$q_2 = -\tfrac{1}{2} \cos \left(\tfrac{1}{3}\right)^{\frac{1}{2}}t + \tfrac{3}{2} \cos t \tag{23}$$

Just as in the case of our *RC* analysis, we can easily excite any one of the natural frequencies of our *LC* network by simply choosing the initial conditions correctly. Thus, if it is desired to excite only the natural frequency which is the square root of the first eigenvalue, we need only establish initial conditions on the $q_i(0)$ and the $q_i'(0)$ so that $\theta_1(0)$ and/or $\theta_1'(0)$ are not zero, but that all the other $\theta_i(0)$ and $\theta_i'(0)$ are zero. In the case of our example, from (7) we see that

$$q(0) = A\theta(0) = \begin{bmatrix} \left(\tfrac{2}{3}\right)^{\frac{1}{2}} & 0 \\ \dfrac{-1}{6^{\frac{1}{2}}} & \left(\tfrac{1}{2}\right)^{\frac{1}{2}} \end{bmatrix} \begin{bmatrix} k_1 \\ 0 \end{bmatrix} = \begin{bmatrix} k_1\left(\tfrac{2}{3}\right)^{\frac{1}{2}} \\ \dfrac{-k_1}{6^{\frac{1}{2}}} \end{bmatrix} \tag{24}$$

and
$$q'(0) = A\theta'(0) = \begin{bmatrix} (\tfrac{2}{3})^{\frac{1}{2}} & 0 \\ \dfrac{-1}{6^{\frac{1}{2}}} & (\tfrac{1}{2})^{\frac{1}{2}} \end{bmatrix} \begin{bmatrix} k_2 \\ 0 \end{bmatrix} = \begin{bmatrix} k_2(\tfrac{2}{3})^{\frac{1}{2}} \\ \dfrac{-k_2}{6^{\frac{1}{2}}} \end{bmatrix} \tag{25}$$

are conditions which will excite only the sinusoidal frequency of $1/3^{\frac{1}{2}}$ radians per second. This will be true for all values of the real constants k_1 and k_2. For example, we might choose $k_1 = (\tfrac{3}{2})^{\frac{1}{2}}$ and $k_2 = 0$. From (24) and (25), this requires the placing of initial loop charges $q_1(0) = 1$ and $q_2(0) = -\tfrac{1}{2}$. Since the capacitances are of unit value, these represent the total initial voltages placed on the capacitors in the first and second loops, respectively.

In this section we have adopted the same general procedure as that which was followed in Sec. 6.2. In the earlier section, we analyzed an *RC* network from the viewpoint of the eigenvectors of a linear vector space. In this section we analyzed an *LC* network from the viewpoint of its eigenvalues. Actually, in this section, we have not applied the formalism of the matrix solution of differential equations which was introduced in Sec. 2.11. In a following section, we shall see how a more general specification of the problem may be adopted which will treat not only the *RC* and *LC* cases, but also the *RLC* case.

6.5 *Analysis in the frequency domain*

In the preceding sections of this chapter we studied the behavior of *RC* and *LC* networks from a consideration of their eigenvalues and eigenvectors. The analysis was made in the time domain, i.e., we dealt with variables which were functions of time. It is easy to see that this analysis could also have been made in the complex frequency domain. This section will discuss the analysis of general *RC* and *LC* networks in the frequency domain.

First let us consider the *RC* network. The basic analysis of Sec. 6.2 showed that if the network equations were written on a node basis, they would form a set of equations which could be written in matrix form as

$$Cv' + Gv = 0 \tag{1}$$

The column matrix v represents the scalar nodal voltages which are functions of time. The column matrix v' represents the time derivatives of these quantities. The equation assumes that all the excitation of the network comes from initial conditions alone. These initial conditions may also be represented as the column matrix $v(0)$. If we take the Laplace transform of the voltage variables, each of the elements in the column matrices v and v' is transformed; therefore, we can write a new column matrix which we shall denote as V. The elements of this matrix will be functions of the complex frequency variable p. It should be clear that

$$v(t) \rightarrow V(p)$$
$$v'(t) \rightarrow pV(p) - v(0) \tag{2}$$

where the arrow indicates transformation by means of the Laplace transform. The relations of (1) may now be written in their transformed form as the matrix equation

$$pCV + GV = Cv(0) \tag{3}$$

We may now consider the various $V_i(p)$, i.e., the elements of the column matrix V, as measure numbers defined with respect to a set of orthonormal basis vectors x_i. Thus, we have defined a vector $\bar{V}(p)$ such that

$$\bar{V}(p) = V^t x \tag{4}$$

We may now follow the procedure of Sec. 6.2 to find a matrix A that will simultaneously reduce C to the identity matrix and diagonalize G. Since the matrices C and G have not been changed by the Laplace transformation, the matrix A will have the same elements as it did in Sec. 6.2. We thus have the relationships

$$A^t C A = 1$$
$$A^t G A = D = \begin{bmatrix} \lambda_1 & \cdots & 0 \\ \cdot & \cdots & \cdot \\ 0 & \cdots & \lambda_n \end{bmatrix} \tag{5}$$

If we now define eigenvectors whose measure numbers are the elements of the columns of the matrix A, we may call these eigenvectors the a_i and use them to form a new basis for our space. The measure numbers that relate to these eigenvectors may be considered as $\theta_i(t)$, with transforms $\Theta_i(p)$. Thus we may define our vector $\bar{V}(p)$ as

$$\bar{V}(p) = \Theta^t a \tag{6}$$

where Θ is the column matrix whose elements are the $\Theta_i(p)$. Since the a_i are related to the x_i by the matrix A, i.e., since

$$a = A^t x$$

and since, in the time domain,

$$v = A\theta \tag{7}$$

we see that the initial-condition matrix $v(0)$ in the time domain is related to $\theta(0)$ by the expression

$$v(0) = A\theta(0) \tag{8}$$

Similarly, we may relate the $V_i(p)$ and the $\Theta_i(p)$ in the frequency domain by

$$V = A\Theta \tag{9}$$

If these relations are substituted in (3), we obtain

$$pCA\Theta + GA\Theta = CA\theta(0)$$

If we premultiply both sides of the above equation by A^t, we obtain

$$pA^tCA\Theta + A^tGA\Theta = A^tCA\theta(0) \tag{10}$$

Substituting the relations (5), we obtain

$$(p1 + D)\Theta = 1\theta(0) \tag{11}$$

Thus we have a set of equations for the $\Theta_i(p)$ in the frequency domain; they are:

$$\Theta_1(p) = \frac{\theta_1(0)}{p + \lambda_1}$$
$$\cdots\cdots\cdots\cdots \tag{12}$$
$$\Theta_n(p) = \frac{\theta_n(0)}{p + \lambda_n}$$

The inverse transforms of these are easily seen to be the results of (23) of Sec. 6.2. These solutions may, of course, be recombined in either the time or the frequency domain, using (7) or (9), to find either the column matrix $v(t)$ or the column matrix $V(p)$, thus specifying the behavior of the nodal voltages. The student should work out a physical example of the details of this analysis using the circuit given in Fig. 6.1.

A similar procedure may be followed for the LC network. The reader should review Sec. 6.4 and the development given there for the LC network. We may begin with the matrix equation for the case in which there are no external sources connected to the network. For this case, we have

$$Lq'' + Sq = 0 \tag{13}$$

The variables $q_i''(t)$ and $q_i(t)$ are given in matrix form as q'' and q, respectively. If we apply the Laplace transform to these quantities, we obtain

$$\begin{aligned} q(t) &\rightarrow Q(p) \\ q''(t) &\rightarrow p^2Q(p) - pq(0) - q'(0) \end{aligned} \tag{14}$$

The relations of (13) may now be written in terms of the transformed variables as

$$p^2LQ + SQ = pLq(0) + Lq'(0) \tag{15}$$

The $Q_i(p)$ may be considered as measure numbers defined with respect to a set of orthonormal basis vectors x_i. Thus, we have defined a vector $\bar{Q}(p)$ such that

$$\bar{Q}(p) = Q^tx \tag{16}$$

A matrix A may be found that satisfies the relationships

$$A^tLA = 1$$

$$A^tSA = D = \begin{bmatrix} \lambda_1 & \cdots & 0 \\ \cdots & \cdots & \cdots \\ 0 & \cdots & \lambda_n \end{bmatrix} \tag{17}$$

The columns of A with their measure numbers may be referred to as the A_i, and, on the x_i basis, they define the eigenvectors a_i. We may define the vector $\overline{Q}(p)$ by means of measure numbers $\Theta_i(p)$ with respect to the eigenvectors a_i. Thus we have

$$\overline{Q}(p) = \Theta^t a \tag{18}$$

Since

$$a = A^t x \tag{19}$$

it is easy to see that

$$Q = A\Theta$$
$$q(0) = A\theta(0) \tag{20}$$
$$q'(0) = A\theta'(0)$$

If these relations are substituted in (15), we obtain

$$p^2LA\Theta + SA\Theta = pLA\theta(0) + LA\theta'(0) \tag{21}$$

If we premultiply both sides of (21) by A^t, we obtain

$$p^2A^tLA\Theta + A^tSA\Theta = pA^tLA\theta(0) + A^tLA\theta'(0) \tag{22}$$

The relations of (17) may be substituted in (22) to obtain

$$(p^2 1 + D)\Theta = p\theta(0) + \theta'(0) \tag{23}$$

Thus, instead of solving a set of equations, each containing the n variables $Q_i(p)$, we need only solve a set of equations, each of which contains a single variable $\Theta_i(p)$. The solutions are

$$\Theta_1(p) = \frac{p\theta_1(0) + \theta_1'(0)}{p^2 + \lambda_1}$$
$$\cdots \cdots \cdots \cdots \cdots \cdots \tag{24}$$
$$\Theta_n(p) = \frac{p\theta_n(0) + \theta_n'(0)}{p^2 + \lambda_n}$$

The natural frequencies of the network are the poles of the above expressions. The actual time behavior of the loop charges may be found either by recombining the above terms to find the $Q_i(p)$ and then taking the inverse transform, or by taking the inverse transform of the $\Theta_i(p)$ and recombining the time functions $\theta_i(t)$ to find the $q_i(t)$. The student should follow through the steps of the example of Sec. 6.4 in the frequency domain to illustrate this procedure.

In this section we have shown that the development of the RC and LC networks (the same statements also apply to the RL case) may be considered in the frequency domain as well as in the time domain. The analysis of the networks in terms of their eigenvectors places the natural frequencies clearly in evidence in both cases, and the same conclusions may be drawn with respect to network performance in either domain.

6.6 *Driving functions*

In the last section it was shown that the eigenvalue approach to the solution of two-type-element networks could be applied in the frequency domain as well as in the time domain. The frequency-domain approach is especially easy to extend to the more practical case in which we may be concerned, not only with initial conditions in the network, but also with the effects of various inputs to the nodes or the loops of the network. In this section we shall discuss this extension, i.e., the effect of external driving functions applied to the network.

Let us first consider the RC network. In the time domain we may write the nodal equations for this network, in the form of a matrix equation, as

$$Cv' + Gv = i \tag{1}$$

The nodal voltages $v_i(t)$ have been listed as the elements of the column matrix v, and their time derivatives as the elements of the column matrix v'. The input currents $i_i(t)$ to the various nodes have been listed as the elements of the column matrix i. The G and C matrices are the same as those discussed in Secs. 6.2 and 6.3 and are composed of time-invariant elements.

We may apply the usual Laplace-transformation techniques to the variables $v_i(t)$ and $i_i(t)$, generating the variables $V_i(p)$ and $I_i(p)$. Note that the column matrix whose elements are the $I_i(p)$ will be referred to as I. The symbol 1 will be used for the identity matrix. The transform of the matrix equation (1) is

$$(pC + G)V = Cv(0) + I \tag{2}$$

We may now find a matrix A which satisfies the relations

$$A^t C A = 1$$

$$A^t G A = D = \begin{bmatrix} \lambda_1 & \cdots & 0 \\ \cdots & \cdots & \cdots \\ 0 & \cdots & \lambda_n \end{bmatrix} \tag{3}$$

If we change the basis on which the vector $\bar{V}(p)$ of (4) of Sec. 6.5 is defined, we may define the column matrices $\Theta(p)$ and $\theta(0)$ by the relations

$$V = A\Theta$$
$$v(0) = A\theta(0) \tag{4}$$

Equation (2) now becomes

$$(pC + G)A\Theta = CA\theta(0) + I \tag{5}$$

Premultiplying both sides of (5) by A^t, we obtain

$$(pA^tCA + A^tGA)\Theta = A^tCA\theta(0) + A^tI \tag{6}$$

The relations of (3) may be substituted into this equation to simplify it to the form

$$(p\mathbf{1} + D)\Theta = \theta(0) + A^tI \tag{7}$$

We may now define a set of excitations $\beta_i(p)$, the elements of a column matrix β defined by the relation

$$A^tI = \beta \tag{8}$$

The solution of (7) may now be expressed as

$$\Theta = (p\mathbf{1} + D)^{-1}\theta(0) + (p\mathbf{1} + D)^{-1}\beta \tag{9}$$

This is simply a set of equations in the individual variables $\Theta_i(p)$. These equations are

$$\Theta_1(p) = \frac{\theta_1(0)}{p + \lambda_1} + \frac{\beta_1(p)}{p + \lambda_1}$$
$$\cdots \cdots \cdots \cdots \cdots \cdots \cdots \tag{10}$$
$$\Theta_n(p) = \frac{\theta_n(0)}{p + \lambda_n} + \frac{\beta_n(p)}{p + \lambda_n}$$

The form of (10) tells us that each of the variables $\Theta_i(p)$ is the result of some initial condition $\theta_i(0)$ (in the time domain) and some forcing function $\beta_i(p)$. The latter will usually be a rational function with numerator and denominator polynomials with real coefficients. Thus, $\Theta_i(p)$ will not only have a pole resulting from the natural frequency at $-\lambda_i$ associated with its role as an eigenvector, but it will also have poles which are the result of the specific form of the forcing function. In addition, a forcing function of any given time behavior can be used to excite only a single natural frequency of the network by proper apportionment of the magnitude of this excitation among the various nodes of the network. The proper apportionment is determined by (8), which may be rewritten as

$$I = (A^t)^{-1}\beta \tag{11}$$

From (3) we see that $A^{-1} = A^tC$; therefore, the above equation may be written as

$$I = C^tA\beta \tag{12}$$

Another insight into the behavior of the network may be found by considering the inverse transformation of the equations (10), which become

$$\theta_1(t) = \theta_1(0)e^{-\lambda_1 t} + \mathcal{L}^{-1}\frac{\beta_1(p)}{p + \lambda_1}$$

$$\cdots\cdots\cdots\cdots\cdots\cdots\cdots\cdots\cdots \quad (13)$$

$$\theta_n(t) = \theta_n(0)e^{-\lambda_n t} + \mathcal{L}^{-1}\frac{\beta_n(p)}{p + \lambda_n}$$

The initial conditions thus have the effect of impulse functions and produce the first right-hand term in each of the above expressions. The inverse transformation of the second right-hand term will, in general, have the time behavior represented, not only by the inverse transformation of the poles of $\beta_i(p)$, but by the natural frequency of the particular eigenvector as well.

It is important to realize here that an arbitrary excitation of almost any time variation applied at any of the nodes of a network will, in general, excite all the natural frequencies of the network. The resulting time variation of the nodal voltages will thus be a function of all the natural frequencies of the network, as well as the time variation of the input. Equations (10), however, tell us that it is possible to apply an excitation of arbitrary time variation to a network and still excite only a single natural frequency of the network itself. Thus, the resulting time variation of the nodal voltages in this case will be a function of the excitation and only one of the natural frequencies of the network. We may summarize all this by simply saying that regardless of our method of excitation, whether it be impulse functions (i.e., initial conditions) or driving functions, we may still exert complete control over the number of natural frequencies of the network which are excited.

As an example of the use of driving functions in the excitation of networks, let us consider the RC network which was used as an example in Sec. 6.3. It is shown in Fig. 6.8. Driving sources in the form of current

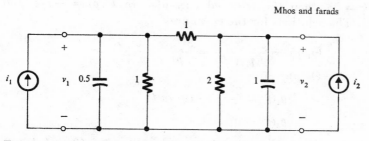

Figure 6.8 An RC network with driving sources.

generators have been added at each of the nodes of this network. The transformed network equations corresponding with (2) are

$$\left\{ p \begin{bmatrix} \frac{1}{2} & 0 \\ 0 & 1 \end{bmatrix} + \begin{bmatrix} 2 & -1 \\ -1 & 3 \end{bmatrix} \right\} \begin{bmatrix} V_1(p) \\ V_2(p) \end{bmatrix} = \begin{bmatrix} \frac{1}{2} & 0 \\ 0 & 1 \end{bmatrix} \begin{bmatrix} v_1(0) \\ v_2(0) \end{bmatrix} + \begin{bmatrix} I_1(p) \\ I_2(p) \end{bmatrix}$$

The matrix A of (3) was found in (11) in Sec. 6.3 for this network. It is

$$A = \frac{1}{3^{\frac{1}{2}}} \begin{bmatrix} -2 & 2^{\frac{1}{2}} \\ 1 & 2^{\frac{1}{2}} \end{bmatrix}$$

The relations between $I(p)$ and $\beta(p)$ may be found from (8) and (12). We see that

$$\beta(p) = \begin{bmatrix} \beta_1(p) \\ \beta_2(p) \end{bmatrix} = \frac{1}{3^{\frac{1}{2}}} \begin{bmatrix} -2 & 1 \\ 2^{\frac{1}{2}} & 2^{\frac{1}{2}} \end{bmatrix} \begin{bmatrix} I_1(p) \\ I_2(p) \end{bmatrix} = A^t I(p) \qquad (14)$$

and $\quad I(p) = \begin{bmatrix} I_1(p) \\ I_2(p) \end{bmatrix} = \begin{bmatrix} \frac{1}{2} & 0 \\ 0 & 1 \end{bmatrix} \frac{1}{3^{\frac{1}{2}}} \begin{bmatrix} -2 & 2^{\frac{1}{2}} \\ 1 & 2^{\frac{1}{2}} \end{bmatrix} \begin{bmatrix} \beta_1(p) \\ \beta_2(p) \end{bmatrix} = C^t A \beta(p) \qquad (15)$

The eigenvalues associated with the eigenvectors whose measure numbers are the columns of A are 5 and 2. Thus, the set of equations (10) becomes, for this case,

$$\Theta_1(p) = \frac{\theta_1(0)}{p + 5} + \frac{\beta_1(p)}{p + 5}$$

$$\Theta_2(p) = \frac{\theta_2(0)}{p + 2} + \frac{\beta_2(p)}{p + 2} \qquad (16)$$

Suppose it is desired to excite only the first natural frequency of the network by applying step inputs of current at the two nodes. We shall assume that the network is initially at rest, i.e., that $\theta_1(0)$ and $\theta_2(0)$ are both zero. To excite the first natural frequency only, we must have $\beta_1(p) = k/p$ and $\beta_2(p) = 0$. The nodal currents can be found from (15):

$$\begin{bmatrix} I_1(p) \\ I_2(p) \end{bmatrix} = \begin{bmatrix} \frac{1}{2} & 0 \\ 0 & 1 \end{bmatrix} \frac{1}{3^{\frac{1}{2}}} \begin{bmatrix} -2 & 2^{\frac{1}{2}} \\ 1 & 2^{\frac{1}{2}} \end{bmatrix} \begin{bmatrix} \frac{k}{p} \\ 0 \end{bmatrix} = \begin{bmatrix} \dfrac{-k}{3^{\frac{1}{2}}p} \\ \dfrac{k}{3^{\frac{1}{2}}p} \end{bmatrix}$$

If we let $k = 3^{\frac{1}{2}}$, then the required currents are $I_1(p) = -1/p$ and $I_2(p) = 1/p$. The solutions for the $\Theta_i(p)$ are

$$\Theta_1(p) = \frac{3^{\frac{1}{2}}}{p(p + 5)} = \frac{3^{\frac{1}{2}}/5}{p} - \frac{3^{\frac{1}{2}}/5}{p + 5}$$

$$\Theta_2(p) = 0$$

Therefore,
$$\theta_1(t) = \frac{3^{\frac{1}{2}}}{5} (1 - e^{-5t})u(t)$$

$$\theta_2(t) = 0$$

where $u(t)$ is the unit step function, i.e., $u(t) = 0, t < 0$; $u(t) = 1, t > 0$.

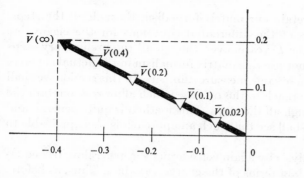

Figure 6.9   *The voltage vector as a function of time.*

The actual nodal voltages are easily found from the relation $v = A\theta$; thus

$$\begin{bmatrix} v_1(t) \\ v_2(t) \end{bmatrix} = \frac{1}{3^{\frac{1}{2}}} \begin{bmatrix} -2 & 2^{\frac{1}{2}} \\ 1 & 2^{\frac{1}{2}} \end{bmatrix} \begin{bmatrix} \dfrac{3^{\frac{1}{2}}}{5}(1 - e^{-5t})u(t) \\ 0 \end{bmatrix} = \begin{bmatrix} \dfrac{-2}{5}(1 - e^{-5t})u(t) \\ \dfrac{1}{5}(1 - e^{-5t})u(t) \end{bmatrix}$$

It is easily seen from the above that the vector $\bar{V}(t)$, describing the nodal voltages of the network, starts at the origin, i.e., $\bar{V}(0) = 0x_1 + 0x_2$, and proceeds outward along the a_1 eigenvector of Fig. 6.4. The position of the vector $\bar{V}(t)$ as a function of time is shown in Fig. 6.9.

The procedure illustrated above may be easily followed to show that a set of nodal currents $I_1(p) = 1/p$ and $I_2(p) = 2/p$ will result in only the second natural frequency being excited. The vector $\bar{V}(t)$ will again start at the origin, but in this case it will follow along the vector a_2 of Fig. 6.4, finally coming to rest at a position corresponding with $v_1 = 1$ and $v_2 = 1$. This is the steady-state condition. Thus we may write $\bar{V}(\infty) = 1x_1 + 1x_2$.

Although the discussion and example of this section have been given for an RC network, the same formalism applies directly to driving functions in the form of voltage sources applied in the loops of an RL network, and, with minor variations, the same technique may be applied to the LC case. We shall leave the illustration of these to the student as an exercise. It is perhaps not amiss, however, to point out here that the basic principle which has been applied in this section is superposition. Thus, (10) predicates the solution to the network equations as the superposition of the effects produced by the initial conditions onto the effects produced by the driving forces connected to the network.

6.7   *A more general method of analysis*

In the preceding sections on RC and LC networks, a difference in the procedure occurred in the final steps of the analysis. Specifically, in the RC

case we were able to retain our matrix formalism through all the steps, including the solutions of the differential equations for the eigenvalue measure numbers; in the LC case, even though all the preliminary steps were the same, we did not use this matrix formalism in the actual achievement of solutions for these same measure numbers. In this section we shall discuss a method of approach to the LC case which allows us to retain the matrix formalism through all the steps. This method is quite general, and in the next section we shall see that such an approach is also applicable to the RLC case.

Let us begin our analysis by again considering the general matrix equation for the LC network in terms of the charge variables. Thus, as before, we have

$$Lq'' + Sq = 0 \tag{1}$$

The q_i are, of course, the measure numbers referred to an orthonormal set of basis vectors x_i. Now let us define a new set of variables ρ_i by the relations

$$q_i' = \rho_i \qquad q_i'' = \rho_i' \tag{2}$$

In matrix form, we may write

$$q' = \rho \qquad q'' = \rho' \tag{3}$$

Our original equation (1) may now be written

$$L\rho' + Sq = 0 \tag{4}$$

Finally, we may combine the information in (3) and (4) in a single matrix equation:

$$\begin{bmatrix} q' \\ \rho' \end{bmatrix} = \begin{bmatrix} 0 & 1 \\ -L^{-1}S & 0 \end{bmatrix} \begin{bmatrix} q \\ \rho \end{bmatrix} \tag{5}$$

where

$$\begin{bmatrix} q' \\ \rho' \end{bmatrix} = \begin{bmatrix} q_1' \\ \cdot\cdot \\ q_n' \\ \rho_1' \\ \cdot\cdot \\ \rho_n' \end{bmatrix} \qquad \begin{bmatrix} q \\ \rho \end{bmatrix} = \begin{bmatrix} q_1 \\ \cdot\cdot \\ q_n \\ \rho_1 \\ \cdot\cdot \\ \rho_n \end{bmatrix} \tag{6}$$

Equation (5) contains all the information that was originally in (1), but in a different form. In the first place, we have been able to replace a second-order differential equation by a first-order differential equation, thus achieving some simplicity of representation. Of course, we have paid a price for this simplicity, since we have doubled the number of variables that we have to deal with, i.e., we have gone from n variables to $2n$ variables. There might also be some question as to whether or not the square matrix of (5) always exists, since it involves the inverse of the L matrix, and at this point we have no assurance that L has an inverse. Let us bypass this problem by assuming that if L^{-1} does not exist, small incremental inductors may be added to the circuit in such a manner as to provide L with an inverse. We shall now simplify our representation by defining the matrices η, η', and B, where

$$\eta = \begin{matrix} q \\ \rho \end{matrix} \right] \qquad \eta' = \begin{matrix} q' \\ \rho' \end{matrix} \right] \qquad B = \begin{bmatrix} 0 & 1 \\ -L^{-1}S & 0 \end{bmatrix} \qquad (7)$$

Equation (5) may now be written in the simple form

$$\eta' = B\eta \qquad (8)$$

At this point, it should be clear to the reader that η represents a column matrix of measure numbers which we shall call η_i. These measure numbers are functions of time, i.e., they may be written $\eta_i(t)$, and they are defined with respect to an orthonormal set of basis vectors x_i. Physically, some of these measure numbers represent the loop charges q_i, and some of them represent the loop currents q_i' (or i_i). The elements of the matrix B are real scalars which are functions of the specific circuit configuration. For the time-invariant networks we have been studying, these scalars will, of course, be time invariant. The measure numbers $\eta_i(t)$ and the basis vectors x_i to which they are referred serve to define a vector in a phase space. If we call this vector $\overline{Y}$, we may employ our usual representation to write

$$\overline{Y} = \eta^t x \qquad (9)$$

We may now proceed to find the eigenvalues and eigenvectors of the matrix B. However, these will be significantly different from the eigenvalues and eigenvectors of the cases previously discussed. Since the matrix B is not symmetric, in general, the eigenvalues will be complex, and the measure numbers of the related eigenvectors will also be complex. Actually, we shall see that for the LC case under discussion, the eigenvalues will be purely imaginary. One other restriction will be found to be true in the general case. That is, the eigenvalues will always occur in complex-conjugate pairs, and the measure numbers of the related eigenvectors will also be complex conjugates.

Let us refer to the eigenvectors as a_i, and let the column matrices of measure numbers which define these eigenvectors on the x_i basis be A_i. We may write

$$a_i = A_i{}^t x$$

The relation between the eigenvector basis and the original basis may now be expressed as

$$a = A^t x \qquad (10)$$

where A is the matrix whose columns are A_i. The vector $\overline{Y}$ may now be defined in phase space by a set of measure numbers $\alpha_i(t)$ referred to the a_i basis vectors. Thus we may write

$$\overline{Y} = \alpha^t a \tag{11}$$

From a consideration of the above equations and the time derivatives of these equations, we see that we may write

$$\begin{aligned} \eta(t) &= A\alpha(t) \\ \eta'(t) &= A\alpha'(t) \\ \eta(0) &= A\alpha(0) \end{aligned} \tag{12}$$

If the first two relations of (12) are substituted into the original equation (8), we obtain

$$A\alpha' = BA\alpha \tag{13}$$

Since the columns of A, i.e., the A_i, are the eigenvectors, we see that

$$BA_i = \lambda_i A_i \tag{14}$$

Therefore we may write

$$BA = AD \tag{15}$$

where D is the diagonal matrix consisting of the eigenvalues λ_i of the matrix B. Substituting this result into (13) gives us

$$A\alpha' = AD\alpha$$

If we premultiply both sides of the above equation by A^{-1}, we obtain

$$\alpha' = D\alpha \tag{16}$$

Thus we have a separate set of equations in the variables $\alpha_i(t)$, which may be written

$$\begin{aligned} \alpha_1'(t) &= \lambda_1 \alpha_1(t) \\ &\cdots\cdots\cdots \\ \alpha_n'(t) &= \lambda_n \alpha_n(t) \end{aligned} \tag{17}$$

The solutions of these equations are easily seen to be

$$\begin{aligned} \alpha_1(t) &= \alpha_1(0)e^{\lambda_1 t} \\ &\cdots\cdots\cdots \\ \alpha_n(t) &= \alpha_n(0)e^{\lambda_n t} \end{aligned} \tag{18}$$

Just as the eigenvalues and the measure numbers which define the eigenvectors occur in complex-conjugate sets, the constants $\alpha_i(0)$ will also occur as complex conjugates, and thus the quantities $\alpha_i(t)$ will be complex conjugates. For example, if $\lambda_2 = \lambda_1^*$, $\alpha_2(0)$ will equal $\alpha_1^*(0)$. Thus we can conclude that $\alpha_2(t)$ will be the complex conjugate of $\alpha_1(t)$. These complex-conjugate properties are exactly the conditions which are required to ensure that the quantities $\eta_i(t)$ will be real, i.e., that they will *not* be complex. Since the $\eta_i(t)$ are physical quantities, i.e., charges and currents, this is necessary. To see this, consider the following result from the first of equations (12):

$$\eta_1(t) = \alpha_1(t)a_{11} + \alpha_2(t)a_{12} + \cdots$$

The quantities $\alpha_1(t)$, $\alpha_2(t)$, a_{11}, and a_{12} are all complex quantities; however, if $\alpha_2(t) = \alpha_1^*(t)$, and $a_{12} = a_{11}^*$, then

$$\eta_1(t) = \alpha_1(t)a_{11} + \alpha_1^*(t)a_{11}^* + \cdots = 2\,\mathrm{Re}\,[\alpha_1(t)a_{11}] + \cdots \quad (19)$$

and clearly $\eta_1(t)$ is real.

The conclusions that were previously made for the LC case are easily applicable to our results here. We can now excite any given combination of the natural frequencies of a network, just as we could before. Only one precaution is necessary: when one of the eigenvalues is excited, its complex-conjugate companion must also be excited. In effect, we are simply saying that if a network has a pair of complex-conjugate poles, it is not possible to excite only one of these poles; they must both be excited simultaneously.

The above concepts may be best illustrated by an example. Let us use the same example which was presented in Sec. 6.4. The network is shown in Fig. 6.7. The L and S matrices are

$$L = \begin{bmatrix} 2 & 1 \\ 1 & 2 \end{bmatrix} \qquad S = \begin{bmatrix} 1 & 1 \\ 1 & 2 \end{bmatrix}$$

The matrix $-L^{-1}S$ is easily found to be

$$-\tfrac{1}{3}\begin{bmatrix} 2 & -1 \\ -1 & 2 \end{bmatrix}\begin{bmatrix} 1 & 1 \\ 1 & 2 \end{bmatrix} = \tfrac{1}{3}\begin{bmatrix} -1 & 0 \\ -1 & -3 \end{bmatrix}$$

The matrix equation involving the B matrix of (7) now becomes

$$\begin{bmatrix} \eta_1' \\ \eta_2' \\ \eta_3' \\ \eta_4' \end{bmatrix} = \begin{bmatrix} 0 & 0 & 1 & 0 \\ 0 & 0 & 0 & 1 \\ -\tfrac{1}{3} & 0 & 0 & 0 \\ -\tfrac{1}{3} & -1 & 0 & 0 \end{bmatrix} \begin{bmatrix} \eta_1 \\ \eta_2 \\ \eta_3 \\ \eta_4 \end{bmatrix}$$

The η matrix is composed of the charge and current variables for the network. Thus we may write

$$\begin{bmatrix} \eta_1 \\ \eta_2 \\ \eta_3 \\ \eta_4 \end{bmatrix} = \begin{bmatrix} q_1 \\ q_2 \\ i_1 \\ i_2 \end{bmatrix}$$

The usual techniques may be applied to the B matrix to find its eigenvalues and eigenvectors. Thus, we obtain

$$\lambda_1 = -j(\tfrac{1}{3})^{\tfrac{1}{2}} \qquad \lambda_2 = j(\tfrac{1}{3})^{\tfrac{1}{2}} \qquad \lambda_3 = -j1 \qquad \lambda_4 = j1$$

$$A_1 = \begin{bmatrix} j3^{\tfrac{1}{2}} \\ -j3^{\tfrac{1}{2}} \\ 2 \\ 1 \\ -\tfrac{1}{2} \end{bmatrix} \quad A_2 = \begin{bmatrix} -j3^{\tfrac{1}{2}} \\ j3^{\tfrac{1}{2}} \\ 2 \\ 1 \\ -\tfrac{1}{2} \end{bmatrix} \quad A_3 = \begin{bmatrix} 0 \\ j \\ 0 \\ 1 \end{bmatrix} \quad A_4 = \begin{bmatrix} 0 \\ -j \\ 0 \\ 1 \end{bmatrix}$$

It is important to remember here that the usual property of eigenvectors still holds, i.e., they may be multiplied by an arbitrary constant without impairing their function as eigenvectors. In this case, since they are composed of measure numbers which are complex, they may even be multiplied by complex constants without changing their function. Thus, many similar forms for the given eigenvectors are possible.

We may now form the A matrix and specify the relation between the measure numbers η_i on the x_i basis and the measure numbers α_i on the a_i basis. From (12) we see that the A matrix is the square matrix of the equation

$$\eta = \begin{bmatrix} q_1 \\ q_2 \\ i_1 \\ i_2 \end{bmatrix} = \begin{bmatrix} j3^{\tfrac{1}{2}} & -j3^{\tfrac{1}{2}} & 0 & 0 \\ -j3^{\tfrac{1}{2}} & j3^{\tfrac{1}{2}} & & \\ 2 & 2 & j & -j \\ 1 & 1 & 0 & 0 \\ -\tfrac{1}{2} & -\tfrac{1}{2} & 1 & 1 \end{bmatrix} \begin{bmatrix} \alpha_1 \\ \alpha_2 \\ \alpha_3 \\ \alpha_4 \end{bmatrix} = A\alpha \qquad (20)$$

The solutions for the measure numbers $\alpha_i(t)$ are quite straightforward and may be found from (18) as

$$\alpha_1(t) = \alpha_1(0)e^{-jt/(3)^{\tfrac{1}{2}}}$$
$$\alpha_2(t) = \alpha_2(0)e^{jt/(3)^{\tfrac{1}{2}}}$$
$$\alpha_3(t) = \alpha_3(0)e^{-jt}$$
$$\alpha_4(t) = \alpha_4(0)e^{jt}$$

If it is desired to excite only the first natural frequency of the network, i.e., to excite only the first *two* eigenvalues, then we need only select $\alpha_1(0)$, and thus $\alpha_2(0)$, as nonzero (they must, however, be complex conjugates), and $\alpha_3(0)$ and $\alpha_4(0)$ as zero. For example, if we pick $\alpha_1(0) = jk_b$, then $\alpha_2(0)$ will equal $-jk_b$. From (20) we find that this makes $q_1(0) = -2(3)^{\tfrac{1}{2}}k_b$ and $q_2(0) = 3^{\tfrac{1}{2}}k_b$, while $i_1(0)$ and $i_2(0)$ are zero. If we choose $k_b = -1/2(3)^{\tfrac{1}{2}}$, then $q_1(0) = 1$, and $q_2(0) = -\tfrac{1}{2}$. This is exactly the situation that was discussed in connection with (24) and (25) in Sec. 6.4, and the choice of the constants $k_1 = (\tfrac{3}{2})^{\tfrac{1}{2}}$ and $k_2 = 0$ in that section. On the other hand, if we pick $\alpha_1(0) = \alpha_2(0) = k_a$ and $\alpha_3(0) = \alpha_4(0) = 0$, then from (20) we see that $q_1(0) = q_2(0) = 0$, $i_1(0) = 2k_a$, and $i_2(0) = -k_a$. This would correspond to the situation in Sec. 6.4 in which $k_1 = 0$ but $k_2 \neq 0$. In general, then, we may write

$$\alpha_1(0) = k_a + jk_b$$
$$\alpha_2(0) = k_a - jk_b$$

The constant k_a will specify the placing of initial currents in the loops of the network, and the constant k_b will specify the placing of initial charges in the network. The effect of any of these initial currents or charges or any combination of them, however, will still be to excite only the first natural frequency. From (20), if $\alpha_3(0) = \alpha_4(0) = 0$, we can solve for the charge variables. We see that

$$q_1(t) = -2(3)^{\frac{1}{2}}k_b \cos \frac{t}{3^{\frac{1}{2}}} + 2(3)^{\frac{1}{2}}k_a \sin \frac{t}{3^{\frac{1}{2}}}$$

$$q_2(t) = 3^{\frac{1}{2}}k_b \cos \frac{t}{3^{\frac{1}{2}}} - 3^{\frac{1}{2}}k_a \sin \frac{t}{3^{\frac{1}{2}}}$$

A similar series of steps can be carried out to show the effect of the real and imaginary parts of $\alpha_3(0)$ and $\alpha_4(0)$ in specifying the initial values of current and charge, respectively, that are required to excite the natural frequency associated with λ_3 and λ_4, i.e., the second natural frequency of the network. It should be pointed out that the association of the real part of the constants $\alpha_1(0)$ and $\alpha_2(0)$ with initial currents was a direct result of the specific measure numbers selected for the eigenvectors a_1 and a_2. Some other choice of the measure numbers of these eigenvectors would have resulted in a different effect of the real and imaginary parts of these constants. Thus, we might have chosen our eigenvectors so that the real parts of the constants would correspond with equal magnitudes of both charge and current in the initial conditions of the network, etc. There are infinitely many other possibilities.

In this section we have shown that a second-order matrix differential equation may be rewritten as a first-order differential equation, and the eigenvalues and eigenvectors of the resulting matrix may be used to place in evidence the natural frequencies of the given network. In addition, all the other concepts of the linear-vector-space approach, such as the conditions that must be impressed on the network in order to excite only a single one of its natural frequencies, may be applied to this situation. It should be pointed out, however, that for the LC case it is usually easier to approach the situation by the method of Sec. 6.4 than by the method of this section. This eliminates the need for dealing with the complex quantities that resulted from the latter approach. However, the real value of the techniques developed in this section is that they apply directly to the more general network in which all three types of elements are considered. This will be discussed in the next section.

6.8 *The RLC network*

In the previous sections of this chapter we have investigated two-type-element networks in terms of their representation in a linear vector space. We have used the concept of eigenvectors to simplify the differential equations describing the networks, and we have shown the direct correspondence between the eigenvalues and the natural frequencies. Thus, it was shown that the natural frequencies of the *RC* network correspond with real exponential behavior in the time domain; i.e., the poles of the network are on the real axis of the complex frequency plane. It was pointed out that the *RL* case could be treated in exactly the same manner as the *RC* case, with similar results in the time and frequency domains. Similarly, the natural frequencies of the *LC* network correspond with imaginary exponentials occurring in conjugate pairs and representing sinusoidal time behavior; i.e., the poles of the network are on the imaginary axis of the complex frequency plane. Thus, we have covered all the possibilities for passive networks which involve only two kinds of elements. In this section we shall extend our analysis to networks which include all three types of elements, i.e., *RLC* networks. Our treatment of this topic will follow the method introduced in the last section.

We may begin our analysis by considering the form that the mesh equations will have for an *RLC* network. In general, they will involve terms such as

$$l_{ij}i_j'' + r_{ij}i_j + s_{ij}\!\int i_j\,dt \tag{1}$$

As in the *LC* case, however, we shall use charge as our variable rather than current. Thus we shall make the substitution $q_j''(t) = i_j'(t)$ in the above expression. The terms from our mesh analysis will then have the form

$$l_{ij}q_j'' + r_{ij}q_j' + s_{ij}q_j \tag{2}$$

We may now write the general equations for all the mesh variables $q_i(t)$ in matrix form. We shall assume that there are no external sources connected to the network. Our general matrix equation is

$$\boldsymbol{Lq'' + Rq' + Sq = 0} \tag{3}$$

At this point we see that our procedure must diverge somewhat from that of Secs. 6.2 and 6.4. The techniques which we developed for the simultaneous diagonalization of two square matrices are not applicable in this case, since there are three square matrices in the problem under consideration. To treat this situation, we shall apply the method of the last section, whereby the matrix differential equation of second order given in (3) may be reduced to a first-order matrix differential equation. It is interesting to note that this technique might also be applied to the solution of differential equations of higher order.

We may start this procedure by considering the variables $i_i(t)$, where

$$i_i(t) = \frac{dq_i(t)}{dt} \tag{4}$$

Thus, in matrix form, we may write

$$i = q' \tag{5}$$

and

$$i' = q'' \tag{6}$$

If (5) and (6) are substituted in (3), the matrix equation for our general *RLC* network becomes

$$Li' + Ri + Sq = 0 \tag{7}$$

Let us assume that L has an inverse; then we may premultiply (7) by L^{-1} to obtain

$$i' + L^{-1}Ri + L^{-1}Sq = 0 \tag{8}$$

We may now combine the information of equations (5) and (8) in a single matrix equation which may be written

$$\begin{bmatrix} q' \\ i' \end{bmatrix} = \begin{bmatrix} 0 & 1 \\ -L^{-1}S & -L^{-1}R \end{bmatrix} \begin{bmatrix} q \\ i \end{bmatrix} \tag{9}$$

If we define

$$\eta = \begin{bmatrix} q \\ i \end{bmatrix} \qquad \eta' = \begin{bmatrix} q' \\ i' \end{bmatrix} \qquad B = \begin{bmatrix} 0 & 1 \\ -L^{-1}S & -L^{-1}R \end{bmatrix}$$

then (9) may be written

$$\eta' = B\eta \tag{10}$$

Equation (10) is in the form of the general first-order differential equation whose solution was discussed in the last section. Thus we see that we have again changed our problem from the solution of a second-order differential equation involving the n variables $q_i(t)$ to the solution of a first-order differential equation involving $2n$ variables, namely, the n variables $q_i(t)$ and the n variables $i_i(t)$. Frequently it is possible to reduce the size of the matrix B by a different choice of the circuit variables of voltage, current, charge, etc.[1] An example of this procedure will be given later in this section.

When the equations for the *RLC* network have been put in the form

---

[1] See T. R. Bashkow, The A Matrix, New Network Description, *IRE Trans. on Circuit Theory*, vol. CT-4, no. 3, pp. 117–119, September, 1957.

of (10), we may follow the procedure of the last section to analyze the given network according to its natural frequencies. In other words we will look for the eigenvectors a_i of the matrix $\boldsymbol{B}$, then use these eigenvectors as a basis for our phase space, and finally describe the network behavior by a set of measure numbers $\alpha_i(t)$ referred to the eigenvector basis and related to the $\eta_i(t)$ measure numbers which in turn refer to the original basis vectors x_i. The steps from (13) to (17) of Sec. 6.7 then apply directly, and we shall be able to express the time variation of the measure numbers for the RLC network as

$$\alpha_1(t) \;=\; \alpha_1(0)e^{\lambda_1 t}$$
$$\cdots\cdots\cdots\cdots$$
$$\alpha_n(t) \;=\; \alpha_n(0)e^{\lambda_n t}$$

(11)

The eigenvalues for the RLC case will either be real or they will be complex and occur in conjugate pairs. Similarly, the related eigenvectors will have measure numbers which are complex conjugates; thus our functions $\alpha_i(t)$ will also occur in complex-conjugate pairs, and these pairs will yield expressions for the physical variables of the circuit, the $\eta_i(t)$, which are real. The only significant difference between this case and the case discussed in the last section is in the fact that the eigenvalues will, in general, have both real and imaginary components. Thus, each complex-conjugate pair of the natural frequencies of the network will represent real-time behavior which has both a real and an imaginary exponential component, i.e., has a behavior represented by an exponentially damped sinusoid.

As an example, consider the network shown in Fig. 6.10. We shall also use this example to illustrate a simplification that can frequently be made in the formulation of the matrix equation for the network. Thus, rather than finding the R, L, and S matrices for this network and proceeding to develop the square matrix of (9), we may work directly with the circuit variables (along with their derivatives) that are encountered in the network equations. These may be rearranged to give a representation of the type shown in (10), and the solution may be carried out as before. For the

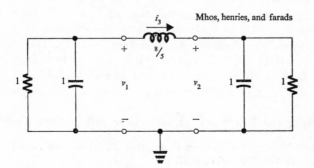

Figure 6.10 An RLC network with two voltage variables and one current variable.

example network we may select as variables the voltages across the capacitors and the current which flows through the inductor. These are indicated as $v_1(t)$, $v_2(t)$, and $i_3(t)$, respectively, in Fig. 6.10. The network equations can be expressed by writing the nodal equations at each of the two nodes and the expression for the voltage drop across the inductor. These equations are

$$
\begin{aligned}
-i_3 &= v_1 + v_1' \\
i_3 &= v_2 + v_2' \\
\tfrac{8}{5}i_3' &= v_1 - v_2
\end{aligned}
\tag{12}
$$

The above equations may be written in the form of (10) as

$$
\begin{bmatrix} v_1' \\ v_2' \\ i_3' \end{bmatrix} =
\begin{bmatrix} -1 & 0 & -1 \\ 0 & -1 & 1 \\ \tfrac{5}{8} & -\tfrac{5}{8} & 0 \end{bmatrix}
\begin{bmatrix} v_1 \\ v_2 \\ i_3 \end{bmatrix}
\tag{13}
$$

It is easy to show that the eigenvalues and a related set of eigenvectors for the network are

$$
\lambda_1 = -1 \qquad\qquad \lambda_2 = -\tfrac{1}{2} + j1 \qquad\qquad \lambda_3 = -\tfrac{1}{2} - j1
$$

$$
A_1 = \begin{bmatrix} 1 \\ 1 \\ 0 \end{bmatrix} \qquad
A_2 = \begin{bmatrix} -\tfrac{1}{2} + j1 \\ \tfrac{1}{2} - j1 \\ \tfrac{5}{4} \end{bmatrix} \qquad
A_3 = \begin{bmatrix} -\tfrac{1}{2} - j1 \\ \tfrac{1}{2} + j1 \\ \tfrac{5}{4} \end{bmatrix}
$$

Thus the relations between the capacitor voltages and the inductor current and the measure numbers $\alpha_i(t)$ which refer to the eigenvector basis are given by the matrix equation

$$
\begin{bmatrix} v_1(t) \\ v_2(t) \\ i_3(t) \end{bmatrix} =
\begin{bmatrix} 1 & -\tfrac{1}{2} + j1 & -\tfrac{1}{2} - j1 \\ 1 & \tfrac{1}{2} - j1 & \tfrac{1}{2} + j1 \\ 0 & \tfrac{5}{4} & \tfrac{5}{4} \end{bmatrix}
\begin{bmatrix} \alpha_1(t) \\ \alpha_2(t) \\ \alpha_3(t) \end{bmatrix}
$$

All the observations which were made for the LC case in the last section also apply to this case. For example, any choice of $\alpha_2(0)$ as an initial condition requires selecting an $\alpha_3(0)$ which is its complex conjugate. If such initial conditions are selected, and if, in addition, $\alpha_1(0)$ is set equal to zero, then only the natural frequency which has a damped exponential sinusoidal time behavior will be excited. Similarly, if $\alpha_2(0)$ and $\alpha_3(0)$ are set equal to zero, the choice of any real number for $\alpha_1(0)$ will excite only the natural frequency which has a real exponential as its time behavior. Similar observations may be made as to the effects of choosing $\alpha_2(0)$ and $\alpha_3(0)$ as real or imaginary quantities on the voltages and currents resulting in the network. These are left to the reader as an exercise.

6.9 *Representation using a reciprocal basis*

In Sec. 5.9 the concept of a reciprocal basis was developed. There we showed that, given a set of basis vectors a_i, we could develop a set of basis vectors u_i such that the relations

$$u_i \cdot a_j = \delta_{ij} \tag{1}$$

were satisfied. The basis consisting of the vectors u_i was called the reciprocal basis. In this section we shall see how the reciprocal basis can be applied to obtain a solution of a matrix differential equation, i.e., an equation which involves a set of variables and their derivatives. The result will be expressed in terms of the natural frequencies of the system. The material presented in this section will reach the same conclusions reached in the earlier sections of this chapter. It will, however, reach them by a different route. The process should help to strengthen the reader's understanding of the fundamental concepts involved.

Let us begin by considering a system described by the matrix differential equation

$$\eta' = B\eta \tag{2}$$

The elements of the column matrix η are the variables $\eta_i(t)$ of the network or system under consideration. The elements of the matrix B are real, although the matrix need not be symmetric. We have seen that it is always possible to put our circuit equations in this form. Now let us consider a vector $\overline{Y}(t)$ describing the state of the system. We may express this vector either in terms of the $\eta_i(t)$ measure numbers which refer to the orthonormal basis or in terms of a new set of measure numbers $\alpha_i(t)$ which refer to the eigenvectors of the matrix B. Let these eigenvectors be expressed by the column matrices A_i. The relation between the two sets of measure numbers has been shown (see Sec. 6.7) to be

$$\eta = A\alpha \tag{3}$$

where A is the square matrix composed of the column matrices A_i. The above expression may be written in a form which is more suitable for our discussion here as

$$\eta = \sum_i \alpha_i(t) A_i \tag{4}$$

Note that the above is a matrix equation which gives the same information as (3) but retains the individual eigenvectors as separate elements of the summation. Since the elements of the A_i are time invariant, we may write

$$\eta' = \sum_i \alpha_i'(t) A_i \tag{5}$$

Thus, our original differential equation (2) may be written

$$\sum_i \alpha_i'(t) A_i \;=\; B \sum_i \alpha_i(t) A_i \tag{6}$$

The matrix B may be moved inside the summation to give

$$\sum_i \alpha_i'(t) A_i \;=\; \sum_i \alpha_i(t) B A_i \tag{7}$$

The A_i, however, are eigenvectors, so the effect on them of the original transformation matrix B may be written

$$B A_i \;=\; \lambda_i A_i \tag{8}$$

If we substitute this relation in (7), our original differential equation (2) becomes

$$\sum_i \alpha_i'(t) A_i \;=\; \sum_i \lambda_i \alpha_i(t) A_i \tag{9}$$

Now let us define a basis with vectors u_i whose measure numbers are given by the column matrices U_i. We will select this basis so that it is reciprocal to the eigenvector basis. In terms of the column matrices of measure numbers which define these vectors, we may write the defining scalar-product relations for the reciprocal basis as

$$U_j{}^t A_k \;=\; \delta_{jk} \tag{10}$$

If we premultiply both sides of (9) by $U_1{}^t$ and apply the above relationship, we obtain

$$\alpha_1'(t) \;=\; \lambda_1 \alpha_1(t) \tag{11}$$

This process may be continued with the other $U_j{}^t$ row matrices to obtain other equations, each of which involves only one of the $\alpha_i(t)$ variables and its first derivative. Thus, we now have a set of equations

$$\begin{aligned} \alpha_1'(t) &= \lambda_1 \alpha_1(t) \\ &\cdots\cdots\cdots \\ \alpha_n'(t) &= \lambda_n \alpha_n(t) \end{aligned} \tag{12}$$

The only additional information needed for the solution of the equations (12) is the initial values of the variables. Since (4) is valid for all values of the variable t, it is valid for $t = 0$. Thus, we may write

$$\eta(0) \;=\; \sum_i \alpha_i(0) A_i \tag{13}$$

If we premultiply both sides of this equation by $U_1{}^t$, from (10) we obtain

$$U_1{}^t\boldsymbol{\eta}(0) = \alpha_1(0) \tag{14}$$

Similarly, the value of any $\alpha_j(0)$ may be found by premultiplying both sides of (13) by $U_j{}^t$. Our initial conditions may now be written

$$\alpha_1(0) = U_1{}^t\boldsymbol{\eta}(0)$$
$$\cdots\cdots\cdots\cdots \tag{15}$$
$$\alpha_n(0) = U_n{}^t\boldsymbol{\eta}(0)$$

where the U_i are the column matrices of measure numbers of the reciprocal basis vectors. We now have achieved the solution for the quantities $\alpha_i(t)$. These are

$$\alpha_1(t) = [U_1{}^t\boldsymbol{\eta}(0)]e^{\lambda_1 t}$$
$$\cdots\cdots\cdots\cdots\cdots \tag{16}$$
$$\alpha_n(t) = [U_n{}^t\boldsymbol{\eta}(0)]e^{\lambda_n t}$$

The solutions for our actual network variables, the $\eta_i(t)$, may now be written directly by substituting (16) in (4). Thus, we obtain

$$\boldsymbol{\eta} = \sum_i [U_i{}^t\boldsymbol{\eta}(0)]e^{\lambda_i t}A_i \tag{17}$$

This is the solution of our original differential equation (2).

As an example of this technique, consider the network which was discussed in Sec. 6.3 and is shown in Fig. 6.11. The network equations are

$$\tfrac{1}{2}v_1' + 2v_1 - v_2 = 0$$
$$v_2' - v_1 + 3v_2 = 0$$

These equations may be written in matrix form as

$$\begin{bmatrix} v_1' \\ v_2' \end{bmatrix} = \begin{bmatrix} -4 & 2 \\ 1 & -3 \end{bmatrix} \begin{bmatrix} v_1 \\ v_2 \end{bmatrix}$$

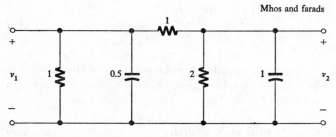

Figure 6.11   An RC network with two voltage variables.

where, for convenience, the upper equation has been multiplied by 2. The eigenvalues and normalized eigenvectors are easily found by the usual techniques. They are

$$\lambda_1 = -2 \qquad \lambda_2 = -5$$

$$A_1 = \begin{bmatrix} \dfrac{1}{2^{\frac{1}{2}}} \\[2ex] \dfrac{1}{2^{\frac{1}{2}}} \end{bmatrix} \qquad A_2 = \begin{bmatrix} \dfrac{-2}{5^{\frac{1}{2}}} \\[2ex] \dfrac{1}{5^{\frac{1}{2}}} \end{bmatrix}$$

We may solve for the reciprocal basis vectors by finding the matrix $U = (A^t)^{-1}$ as was done in Sec. 5.9. The A matrix, of course, is composed of the column matrices of eigenvector measure numbers A_i. We see that

$$U = (A^t)^{-1} = \begin{bmatrix} \dfrac{2^{\frac{1}{2}}}{3} & \dfrac{-5^{\frac{1}{2}}}{3} \\[2ex] \dfrac{2(2)^{\frac{1}{2}}}{3} & \dfrac{5^{\frac{1}{2}}}{3} \end{bmatrix}$$

The reciprocal basis vectors have the measure numbers given in the columns of the U matrix. Thus, we see that

$$U_1 = \begin{bmatrix} \dfrac{2^{\frac{1}{2}}}{3} \\[2ex] \dfrac{2(2)^{\frac{1}{2}}}{3} \end{bmatrix} \qquad U_2 = \begin{bmatrix} \dfrac{-5^{\frac{1}{2}}}{3} \\[2ex] \dfrac{5^{\frac{1}{2}}}{3} \end{bmatrix}$$

where U_1 gives the measure numbers of the reciprocal basis vector u_1, and U_2 gives the measure numbers of the reciprocal basis vector u_2. The eigenvectors a_i and the reciprocal basis vectors u_i, together with the orthonormal basis vectors x_i (with respect to which the numbers of the eigenvectors and the reciprocal basis vectors are defined), are shown in Fig. 6.12. The reader should verify that the relationships (10) are satisfied.

We may now write the solution for our network variables in the form of (17) as

$$\begin{bmatrix} v_1(t) \\[2ex] v_2(t) \end{bmatrix} = \underbrace{\begin{bmatrix} \dfrac{2^{\frac{1}{2}}}{3} & \dfrac{2(2)^{\frac{1}{2}}}{3} \end{bmatrix} \begin{bmatrix} v_1(0) \\[2ex] v_2(0) \end{bmatrix}}_{} e^{-2t} \begin{bmatrix} \dfrac{1}{2^{\frac{1}{2}}} \\[2ex] \dfrac{1}{2^{\frac{1}{2}}} \end{bmatrix} + \underbrace{\begin{bmatrix} \dfrac{-5^{\frac{1}{2}}}{3} & \dfrac{5^{\frac{1}{2}}}{3} \end{bmatrix} \begin{bmatrix} v_1(0) \\[2ex] v_2(0) \end{bmatrix}}_{} e^{-5t} \begin{bmatrix} \dfrac{-2}{5^{\frac{1}{2}}} \\[2ex] \dfrac{1}{5^{\frac{1}{2}}} \end{bmatrix}$$

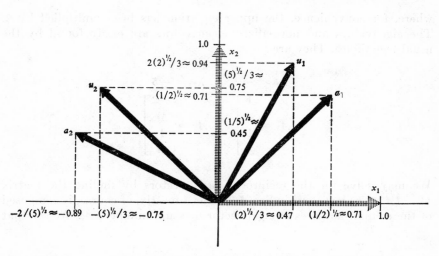

Figure 6.12   *The eigenvector basis a_i and the reciprocal basis u_i.*

If we assume initial conditions $v_1(0) = 2$ and $v_2(0) = 1$, the solution for our nodal voltages is

$$\begin{bmatrix} v_1(t) \\ v_2(t) \end{bmatrix} = \begin{bmatrix} \frac{4}{3}e^{-2t} + \frac{2}{3}e^{-5t} \\ \frac{4}{3}e^{-2t} - \frac{1}{3}e^{-5t} \end{bmatrix}$$

The reader should compare the steps of this development with the one given in Sec. 6.3, where the same initial conditions were chosen.

If we apply the above procedure to the *RLC*-network case, we find that the same steps may be followed. The reciprocal basis vectors in this case may have complex measure numbers. If they do, they will occur in conjugate pairs. Graphical representations for the variables are also possible in this case. The details may be found in the literature to which the interested reader is referred.[1]

In this section we have presented a second method of applying the concepts of linear vector spaces to the general network situation. The notation is somewhat different from the notation used in the earlier sections of this chapter; however, the reciprocal basis is frequently used in the literature, and the reader should be aware of the techniques and the notation involved. These techniques may also be applied to the frequency domain and to the use of forcing functions. The procedure follows quite closely that used in Secs. 6.5 and 6.6, and the details are left to the reader as an exercise.

[1] See C. A. Desoer, Modes in Linear Circuits, *IRE Trans. on Circuit Theory*, vol. CT-7, pp. 211–223, September, 1960.

PROBLEMS

6.1 Find the eigenvectors and eigenvalues of the network shown in Fig. P6.1 by solving the equations in the time domain.

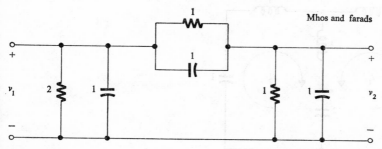

Figure P6.1

6.2 Find the eigenvectors and eigenvalues of the network shown in Fig. P6.1 by solving the equations in the frequency domain.

6.3 What initial conditions must be established to excite each of the natural frequencies of the network shown in Fig. P6.1?

6.4 Find the eigenvectors and eigenvalues of the network shown in Fig. P6.4 by solving the equations in the time domain.

Ohms and henries

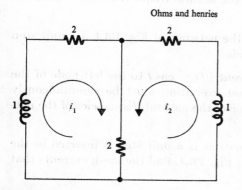

Figure P6.4

6.5 Find the eigenvalues and eigenvectors of the network shown in Fig. P6.4 by solving the equations in the frequency domain.

6.6 What are the initial conditions that must be established to excite each of the natural frequencies of the network shown in Fig. P6.4?

6.7 Find the eigenvectors and eigenvalues of the network shown in Fig. P6.7 by solving the equations in the time domain. Use the method of Sec. 6.4.

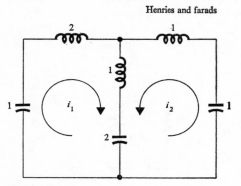

Henries and farads

Figure P6.7

6.8 Find the eigenvectors and eigenvalues of the network shown in Fig. P6.7 by solving the equations in the frequency domain.

6.9 Find a set of initial voltages for the capacitors of the network shown in Fig. P6.7 such that only one of the natural frequencies will be excited.

6.10 Find a set of initial currents for the inductors of the network shown in Fig. P6.7 such that only one of the natural frequencies of the network will be excited.

6.11 Find the nodal voltages in the network of Fig. P6.1 if a unit step of current is applied at the left node.

6.12 It is desired to apply a current $i(t) = \cos t$ to the left node of the network shown in Fig. P6.1. What excitation must be simultaneously applied to the right node if only one of the natural frequencies of the network is to be excited?

6.13 If a voltage source whose output is a unit step is inserted in the center leg of the network shown in Fig. P6.4, find the mesh currents that result.

6.14 If voltage sources are inserted in the outside legs of the network shown in Fig. P6.4, what voltages must be applied so that only one of the natural frequencies of the network is excited?

6.15 It is desired to excite the network shown in Fig. P6.7 with a sinusoidal frequency which is the same as one of the natural frequencies of the network. Is it possible to obtain stable loop currents if this excitation is applied by means of a voltage source in the center leg of the network? Why or why not?

6.16 If voltage sources are placed in each of the outer legs of the network shown in Fig. P6.7, and if the output of these sources is a sinusoid whose frequency is the same as the lower natural frequency of the network, find the magnitude of the excitation such that the network currents will be stable.

6.17 In the matrix equation

$$y''' + Ay'' + By' + Cy = 0$$

y is a column matrix consisting of n elements $y_i(t)$. A, B, and C are non-singular $n \times n$ square matrices with real, time-invariant elements. The equation involves the first, second, and third derivatives of the y_i. Rewrite this equation as a first-order differential equation with a single $3n \times 3n$ matrix relating the variables and their derivatives.

6.18 Find the eigenvalues and eigenvectors of the network shown in Fig. P6.7 by the method of Sec. 6.7.

6.19 Verify the effects of the real and imaginary components of the constants $\alpha_3(0)$ and $\alpha_4(0)$ in specifying the initial values of charge and current, respectively, in the example of Sec. 6.7.

6.20 Select a different set of eigenvectors for the example given in Sec. 6.7, so that the effects of the real and the imaginary components of the constants $\alpha_1(0)$ and $\alpha_2(0)$ are interchanged.

6.21 Find the eigenvectors and eigenvalues of the network shown in Fig. P6.21.

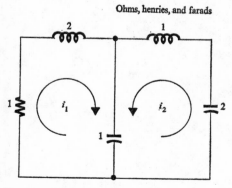

Ohms, henries, and farads

Figure P6.21

6.22 Show that the same natural frequencies will result if the example given in Sec. 6.8 is set up as a 4×4 matrix according to the method given in the section.

6.23 Use the method of Sec. 6.9 to solve for the nodal voltages of the circuit in Fig. P6.1. Assume initial conditions of 1 volt on each of the capacitors.

6.24 Develop an analysis, parallel to the one given in Sec. 6.9, for the frequency domain. Include the effect of external excitations.

Just as the indefinite-admittance matrix of Sec. 3.5 provides a means of determining the properties of networks formed by the *parallel* connection of multiterminal networks, so we may define a procedure whereby we may compute the over-all properties of multiterminal networks connected in *cascade*. The matrix we shall use to accomplish this is called the *indefinite-transfer matrix*.[1]

Consider the $2n$-terminal network shown in Fig. A.1. As the figure indicates, we shall consider the first n of the terminals and their associated voltage and current variables as input terminals, and the other n terminals with their voltage and current variables as output terminals. The input and output variables may be arranged in a form quite similar to that of the two-port transmission parameters discussed in Sec. 3.3. Thus, we may

[1] J. Shekel, Matrix Analysis of Multi-terminal Transducers, *Proc. IRE*, vol. 42, no. 5, pp. 840–847, May, 1954.

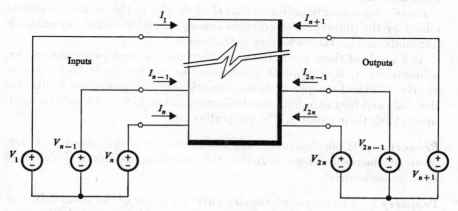

Figure A.1   The voltage and current variables for the indefinite-transfer matrix of a 2n-terminal network.

write

$$
\begin{bmatrix} V_1 \\ \cdot \cdot \\ V_n \\ \hline I_1 \\ \cdot \cdot \\ I_n \end{bmatrix} = \left[\begin{array}{ccc|ccc} a_{11} & \cdots & a_{1n} & b_{11} & \cdots & b_{1n} \\ \multicolumn{6}{c}{\cdots\cdots\cdots\cdots\cdots\cdots} \\ a_{n1} & \cdots & a_{nn} & b_{n1} & \cdots & b_{nn} \\ \hline c_{11} & \cdots & c_{1n} & d_{11} & \cdots & d_{1n} \\ \multicolumn{6}{c}{\cdots\cdots\cdots\cdots\cdots\cdots} \\ c_{n1} & \cdots & c_{nn} & d_{n1} & \cdots & d_{nn} \end{array} \right] \begin{bmatrix} V_{n+1} \\ \cdots \\ V_{2n} \\ \hline -I_{n+1} \\ \cdots \\ -I_{2n} \end{bmatrix} \tag{1}
$$

The $2n \times 2n$ matrix is termed the indefinite-transmission matrix. Equation (1) may be written (with the indicated partitioning) in terms of submatrices as

$$
\begin{bmatrix} V_a \\ \hline I_a \end{bmatrix} = \left[\begin{array}{c|c} A & B \\ \hline C & D \end{array} \right] \begin{bmatrix} V_b \\ \hline -I_b \end{bmatrix} \tag{2}
$$

where

$$
V_a = \begin{bmatrix} V_1 \\ \cdot \cdot \\ V_n \end{bmatrix} \qquad V_b = \begin{bmatrix} V_{n+1} \\ \cdots \\ V_{2n} \end{bmatrix} \qquad A = \begin{bmatrix} a_{11} & \cdots & a_{1n} \\ \cdots\cdots\cdots\cdots \\ a_{n1} & \cdots & a_{nn} \end{bmatrix} \qquad \cdots
$$

It is convenient to make the following restrictions on the network shown in Fig. A.1:

Restriction 1.   The sum of all the input currents I_i ($i = 1, 2, \ldots , n$) is zero.

Restriction 2.   The sum of all the output currents I_i ($i = n + 1, n + 2, \ldots , 2n$) is zero (actually, this follows from Restriction 1 and Kirchhoff's law).

Restriction 3.   If an arbitrary voltage is added to all the input voltages (or to all the output voltages), the currents at the various terminals remain unchanged.

Restriction 3 simply indicates that the behavior of the network is determined by the differences of voltages among its various input (or output) terminals, not on their absolute potentials.

As a result of these restrictions, we may specify some properties of the submatrices *A*, *B*, *C*, and *D* which compose the indefinite-transmission matrix. We shall not prove these properties here. A procedure similar to that followed for the indefinite-admittance matrix in Sec. 3.5 may be used to establish their validity. The properties are:

Property 1   If the elements in any row or column of the submatrix *C* are summed, the result is zero (note that this matrix is, in effect, an indefinite-admittance matrix).

Property 2   The sum of all the elements in any *row* of the submatrix *A* is the same as the sum of all the elements in any other row of *A* (this sum will not necessarily be equal to zero).

Property 3 The sum of all the elements in any *column* of the submatrix **D** is the same as the sum of all the elements in any other column of **D** (again, this sum will not necessarily be equal to zero).

In a manner analogous to that in which we proceeded with the indefinite-admittance matrix, it is now desired to select a certain terminal from among the input terminals and a terminal from among the output terminals and use them as reference or ground terminals. For convenience we will ground terminals n and $2n$. To do this, it is necessary to define two matrices **P** and **Q**. **P** is an $n \times (n-1)$ matrix consisting of an $(n-1) \times (n-1)$ identity submatrix and a $1 \times (n-1)$ zero submatrix. Specifically, we may define

$$P = \begin{bmatrix} 1 & 0 & \cdots & 0 \\ 0 & 1 & \cdots & 0 \\ \cdot & \cdot & \cdots & \cdot \\ 0 & 0 & \cdots & 1 \\ \hline 0 & 0 & \cdots & 0 \end{bmatrix} \begin{array}{c} \uparrow \\ n \\ \text{rows} \\ \downarrow \end{array} \tag{3}$$

$$\xleftarrow{\hspace{1cm}} \begin{array}{c} n-1 \\ \text{columns} \end{array} \xrightarrow{\hspace{1cm}}$$

The matrix **Q** is defined as an $n \times (n-1)$ matrix consisting of an $(n-1) \times (n-1)$ identity submatrix and a $1 \times (n-1)$ submatrix, all of whose elements are -1. Specifically, we may define

$$Q = \begin{bmatrix} 1 & 0 & \cdots & 0 \\ 0 & 1 & \cdots & 0 \\ \cdot & \cdot & \cdots & \cdot \\ 0 & 0 & \cdots & 1 \\ \hline -1 & -1 & \cdots & -1 \end{bmatrix} \begin{array}{c} \uparrow \\ n \\ \text{rows} \\ \downarrow \end{array} \tag{4}$$

$$\xleftarrow{\hspace{1cm}} \begin{array}{c} n-1 \\ \text{columns} \end{array} \xrightarrow{\hspace{1cm}}$$

The effect of the above matrices will be to eliminate the variables V_n, I_n, V_{2n}, and I_{2n} from our matrix equations. Thus, we may express a new set of relations

$$\begin{bmatrix} V'_a \\ I'_a \end{bmatrix} = \begin{bmatrix} A' & B' \\ \hline C' & D' \end{bmatrix} \begin{bmatrix} V'_b \\ -I'_b \end{bmatrix}$$

where

$$V'_a = \begin{bmatrix} V_1 \\ \cdots \\ V_{n-1} \end{bmatrix} \qquad V'_b = \begin{bmatrix} V_{n+1} \\ \cdots \\ V_{2n-1} \end{bmatrix} \qquad A' = \begin{bmatrix} a'_{11} & \cdots & a'_{1,n-1} \\ \cdots & \cdots & \cdots \\ a'_{n-1,1} & \cdots & a'_{n-1,n-1} \end{bmatrix} \qquad \cdots$$

The definite-transfer matrix composed of submatrices A', B', C', and D' may be found as

$$\begin{bmatrix} A' & B' \\ C' & D' \end{bmatrix} = \begin{bmatrix} Q^t & 0 \\ 0 & P^t \end{bmatrix} \begin{bmatrix} A & B \\ C & D \end{bmatrix} \begin{bmatrix} P & 0 \\ 0 & Q \end{bmatrix} \tag{5}$$

By rearranging the variables V_a, V_b, and I_b in (2), it is easy to develop a relation between the indefinite-transfer matrix and the indefinite-admittance matrix. We may define a partitioning of the indefinite-admittance matrix as follows:

$$\begin{bmatrix} I_a \\ I_b \end{bmatrix} = \begin{bmatrix} Y_{11} & Y_{12} \\ Y_{21} & Y_{22} \end{bmatrix} \begin{bmatrix} V_a \\ V_b \end{bmatrix} \tag{6}$$

where I_a, I_b, V_a, and V_b are defined in (2), and where

$$Y_{11} = \begin{bmatrix} y_{11} & \cdots & y_{1n} \\ \cdots & \cdots & \cdots \\ y_{n1} & \cdots & y_{nn} \end{bmatrix} \qquad Y_{12} = \begin{bmatrix} y_{1,n+1} & \cdots & y_{1,2n} \\ \cdots & \cdots & \cdots \\ y_{n,n+1} & \cdots & y_{n,2n} \end{bmatrix} \qquad \cdots$$

We may now express the indefinite-transfer matrix as

$$\begin{bmatrix} A & B \\ C & D \end{bmatrix} = \begin{bmatrix} -Y_{21}^{-1}Y_{22} & -Y_{21}^{-1} \\ Y_{12} - Y_{11}Y_{21}^{-1}Y_{22} & -Y_{11}Y_{21}^{-1} \end{bmatrix} \tag{7}$$

The details are left to the student as an exercise. It should be noted that frequently this provides an easy way to determine the indefinite-transfer matrix. The result of (7) should be compared with the relation between the *ABCD* parameters and the y parameters given in Table 3.1 for a two-port network. When the submatrices Y_{ij} become single elements, the relations are identical.

Appendix B *Gyrators and gyration admittance*

In Sec. 4.7, the concept of a gyrator was introduced. The gyration constant G was treated as a real number, and because of its dimensions we referred to it as a *gyration conductance*. In this section we shall see that it is also possible to specify a gyrator in terms of a function of the complex frequency variable p. In this case, we refer to a *gyration admittance*. As an interesting result of this concept, we shall see that it is possible to realize transformers with complex turns ratios.

Let us first consider the ideal three-terminal gyrator shown in Fig. B.1a. We shall assume that it has a gyration conductance of G, where G is a real number. In Fig. B.1b, the admittances Y_1 and Y_2 have been added in series to two of the terminals of the ideal gyrator. The result can be considered as a five-terminal device, with the terminals numbered as shown. We may apply the concepts of Sec. 3.5 to find the indefinite-admittance matrix for this network. It is

$$\begin{bmatrix} Y_1 & 0 & 0 & -Y_1 & 0 \\ 0 & Y_2 & 0 & 0 & -Y_2 \\ 0 & 0 & 0 & G & -G \\ -Y_1 & 0 & -G & Y_1 & G \\ 0 & -Y_2 & G & -G & Y_2 \end{bmatrix} \tag{1}$$

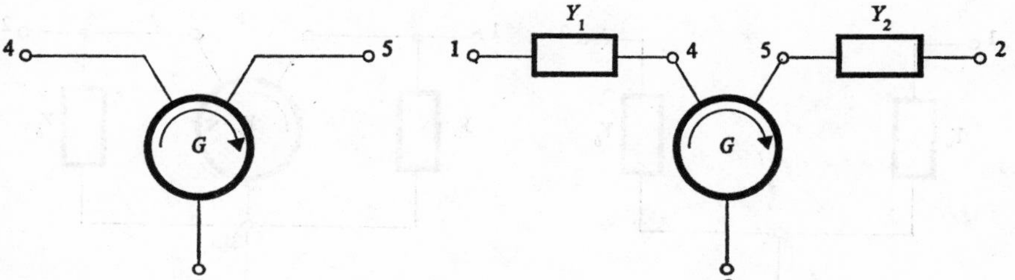

Figure B.1 *A three-terminal gyrator with series admittances.*

Now let us suppress terminals 4 and 5 of the network of Fig. B.1*b* so that we again have a three-terminal device. From (13) in Sec. 3.5 we see that the indefinite-admittance matrix for the resulting three-terminal network is given by

$$
\begin{bmatrix} Y_1 & 0 & 0 \\ 0 & Y_2 & 0 \\ 0 & 0 & 0 \end{bmatrix} - \begin{bmatrix} -Y_1 & 0 \\ 0 & -Y_2 \\ G & -G \end{bmatrix} \begin{bmatrix} Y_1 & G \\ -G & Y_2 \end{bmatrix}^{-1} \begin{bmatrix} -Y_1 & 0 & -G \\ 0 & -Y_2 & G \end{bmatrix} \quad (2)
$$

After simplification, we have

$$
\frac{G}{Y_1 Y_2 + G^2} \begin{bmatrix} Y_1 G & Y_1 Y_2 & -Y_1 Y_2 - Y_1 G \\ -Y_1 Y_2 & Y_2 G & Y_1 Y_2 - Y_2 G \\ Y_1 Y_2 - Y_1 G & -Y_1 Y_2 - Y_2 G & Y_1 G + Y_2 G \end{bmatrix}
$$

If we now ground terminal 3, we need only delete the third row and column of the above indefinite-admittance matrix, which yields

$$
\frac{G}{Y_1 Y_2 + G^2} \begin{bmatrix} Y_1 G & Y_1 Y_2 \\ -Y_1 Y_2 & Y_2 G \end{bmatrix} \quad (3)
$$

The matrix in (3) can be considered as the y-parameter matrix for the three-terminal network. It may also be written as the sum of two matrices, thus representing the parallel connection of a pair of three-terminal networks. Thus (3) may be written as

$$
\frac{G}{Y_1 Y_2 + G^2} \begin{bmatrix} Y_1 G & 0 \\ 0 & Y_2 G \end{bmatrix} + \frac{G}{Y_1 Y_2 + G^2} \begin{bmatrix} 0 & Y_1 Y_2 \\ -Y_1 Y_2 & 0 \end{bmatrix} \quad (4)
$$

The first matrix of (4) represents a network consisting of two admittances Y_a and Y_b connected as shown in Fig. B.2*a*, where

$$
Y_a = \frac{Y_1 G^2}{Y_1 Y_2 + G^2} \qquad Y_b = \frac{Y_2 G^2}{Y_1 Y_2 + G^2} \quad (5)
$$

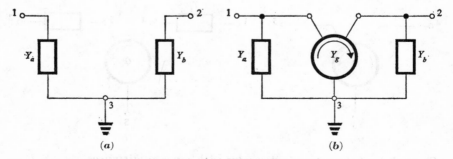

Figure B.2   *A three-terminal gyrator with shunt admittances.*

If we compare the second matrix of (4) with the equations (7) of Sec. 4.7 defining a gyrator, we see that this matrix represents a gyrator with gyration admittance Y_g, where

$$Y_g = \frac{Y_1 Y_2 G}{Y_1 Y_2 + G^2} \tag{6}$$

The over-all network represented by (3) is shown in Fig. B.2*b*. This network does not represent an ideal gyrator, since it has admittances shunting the input and output ports. It may be made ideal, however, by shunting these admittances with negative admittances of the same value. Thus we can produce an *ideal* gyrator with a complex gyration admittance.

As an example of this procedure, suppose it is desired to produce a gyrator with gyration admittance $Y_g = p/(p + 1)$. From (6) we see that

$$Y_1 Y_2 = \frac{Y_g G^2}{(G - Y_g)} \tag{7}$$

Let us assume that our original ideal gyrator has a gyration conductance of unity, i.e., that $G = 1$. Substituting in (7) yields the result $Y_1 Y_2 = p$. This is easily satisfied by letting $Y_1 = p$ and $Y_2 = 1$. In Fig. B.3*a* are shown the original ideal gyrator with $G = 1$ and the appropriate compensating networks Y_1 and Y_2. This circuit is equivalent to the circuit shown in Fig. B.3*b*; i.e., it is equivalent to a gyrator with gyration admittance $p/(p + 1)$, shunted with the networks shown. In Fig. B.4*a* compensating networks have been added to the original network of Fig. B.3*a* to produce an ideal gyrator with a gyration admittance $p/(p + 1)$, as shown in Fig. B.4*b*. Thus the two networks shown in Fig. B.4 are equivalent. The reader should study these figures to make certain he understands all the steps in their development.

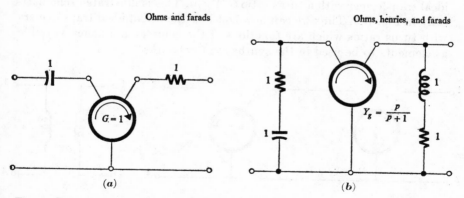

Ohms and farads   Ohms, henries, and farads

(*a*)   (*b*)

Figure B.3   Two networks, one with an ideal gyrator G = 1, the other with an ideal gyrator $Y_g = p/(p + 1)$, both of which have the same y-parameter matrix.

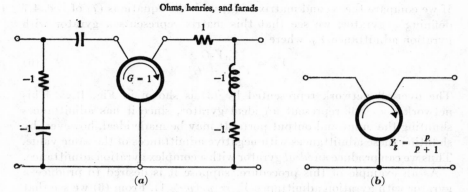

Figure B.4   Two networks with the same y-parameter matrix.

Gyrators which have gyration admittances which are functions of the complex frequency variable p provide an interesting addition to our collection of network devices. As an example, consider the case in which a gyrator with gyration admittance $Y_g(p)$ is cascaded with a gyrator with a real gyration conductance G. The transmission parameters of the cascade are found by multiplying the individual transmission-parameter matrices. We see that

$$
\begin{bmatrix} 0 & \dfrac{1}{Y_g} \\ Y_g & 0 \end{bmatrix}
\begin{bmatrix} 0 & \dfrac{1}{G} \\ G & 0 \end{bmatrix}
=
\begin{bmatrix} \dfrac{G}{Y_g} & 0 \\ 0 & \dfrac{Y_g}{G} \end{bmatrix}
\tag{8}
$$

The transmission-parameter matrix that results, however, is that of an ideal transformer with a turns ratio $G/Y_g(p)$. This is illustrated schematically in Fig. B.5. Thus we can now consider the use of ideal transformers with turns ratios which are functions of the complex frequency variable as elements to be used in the synthesis of networks.

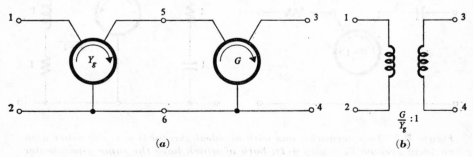

Figure B.5   An ideal transformer with a complex turns ratio.

Appendix C   Network realization by transformation methods

In the various sections of Chap. 6, we showed how the network variables voltage, charge, and current could be redefined so as to simplify the solution of the network equations. Specifically, we chose new variables which were linear combinations of the original ones. Thus, if the $v_i(t)$ were our original network variables, we selected a set of variables $\theta_i(t)$, where the relation between the variables is given in matrix form as $v = A\theta$. The A matrix which was used for this redefinition of variables was the matrix which would simultaneously transform one matrix to the identity matrix and a second matrix to a diagonal matrix. As an example, see (5) of Sec. 6.2, where the C and G matrices are so transformed. The A matrix, of course, is the matrix specified by the eigenvectors of the given network. Here we shall see that another connotation may be given the matrix A, in that this matrix may be used as part of a synthesis procedure to realize the element values of an actual network configuration. There are certain limitations to this method of approach; they will be pointed out as the material is developed.

First let us consider the passive RC network. Let the $V_i(p)$ be the Laplace transforms of the nodal voltages, and the $I_i(p)$ be the transforms of the currents applied to the various nodes of the network. The column matrices composed of these variables are V and I, respectively. If the initial conditions are assumed to be zero, the network equations can be written in the frequency domain as

$$I = YV \tag{1}$$

where Y is the admittance matrix which was introduced in Sec. 3.8. For the case of an RC network, Y will be equal to the sum of a conductance matrix G and a capacitance matrix C. Thus

$$Y = pC + G \tag{2}$$

A matrix A which will simultaneously diagonalize C and G may be found by the techniques of Sec. 5.8. By using this matrix, we can define a diagonal matrix Y', where

$$Y' = A^t Y A = A^t(pC + G)A = pl + D = \begin{bmatrix} p + \sigma_1 & \cdots & 0 \\ \cdots & \cdots & \cdots \\ 0 & \cdots & p + \sigma_n \end{bmatrix} \quad (3)$$

The Y' matrix places the natural frequencies of the network clearly in evidence. They are $-\sigma_1, -\sigma_2, \cdots, -\sigma_n$. Since the C and G matrices are real, symmetric, and positive definite,[1] the various σ_i will all be real and positive. Now let us take the inverse of both sides of (3). We obtain

$$(Y')^{-1} = A^{-1}Y^{-1}(A^t)^{-1} \quad (4)$$

The impedance matrix Z for our network is defined as Y^{-1}. From (4) we see that

$$Z = Y^{-1} = A(Y')^{-1}A^t = A \begin{bmatrix} \dfrac{1}{p + \sigma_1} & \cdots & 0 \\ \cdots & \cdots & \cdots \\ 0 & \cdots & \dfrac{1}{p + \sigma_n} \end{bmatrix} A^t \quad (5)$$

Thus, we see that

$$z_{11} = \frac{a_{11}{}^2}{p + \sigma_1} + \frac{a_{12}{}^2}{p + \sigma_2} + \cdots + \frac{a_{1n}{}^2}{p + \sigma_n} \quad (6)$$

$$z_{12} = \frac{a_{11}a_{21}}{p + \sigma_1} + \frac{a_{12}a_{22}}{p + \sigma_2} + \cdots + \frac{a_{1n}a_{2n}}{p + \sigma_n} \quad (7)$$

and, in general,

$$z_{ij} = \sum_k \frac{a_{ik}a_{jk}}{p + \sigma_k} \quad (8)$$

where the a_{ij} are the elements of the A matrix. The above expressions are simply the partial-fraction expansions for the various z_{ij} terms associated with the given network. Thus we see that we may write definite relations between the elements of the A matrix and the residues of the various z_{ij} terms at the poles of the network.[2] For example, (6) indicates that the first row of the A matrix specifies the residues of the z_{11} term. Similarly, from (7) we see that the residues of the z_{12} term are specified by the product of the elements in the first and second rows of the A matrix, and so on.

[1] Actually, these matrices can also be positive semidefinite; however, we shall restrict ourselves to the positive-definite case.

[2] E. A. Guillemin, An Approach to the Synthesis of Linear Networks Through Use of Normal Coordinate Transformations Leading to More General Topological Configurations, *IRE Trans. on Circuit Theory*, vol. CT-7, Special Supplement, pp. 40–48, August, 1960.

We may now take the opposite viewpoint and start with a matrix $(Y')^{-1}$ specifying the natural frequencies it is desired to have in a given network. We may then specify the extent to which each of these natural frequencies is present in a given term of the impedance matrix by specifying the elements of the A matrix. Since the A matrix will also satisfy the relations

$$A^t C A = 1$$
$$A^t G A = D \tag{9}$$

we can find the C and G matrices directly from the A and D matrices as

$$C = (A^t)^{-1} A^{-1}$$
$$G = (A^t)^{-1} D A^{-1} \tag{10}$$

Thus, specifying the A matrix according to the desired residues also specifies the conductance matrix and the capacitance matrix, and thus specifies the configuration and the element values of the network. The procedure is basically simple, but there are some limitations. For example, it is not possible, in general, to specify all the parameters of the network simultaneously. Thus, specific choices for all the residues of all the z_{ij} terms for $i = j$ would completely determine the elements of the A matrix. In this case, no specification of the residues for the mutual terms z_{ij} for $i \neq j$ could be made. Another limitation is the form that the C and G matrices must have if the network is to be realized with passive components. This result also places a limitation on the elements of the A matrix. In simple cases, the above limitations may be seen directly. This is best illustrated by an example:

Suppose it is desired to realize a network which has the following open-circuit driving-point impedance:

$$z_{11} = \frac{1}{p + 1} + \frac{4}{p + 2}$$

The Y' matrix must then consist of elements corresponding to the desired natural frequencies. Thus,

$$Y' = \begin{bmatrix} p + 1 & 0 \\ 0 & p + 2 \end{bmatrix}$$

The first row of the A matrix is specified by the square roots of the desired residues, but the other elements are free to be chosen. We see that

$$A = \begin{bmatrix} 1 & 2 \\ a & b \end{bmatrix} \qquad A^{-1} = \frac{1}{b - 2a} \begin{bmatrix} b & -2 \\ -a & 1 \end{bmatrix}$$

where a and b are still to be determined. We may now compute our C and G matrices. From (10) we obtain

$$C = (A^t)^{-1}A^{-1} = \begin{bmatrix} b & -a \\ -2 & 1 \end{bmatrix}\begin{bmatrix} b & -2 \\ -a & 1 \end{bmatrix}\frac{1}{(b-2a)^2}$$

$$= \frac{1}{(b-2a)^2}\begin{bmatrix} b^2 + a^2 & -2b - a \\ -2b - a & 5 \end{bmatrix}$$

$$G = (A^t)^{-1}DA^{-1} = \begin{bmatrix} b & -a \\ -2 & 1 \end{bmatrix}\begin{bmatrix} 1 & 0 \\ 0 & 2 \end{bmatrix}\begin{bmatrix} b & -2 \\ -a & 1 \end{bmatrix}\frac{1}{(b-2a)^2}$$

$$= \frac{1}{(b-2a)^2}\begin{bmatrix} b^2 + 2a^2 & -2b - 2a \\ -2b - 2a & 6 \end{bmatrix}$$

For simplicity, let us choose $a = 0$; then our C and G matrices become

$$C = \begin{bmatrix} 1 & \dfrac{-2}{b} \\ \dfrac{-2}{b} & \dfrac{5}{b^2} \end{bmatrix} \qquad G = \begin{bmatrix} 1 & \dfrac{-2}{b} \\ \dfrac{-2}{b} & \dfrac{6}{b^2} \end{bmatrix}$$

For these to be realizable, the matrices must be dominant (see Sec. 4.8). Thus, the conditions on b sufficient for the network to be realizable with passive components are

$$b > 0 \qquad 2 \leq b \qquad b \leq 2.5$$

If we choose $b = 2.5$, we obtain

$$C = \begin{bmatrix} 1 & -0.8 \\ -0.8 & 0.8 \end{bmatrix} \qquad G = \begin{bmatrix} 1 & -0.8 \\ -0.8 & 0.96 \end{bmatrix}$$

The network realization is shown in Fig. C.1. Note that this realization actually has one more element than a realization made directly from the equations of Fig. 4.26 would have. The significant point of this realization,

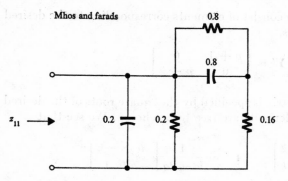

Figure C.1 A network realization with a specified driving-point impedance.

however, is that the G and C matrices, and thus the network configuration, have been directly specified. It should be apparent that the same technique can be applied to cases in which the network has more natural frequencies, and thus greater complexity. The realization conditions which will have to be solved in these cases will, of course, be more complicated, and it may be necessary to use computation facilities to achieve a solution. If, however, we do not restrict ourselves to passive components in our solution, but permit the use of negative- as well as positive-valued elements, then the solution will always be readily apparent for any choice of the z_{ij} residues.

Let us now consider a somewhat different interpretation of the formalism which we have followed in this section. Instead of considering the matrix A as a means by which two matrices are simultaneously diagonalized, let us consider it as a means of defining new current and voltage variables. Let these transformed variables be $V_i'(p)$ and $I_i'(p)$, and let V' and I' be the column matrices composed of these variables. Thus, we can define a matrix Y', where

$$I' = Y'V' \tag{11}$$

If the definition of Y' from (3) is substituted in the above, and if the terms are rearranged, we see that

$$(A^t)^{-1}I' = YAV' \tag{12}$$

Comparing this with (1), we see that

$$I = (A^t)^{-1}I'$$
$$V = AV'$$

or that

$$I' = A^tI$$
$$V' = A^{-1}V \tag{13}$$

In terms of the above equations we can describe the procedure that has been presented in this appendix in a new way. We can say that the original network, as defined by the Y matrix, has been treated in terms of redefined voltage and current variables (denoted by the prime notation) which consist of appropriate linear combinations of the original voltage and current variables. This concept can be extended. For example, it is possible to consider cases in which only linear combinations of the voltage *or* of the current variables are treated. Thus, we might consider the case in which the behavior of a network is to be described by the equations

$$I = YBV' \tag{14}$$

If we compare this with the original equation $I = YV$, we see that we may either say that the performance of our original network as defined by the matrix Y is being evaluated in terms of the linear combinations $V_i'(p)$ of

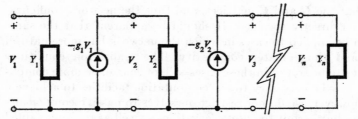

Figure C.2 A cascade of $n - 1$ unilateral networks.

the actual voltages $V_i(p)$, where $V' = B^{-1}V$, or we may say that the original network has been replaced with one whose elements are specified by the matrix Y', where $Y' = YB$, and that this network has nodal voltages $V_i'(p)$.

An interesting example of the application of such logic may be seen by the following example:[1] Consider a ladder network composed of a cascade of $n - 1$ unilateral stages, each consisting of a current generator and a shunt admittance, as shown in Fig. C.2. The ladder is terminated in an admittance Y_n. The Y matrix for this network is

$$Y = \begin{bmatrix} Y_1 & 0 & 0 & \cdots & 0 & 0 \\ g_1 & Y_2 & 0 & \cdots & 0 & 0 \\ 0 & g_2 & Y_3 & \cdots & 0 & 0 \\ \multicolumn{6}{c}{\cdots\cdots\cdots\cdots\cdots\cdots\cdots} \\ 0 & 0 & 0 & \cdots & g_{n-1} & Y_n \end{bmatrix} \tag{15}$$

Let us now consider a transformation matrix B which has two diagonal lines of elements and whose other elements are zero. This will have the form

$$B = \begin{bmatrix} b_{11} & b_{12} & 0 & \cdots & 0 & 0 \\ 0 & b_{22} & b_{23} & \cdots & 0 & 0 \\ \multicolumn{6}{c}{\cdots\cdots\cdots\cdots\cdots\cdots\cdots\cdots} \\ 0 & 0 & 0 & \cdots & b_{n-1,n-1} & b_{n-1,n} \\ 0 & 0 & 0 & \cdots & 0 & b_{nn} \end{bmatrix} \tag{16}$$

The Y' matrix, where $Y' = YB$, will have three diagonal lines of elements, and its other elements will be zero. Thus,

$$Y' = \begin{bmatrix} y_{11}' & y_{12}' & 0 & \cdots & 0 & 0 \\ y_{21}' & y_{22}' & y_{23}' & \cdots & 0 & 0 \\ 0 & y_{32}' & y_{33}' & \cdots & 0 & 0 \\ \multicolumn{6}{c}{\cdots\cdots\cdots\cdots\cdots\cdots\cdots\cdots} \\ 0 & 0 & 0 & \cdots & y_{n-1,n-1}' & y_{n-1,n}' \\ 0 & 0 & 0 & \cdots & y_{n,n-1}' & y_{nn}' \end{bmatrix} \tag{17}$$

[1] E. A. Guillemin, Transformation Theory Applied to Linear Active and/or Nonbilateral Networks, *IRE Trans. on Circuit Theory*, vol. CT-4, pp. 106–110, September, 1957.

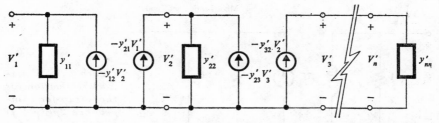

Figure C.3   *A cascade of $n-1$ networks with transmission in both directions.*

The network represented by the Y' matrix will be composed of a cascade of $n-1$ stages, each consisting of two current generators and a shunt admittance, as shown in Fig. C.3. The cascade will be terminated in an admittance y'_{nn}. The elements of the B matrix may be chosen so as to make the elements y'_{ij} $(i \neq j)$ of the Y' matrix real numbers. These may be realized as dependent current sources. If the element b_{nn} is real, then we see that since $V = BV'$, we may write $V_n = b_{nn}V'_n$. Thus $V_n(p)$ and $V'_n(p)$ are related by a simple constant, and if the networks shown in Figs. C.2 and C.3 are driven by a single current source at the first node, they will have the same transfer impedance (within a constant multiplier). In other words, if we specify the transfer function of a network in which unilateral active devices are present (this is relatively easy, owing to the isolation between stages that is provided by the unilateral elements), we can find a network which will have the same transfer function even though it is comprised of devices with transmission in both directions. This may be done by transforming the admittance matrix of the original network. In effect we can thus design transistor amplifier stages in terms of related vacuum-tube amplifier stages.

As a numerical example, suppose it is desired to realize the transfer function

$$\frac{V_2}{I_1} = \frac{2p}{(p+1)(p+2)}$$

The transfer function for the network shown in Fig. C.4 is

$$\frac{V_2}{I_1} = \frac{-g}{Y_1 Y_2}$$

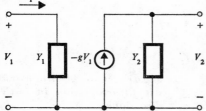

Figure   C.4   A   unilateral   network
with shunt admittances.

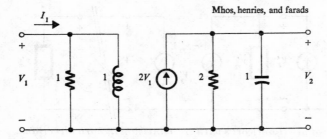

Mhos, henries, and farads

Figure C.5 A network realization for the transfer impedance $2p/[(p + 1)(p + 2)]$.

If we assume that the available active unilateral device has a transconductance of -2, then $g = -2$. We may choose

$$Y_1 = \frac{p + 1}{p} \qquad Y_2 = p + 2$$

The **Y** matrix for this circuit is thus

$$Y = \begin{bmatrix} 1 + \dfrac{1}{p} & 0 \\ -2 & p + 2 \end{bmatrix}$$

The network realization for this transfer function is shown in Fig. C.5.

Now let us consider an active device of the type shown in Fig. C.6. If we assume that this device has a forward transconductance of 3 mhos and a reverse transconductance of 1 mho, then $g_1 = -3$, $g_2 = -1$, and the matrix **Y′** for this network is

$$Y' = \begin{bmatrix} Y_a & -1 \\ -3 & Y_b \end{bmatrix}$$

The **Y′** matrix, however, may be realized from the matrix product **YB**, which is

$$YB = \begin{bmatrix} 1 + \dfrac{1}{p} & 0 \\ -2 & p + 2 \end{bmatrix} \begin{bmatrix} b_{11} & b_{12} \\ 0 & b_{22} \end{bmatrix} = \begin{bmatrix} \dfrac{b_{11}(p + 1)}{p} & \dfrac{b_{12}(p + 1)}{p} \\ -2b_{11} & -2b_{12} + b_{22}(p + 2) \end{bmatrix}$$

A comparison of the matrix **Y′** and the matrix product **YB** shows that if

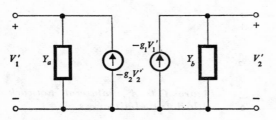

Figure C.6 A network with transmission in both directions.

$Y' = YB$, then

$$b_{11} = \tfrac{3}{2} \qquad b_{12} = \frac{-p}{p+1}$$

If we choose b_{22} as unity, then the voltages V_2 and V_2' are the same, and the Y' matrix is

$$Y' = \begin{bmatrix} \dfrac{3(p+1)}{2p} & -1 \\[2ex] -3 & p+2+\dfrac{2p}{p+1} \end{bmatrix}$$

The network realization is shown in Fig. C.7. This network uses a specified device with transmission in two directions, but it has exactly the same transfer function as the network shown in Fig. C.5. In other words, we have synthesized a specified transfer function through the use of a given element, with the necessary networks realized on the basis of a transformation of the admittance matrix of a network which uses a unilateral element.

The techniques illustrated in this appendix are not completely general. There are many cases in which solutions for the elements of the transformation matrix cannot be found. They are, however, illustrative of the potential of a relatively unexplored area of network theory. Many answers remain to be found in the application of these techniques to actual network situations. If the student finds himself stimulated by the material which has been presented, and if he chooses to pursue these topics further, then this presentation will have been well worth while.

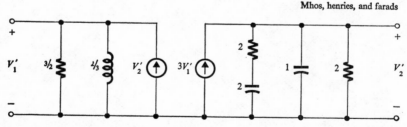

Figure C.7   A network realization for the transfer impedance $2p/[(p+1)(p+2)]$.

Index